MIND: PERCEPTION AND THOUGHT

IN THEIR CONSTRUCTIVE ASPECTS

MIND: PERCEPTION AND THOUGHT IN THEIR CONSTRUCTIVE ASPECTS

By PAUL SCHILDER

New York · Columbia University Press · 1942

TO MY CO-WORKERS

THE PAUL F. SCHILDER
MEMORIAL FUND COMMITTEE

FOLLOWING the death of Dr. Schilder on December 8, 1940, The Society for Psychotherapy and Psychopathology, New York, of which he was the founder and first president, decided to arrange for the publication of his two unpublished books, *The Goals and Desires of Man* and *Mind: Perception and Thought in Their Constructive Aspects.* The Paul F. Schilder Memorial Fund Committee was organized and it is largely due to the response of all Dr. Schilder's friends and followers to the appeal of this Committee that these books now appear.

Considerable editorial work was necessary for the final preparation of the manuscripts, although they were completed by the author as they are now published. The editing was done under the supervision of Dr. Lauretta Bender (Mrs. Paul F. Schilder), who was closely associated with Dr. Schilder at the time this book was written and also during the time that much of the material was accumulated for them; she knew what he wanted to say. There were many who would have gladly assisted with this work and without the generous and valuable aid of those who did help, the manuscripts would never have been published. For the present volume these include especially Eugene Pumpian-Mindlin, Olga Frankel, Heinz Hartmann, and William Q. Wolfson.

BERNARD GLUECK, M.D., *Chairman*
FRANK J. CURRAN, M.D., *Secretary-Treasurer*
LAURETTA BENDER, M.D.
FRITZ WITTELS, M.D.
SÁNDOR LORAND, M.D.
ROBERT B. McGRAW, M.D.
CLARENCE P. OBERNDORF, M.D.

New York, N.Y.
June, 1942

FOREWORD

ALMOST since the beginning of my scientific activities I was fortunate enough to have had co-workers to whom I do not only acknowledge help, but valuable inspiration. Among those I feel particularly indebted to S. Betlheim, Joseph Gerstmann, Heinz Hartmann, Hans Hoff, Otto Kauders, and Erwin Stengel, with whom I have worked in Vienna. In America I had, in the Phipps Clinic, an opportunity to work with Leo Kanner and Elmer Klein. In Bellevue Hospital I have worked in close association with Walter Bromberg, Frank J. Curran, Sam Parker, Sylvan Keiser, Nathaniel Ross, David Wechsler, and, especially, with Lauretta Bender. Her work on gestalt constitutes, in my opinion, a contribution of great value to this fundamental problem. It has helped me considerably in the formulation of many of the problems with which this book deals.

In the Preface to my book *The Image and Appearance of the Human Body* I tried to clarify my general attitudes and principles concerning psychological problems. The principles and the results gained in the investigation of the body image are used here in an attempt to investigate the principles of perception and thought. I extend the results and methods of modern psychology into a field which so far has not been studied from this point of view. As is every serious worker in this field, I am deeply influenced by Freud. However, guided by my own efforts and by my own material, I have developed my own ideas. Freud's work is an era in psychology. In order to utilize it fully, new, independent efforts are necessary.

PAUL SCHILDER

New York, N.Y.
November, 1940

CONTENTS

Part I. *Perception and Action*

Part II. *Higher Mental Functions*

PART I

PERCEPTION AND ACTION

CHAPTER I

IN SEARCH OF PRIMITIVE EXPERIENCE

CONDILLAC fantasied a marble statue gradually awakening. Sensations enter. The ego is the sum of sensations. The senses do not give objective data but merely a modification of the soul. These impressions leave a memory, provoke attention and judgment by their differences and form a chain by association. However now we do not doubt that sensations are not the primitive units out of which more complicated experiences are developed but rather are artificial abstractions.

The term "sensation" should merely mean that we are less interested in the outer world than in the experience of our own body. Sensations are not isolated since they are always closely related to the body image and are not in direct correlation to the stimulus. From the point of view of physiology they are a reaction of the total organism. The experience of the child and of the primitive human being certainly does not consist of simple sensations. The primitive experience seems to be much more complex and diffuse than does the completely developed perception. We therefore come to the conclusion that sensations as far as they exist as units which can be isolated cannot be considered as primitive experiences. Experience is not only something going on in the body but also something occurring in the world, and every sensation is directed toward the outer world.

It is difficult to discover what methodologic procedure leads the exponents of the atomistic theory to the conception of sensation as primitive experience. Do we have any methods by which we may expect to isolate such a primitive experience? We might assume that a process of experience needs time, and that we may catch the primitive experience if we interrupt the process early enough. This conception has been used by W. Baade but it is also the basis for a great deal of tachistoscopic experimentation. I may mention the experiments of F. Schumann on reading, the experiments of Otto Poetzl, and especially those of E. Lindemann concerning the genesis and disappearance of configurations.

When we look at something exposed tachistoscopically we certainly have an experience which is incomplete. It is merely an easy assumption that this incomplete experience is also a primitive one. We may, however, learn something in this way about the process of the development of perception; and may safely say that nowhere does this process of development contain simple sensations or simple perceptions. Primitive configurations exist, and, if one desires, they may be called simple configurations. A short word does not need so long a time of exposure as a letter in order to be recognized. When a person reads the tachistoscopically exposed *Pankt* as *Punkt* (point) or as *Paket* (package) it is difficult to say that *Punkt* is less complicated than *Pankt*. On the contrary, if there should be a difference, one would have to suppose that the early process of recognition is more complicated than the perfected process of recognition. The tachistoscopic method allows us to formulate a preliminary idea of primitiveness.

The primitive experience might be sought for by diminishing the intensity of the stimuli by progressively dimming the light, but this method also has its difficulties. With the darkening of the room, color perception is not only changed quantitatively but qualitatively; for instance, red becomes darker than blue (Purkinje phenomenon). When a room is completely darkened, then the idioretinal light appears. This is undoubtedly a really primitive experience. It is questionable whether the mechanism of the dark adaptation of the eye is more primitive than the mechanism of light adaptation, but it is probable that this is so. One difficulty is that we do not know what "more primitive" means. Does it mean the form experiences take at birth and in early childhood, or the experience of animals, or the experience in the beginning of phylogenesis? F. Sander obtained valuable results in this connection by diminishing the size of a specific configuration. It is possible that the small figure is more primitive than the large, or that more primitive mechanisms of experience operate when the individual has difficulty in perceiving the object clearly. Such a difficulty may be caused by either too short an exposure of the impression or too little intensity or extensity. It is probable that the less the stimulus presents itself to perception, the more the organism must use its own resources. In the idioretinal light, we meet the preparedness of the sense organ which has no chance to develop itself in contact with the outer world.

The experience of the congenitally blind person who has gained the power of vision through operation and the experience of the cortically blind individual who has regained his vision have been studied and yield valuable results. The blind individuals who have been operated on suffer pain and are in a very abnormal psychological situation. The cortically blind who regain vision do not necessarily show primitive vision in the beginning.

Perhaps we should turn to primitive man and to the child in the earliest stages of his development. But modern science has some doubts concerning the primitiveness of "primitive man." At any rate his senses are far from being primitive in their function. We cannot learn anything from him concerning primitive perception. The child might tell us, if he could talk, but he is nearly as speechless as the animal concerning the problems in which we are interested. It is possible to overcome these difficulties by ingenious experimentation, and Lauretta Bender has done this by urging children to draw. But so far we have no definite criteria whether primitiveness in the experience of children possesses the same features as the primitiveness in the vision of the operated congenitally blind.

The study of states of diminished consciousness before falling asleep and after awakening, and of the changes of consciousness caused by drugs or pathological lesions may yet yield further information. Attempts have been made to find drugs which make sensual experience directly more primitive. The investigations of Kurt Beringer, W. Mayer-Gross and H. Stein, and H. Kluever are interesting in this respect but do not offer definite proof of the primitive character of the experiences of senses under intoxication. Pathological influences may possibly hinder the perfection of experience and so give hints as to what primitive perception might be. Localized lesions of the brain which provoke agnosias might have a similar effect. The work of Otto Poetzl on this topic is particularly suggestive.

None of these methods alone can teach us what primitive experience and primitive perception actually are but all of them together at any rate might give us an idea that such a thing as primitive experience truly exists. It is important that we should evaluate primitive experiences quantitatively and qualitatively. The search for primitiveness may be a search for a phantom disguised by words. The problems of experience cannot be separated from the problems of action and of objective reality. Primitiveness is therefore a practical problem, and it leads us to the question of the nature of the world with which we deal. Are there different structures which must be examined in different ways? The problem of primitiveness and development is one of effectiveness. It is also concerned with the degree of development of the neural apparatus necessary for the handling of a specific situation. The primitive world is one which corresponds to an earlier stage of development of the neural apparatus. There are different modes of behavior; we cannot understand the behavior of human beings who are highly developed and in the full possession of their sensory and motor apparatus unless we understand the evolution of a given mode of behavior. Both behavior and perception are processes in the development of an organism, and we must understand these processes in their totality.

CHAPTER II

COLOR AND MOTION IN VISUAL EXPERIENCE

IF there is no external stimulation of the eye, the so-called "Eigenlicht" (the idioretinal light) of the retina appears. This is a continuous luminosity which extends in circles to the periphery and disappears. It is like the soft light of rectified spirits, and consists of innumerable small points of light which move vividly on a dark-gray background; there are also dark points, bands, and whitish clouds. Sometimes there is a slight color haze over the whole picture. The restlessness in the picture may be very strong. The patterns may be formed by previous experiences or preoccupations, and are localized close to the observer at about reading distance. C. E. Ferree saw streams of small points moving in broad bands in different directions when he looked toward light with his eyes closed (B. F. Goldschmidt). Franz reported a congenitally blind man, who upon opening his eyes after operation said that he saw a great field of light in which everything was dark, confused, and moving. Otto Poetzl reported that subjective optic phenomena occurred before the regaining of sight in a case of recovery from total cortical blindness: stars flickered and mists moved, often with a reddish glow. A flickering change of light and darkness took place. Mists covered the contours of the outer world. They sometimes came in a spiral, starting from the center of the optic field. Reddish color was in the foreground. Flickering, resembling that in migraine, persisted for a long time. During the first impressions of regaining sight, motion is predominant, and there is apparent movement even in the impression of darkness.

Electric excitation seems to be a rather primitive stimulus for the cortical region. Fedor Krause reports an interesting case of a thirty-four-year-old man who at the age of twenty-five had received a gun-shot wound in the occipital region. When he was wounded he did not lose consciousness, but he saw threatening figures in quick movement in the right visual field. Later on, a right hemianopsia appeared. Eight years later epileptic attacks occurred, in the beginning of which there appeared animals in the midst of fire or soldiers who changed into stars. During an operation electric excitation was used. The patient saw stars and dented circles expanding themselves like waves after a stone has been thrown into water. When one circle disappeared another formed. The center of the circle was black while the periphery was red as fire. In a later epileptic attack the aura consisted of stars and figures of men and animals, which glided quickly to the right side in a field of glaring lightness. This is another hint that primitive optic experiences are not static but in motion. In the first instance cited, the movements are connected with impressions of black and darkness, and in the last instance the red color is in the foreground. In all the cases mentioned the movement is localized outside of the person in space. Therefore these primitive experiences are phenomenologically perception and not mere "sensations". We may also draw the conclusion that primitive experience is not a sensation because the subject does not consider it a part of himself. Phenomenologically, sensation is referred to the body image, but here the subject has something in front of and separated from himself by space.

It seems that when the dark impression changes into color, the color red appears first. It is well known that epileptics often see red in their aura. According to H. Stein, movement from the periphery to the midline is common. An epileptic with a color aura reported, "Before I get the spell I get the red light through the left eye. It shoots out of the eye. All kinds of light come out of the eye—red, blue, white. I see it in front of my left eye. It is like a mist. Once I saw it shoot right out of my eye to a man's clothes. The clothes were covered with all kinds of colors. If I don't get water I go out for five or ten minutes. But I am not unconscious."

However, red is not always in the foreground. Another epileptic reported that before the attack he saw little colored lights—green, blue, and red, like glittering swamp lights. Still another—his epileptic attacks were caused by alcohol—saw pure green in front of his eyes before his attacks. The green had a yellowish tint, and was close to the eyes, moving in spirals of about ten inches in a counterclockwise direction. A patient with marihuana intoxication saw before his eyes a square of ten centimeters like a painted cardboard of bright scarlet, yellow, and green. Finally there were at least ten colors which faded and came back in five minutes. He heard bells, which sounded like a big church bell ringing a couple of blocks away. He also heard somebody talking about him, "We might get him now." He felt that his eyes became larger and larger—they opened wider and wider. He felt dizzy and the time passed slowly so that five minutes seemed like an hour. He said, "The car was driving very slowly. Afterwards I thought it was barely moving. My knees were heavy. When I walked it was as if somebody were holding me back. I felt like walking very slowly or not walking at all."

His color experiences due to marihuana might have been modified by the state of his eyes, for he had a chorioretinitis and optic nystagmus and his pupils were fixed to light and accommodation, apparently due to congenital lues.

In all the cases reported thus far, the colors in motion had no distinct relation to objects. This was also true of the black-white impressions, which floated in space, filling the space or falling onto the objects. In toxic psychoses moving lines and waves in all colors have occasionally been observed. But this is basically the same phenomenon: movement and color without definite relation to a definite object.

Vaguely shaped colors in motion belong to the sphere of more primitive experiences.[1] A thirty-five-year-old Negro reported that during his alcoholic hallucinosis, "The sun came after me. It was a big red ball. The voices showed me a coffin and a shoe box. I could not touch it. My brother was in the coffin. The saloon windows

---

[1] According to Ruth Staples, newborn children show at first no interest in colors; they react merely to brightness. The three-month-old child shows interest in color; later on red leads in interest; yellow, blue, and green follow.

turned green when I stepped on the steps. They were light green and of diamond shape. I ran across the street and the sun came after me. I thought it would burn. I had a fit [patient had a bitten tongue]. God must be after me, or the devil. He said that if I go into another saloon I die. On the steps there were marks which looked like fire. It was buzzing in my ears like an organ. I thought God wanted to take me home."

In this case an epileptic aura with a red sensation played an important part and it is more than probable that the complementary green has to do with the same central process. In this case we do not deal with elementary sensations as in the previous cases. The red color takes the primitive form of a sphere and of the sun and the complementary green is related to the window. We deal here with a beginning of a process of shaping in which primitive forms are brought into connection with the colors. It is true that we know comparatively little so far about primitive forms, but there are some hints in the material. In the case of green vision, there is a vortexlike movement. In the descriptions of the idioretinal light we find points, stars, circles, bands, which move to the periphery, and a multiplicity of shining points. In our experiments on imagination, instead of distinct forms a diffusion, curving, and fragmentation sets in. The circle, or more probably the vortex, seems to be one of the primitive gestalt formations. There is also the irradiation in the form of a star, and one often hears of flames and fire in hallucinations. So it seems that this unshaped material, primitive vortices and funnels, and to some extent waves, are the most primitive forms we encounter in imagination and in hallucinatory experiences. It is astonishing to see how often red prevails. Second in frequency is green, while yellow and blue are decidedly rare as isolated experiences in hallucinations. Santonin intoxication, in which the visual field appears in a yellow color, probably has a different meaning. I have repeatedly quoted the observation of Heinz Hartmann in which the patient's first hallucination was fire. The fire afterwards came out of the eye of the examiner and finally was identified with the fiery eye of the father of whom the patient was afraid. Thus, under the influence of experiences, the primitive hallucination is bound to a specific object. It is as if a free-floating color were finally used in a constructive synthesis. A more complicated instance is that of a patient in an hysterical state who saw fire in her room and tried to jump out of the window. This patient was always afraid of her husband, a drunkard, whom she accused of wanting to set fire to the furniture. Here the psychological experience is in the foreground and probably uses only a part of the primitive red mechanism. Influenced by experiences, situations, and tendencies, primitive space color is drawn nearer to the object, to become a film color and finally a surface color.

Commonly all colors are present in primitive color experiences. The variety of colors in the fortification spectrum in migraine should be particularly noted. In the case of Margaret M., reported later in detail, the patient saw a bear of many colors. "He was sort of a large-sized dog. He was not as big as a bear should be. Every color in creation was on him." She saw the draperies on the windows in all colors and also saw black and green insects and caterpillars. In this case it seems that the primitive colors are already closely bound to the object. In another case to be discussed later, the patient saw everything he touched explode with a glaring white light. The primitive light experience here seems an expression of the wild aggressive tendencies of the patient.

The union between color and object is not an absolute one. The experiences of those who are born blind and recover their vision also point to the fact that colors which at first float are gradually bound to objects. In the film color there is a loose connection between the color and the object. A patient of A. Gelb with an occipital lesion (the exact locus of which was not determined) saw film colors instead of surface colors. In such cases, the outline of the seen object becomes indistinct and a finger which touches the object seems to dip into the color. But even when film colors are present, the color constancy of the object remains intact, disappearing only when the patient sees space colors. E. Hering has pointed out that objects seen between white borderlines retain their color irrespective of changes in the whiteness. Color constancy also seems to be a process gradually adapted to objects which, to offer a reliable basis for actions must remain constant in regard to specific quality. (See my *Medical Psychology*.) As I have mentioned before, eidetic images and optic imaginations very often show film colors instead of surface colors. Imaginations and images do not point as directly to objects as perceptions do, and with the absence of this immediate directness, more primitive qualities of orientation come again into the foreground.

Discussions about isolated colors are of course more or less artificial. In my preliminary remarks I have indicated that there is movement in the colors, and that the primitive color impression is combined with motion. But even this qualification is in a dual sense incomplete. It is doubtful whether we have the right to speak of isolated sense impressions. Objects and impressions generally are objects for all sense-modalities. Charles Hartshorne points out that synesthesia is the basic type of experience. Hartshorne and E. M. von Hornbostel emphasize that there is an immediate relation between the lightness and darkness of sounds, the color of sounds, and optically perceived colors. Furthermore every impression not only involves motion but brings with it a definite set of motor activities as well. W. Metzger has shown that illuminating one eye in humans increases the muscle tone on the illuminated side. The different colors of the spectrum have a different influence. Furthermore, R. Magnus and A. de Kleijn have shown that optic righting reflexes exist in animals. Labyrinthectomized monkeys, for instance, are able to maintain the normal position of the head in space when they look at an object. Even the most primitive optic experiences (and especially color experiences) are connected with a system of tonic attitudes. We deal here with primitive tonic reactions which are coördinated with primitive experiences of light and color. Primitive perceptions have no definite relation to actions in the common sense; the more primitive perception develops into articulated object perception, the more definite actions appear. Perceptual motion has in itself a tendency to be answered by motion (this will later be the topic of a more detailed discussion). Primitive color and light perceptions are connected with tonic responses and with optic tonic reflexes. The motion in the primitive perception invites a more or less phasic action which comes into the foreground with the further development of the perception of the object.

To repeat: Primitive perception (in this particular case color perception) contains motion. Light and color perception is connected with tonic reflexes. With the development and the forming of the objects the tonic reaction is substituted by a phasic reaction.

Even these formulations neglect an important point. Within themselves colors carry the stimuli to particular emotions. The color red implies a threat, a danger; it lies on the active side, and there is something forceful in it. Charles Hartshorne has justly emphasized that something in these colors connects them with sounds and with all other sensory qualities. Every shade of color has its specific emotional value linking it with impressions of the other senses, which have the same emotional values. Red, fire, and threat are typically connected in the optic aura of many patients. One of my patients complained that she saw the enamel of the wash basin in green, a result of poisonous gases sent by her enemies. In a previous study I pointed out that yellow and blue were both connected with negative and depressive effects. They are the colors of death; to one of my patients the world seen in these colors was a dying world. But according to Josef Froebe's textbook (Volume I, page 189): "A landscape gets a warmer hue from it [blue]. Blue seems to recede; it is the color of remoteness and profundity. It makes you long for softness." However, in our cases it is the color of horror, fright, and despair. It may be that different hues are involved. According to Froebe, yellow is serene and clear. Red shows the highest warmth and energy, exciting when the plane is small, disquieting when it is large. He gives similar descriptions of the other colors. One immediately sees that it is very difficult to come to definite decisions concerning these points; indeed, it is questionable whether we, developed as we are, can ever completely separate colors from objects. It is true that brightness of color has a specific effect, and it is remarkable that when nature produces brightness in the color of feathers or in the color of animals in the mating season, the plumage or the fins corresponds to a similar change in the emotional and motor attitude of the animal. I do not doubt that there is an intrinsic emotional and esthetic value in every color. W. Wundt describes the simple feelings connected with the perception of color. He says that the feeling tone is dependent on the color tone, the intensity and the saturation of colors. Goethe called the hues from red to green the "plus" side, and the hues from green to violet the "minus" side of the coloring, indicating that the one is connected with anxiety and the other with depressed feeling tone. The end colors of the spectrum are connected with excited and restless feelings. Red is an energetic color. A great light intensity is connected with a feeling of excitement. The effect of colors is modified by a mixture of white or by a decreased intensity of light. When red is decreased in intensity to rose, the impression becomes one of excited joy. Wundt presented in table form a system of color impressions; he emphasized that colors and sound become related to each other in the effect produced. Unfortunately in all these questions, whenever one goes beyond very vague and general formulations, the results become doubtful and unreliable. The difficulties in getting at pure color impressions, isolated from the other experiences of life, are almost insurmountable. Feelings and emotions are, after all, expressions of total attitudes which are chiefly motoric in their functions and the impression of color can hardly be separated from the expression of movement.

Carl S., at the time of his admission to the Vienna Psychiatric Clinic, was sixteen years old. Five weeks before admission he had grippe with high temperature, lasting for about nine days. After the disappearance of the fever, the patient showed anxiety. He did not want to eat, as he believed his food was poisoned. At the time of the examination the patient did not speak spontaneously, and when urged to speak did so in a low voice. His orientation in space and time was incomplete. He said that there was a petroleum taste in the food. During further observation the patient was anxious, resistive, stood around for hours and showed some waxy flexibility. He was discharged a month later. Four years later he was again examined. Soon after his discharge he had started to work although he was continually troubled with headaches and sleeplessness. He reported his experience in the psychosis. He saw pictures and colored spots, sometimes white, sometimes red, and various colors of the rainbow wherever he looked. Everything was swimming and jumping as if there were waves—everything turned around before him and everything was curved. The floor waved, and therefore he walked slowly. The light phenomena were always in motion. Upon request he drew the moving waves he saw. When he walked on stairs he was dizzy. When he looked at pictures, he said that the figures in the pictures moved their heads. Whatever he took in his hand seemed sharp and could not be held. Wherever he stepped he felt that knives were in the cracks of the floor or as if fire were there. He could not look up because the light was too sharp. There was always a noise as if someone was saying something to him. He heard scolding as if his father or somebody else was scolding him. He was afraid of everybody, and could not look into anyone's eyes. When someone said something to him, he heard it several times. He had the feeling that there was poison in the food—it did not taste right. The black coffee had the taste of petroleum. He did not know where he was. During the night he smelled blood. Before he became ill with the grippe great feelings of happiness overcame him.

During the second examination (four years after discharge) the patient was slightly depressed, quiet and withdrawn. Although twenty years old he had never had heterosexual relations. He had emissions two or three times a month (one testicle was hypoplastic). A month later he complained of itching in his nose and ear. He said he could not sleep and felt restless. On the street everything frightened him. It seemed as if people were willfully noisy. He then felt the smell of blood and became nauseated. The people said: "Here is a lunatic," and spat. When he saw a chest and looked in another direction he would see the chest again. His vestibular apparatus was normal at the time of reëxamination.[2]

This patient showed elementary hallucinations of colors, waves and movements. There is no reason to doubt the purely optic nature of these phenomena although the vestibular apparatus had not been examined during the first psychosis. His dizziness was probably due to his optic experiences. We meet unformed colors, waves, movements, this time as an hallucinatory experience. H. Stein seems convinced that we have the right to consider these experiences as primitive experiences which actually deal with the beginning of optic experiences.

[2] The case is probably one of schizophrenia with a picture of mental confusion after the grippe. In the foreground was hyperesthesia concerning light and touch. It is probable that his sensations of smell and taste had the same origin. His helplessness was connected with the hyperesthesia. The symptoms suggesting catatonia were probably secondary to the sensory disturbances. Pick has described a similar case.

However his material is even more difficult to evaluate than this, for after quoting the experiences about the *Eigenlicht* (idioretinal light), he uses experiences from mescal intoxication almost exclusively as a basis for his deductions. Tachistoscopic studies might be a better approach to his problem. E. Lindemann saw, in tachistoscopic exposure, that figures expand and contract. This movement, which has also been called gamma movement, may manifest itself in a queer restlessness and flickering and changes in the brightness in the figure itself. He also observed a second type of movement having a closer relation to the structure of the figures. In general, in tachistoscopic exposure of figures at rest, movements are perceived. This is one more hint that motion belongs to the most primitive optic experience. Of special interest are the so-called autokinetic phenomena when a point observed in darkness begins to move suddenly. At the present time the general opinion is that we deal with the combination of two different phenomena: *Punktschwanken* (point wavering), small irregular movements of small excursion; *Punktwanderung* (point wandering), slow gliding movements up to thirty—and according to Carr even up to sixty-five degrees. F. B. Hoffman confirms Oehrwall and Hanselmann's opinion that point wavering is connected with the small eye movements which occur during fixation, regardless of one's unawareness of them. We are less concerned with the latter phenomenon, in which eye movements play at least some part, than with the former. I do not think that eye movements alone are responsible for point wandering. Our total orientation is changed in a dark room. The eye movements play only a small part in the attempt to regain orientation.

Point wavering is the problem which deserves our special interest. According to my own experiments it is not true that, as F. B. Hoffman states, if three points are exposed they always move in the same direction. On the contrary, when one produces the phenomenon with three points, one sees distinctly that every point has an independent movement. This movement is a gradual and creeping one, as though the point pushed out an extension. The point changes its shape and does not move as a whole. If a point is drawn near a straight line, it appears to approach the line and then go away. However it is true that point and line or two points never unite. They approach each other but never unite. The movement generally starts at the time when negative contrast phenomena around the point become obvious. The whole figure becomes filled with a more or less glittering light which is similar to flickering. Hoffman himself states that a slow movement of the point speaks against the genesis of the movement from eye movements, but he still returns to his previous interpretation. He did not consider that changes in the shape became obvious if the points are made a little larger. Hoppe has compared these changes in the figure with a moving insect. Even the analysis of the movements of single points makes it clear that the movement is not due to ocular movements but is inherent in the optic process as such. These phenomena can be seen in the daytime as well as in a dark room. The less visibility the point has, the more sharply are the phenomena outlined. However it is much simpler to understand these problems if lines are used instead of points. If one looks at a thin line it seems to tremble and waves appear. At a distance of about 40 cm. the amplitude of the wave is about $\frac{1}{2}$ cm., and the wave length about 2 cm. When one looks at the end of the line it begins to swing like a pendulum. The amplitude of the swinging is up to $1\frac{1}{2}$ cm. The phenomenon requires more time for development when the line is thicker. The quick waves appear on the two borderlines of the thick lines, independently of each other, and the line as a whole moves slowly. Short lines move more than long ones. The phenomena occur more quickly and vividly when the retina is tired, when the lines are seen through dark glasses, or when they are covered with transparent paper. It is of special importance that the same phenomena occur in the afterimage of lines. Movement occurs in the afterimage even if it did not in the illuminated line which was exposed, and becomes more pronounced before the afterimage disappears. There is no doubt that the phenomena on the lines and the phenomena on the points are identical. Neither can be due to ocular movements, but to the optic process as such, and are therefore inherent in it, and arise in certain phases of the optic process—namely, when they are weak, continued too long, or near to its disappearance. The phenomena seem to be related to the phenomena of contrast, and strongly indicate that movement is inherent in optic perception as such. The phenomena of the lines were known to Helmholtz. He incorrectly associated them with the anatomical arrangement of the retinal elements. Knowing that cones and rods are irregularly arranged, he assumed that a line sufficiently thin would be distorted when stimulating this irregular pattern, if sensations are correlated to the stimulation of the single elements. This phenomenon is due to functional processes taking place in the retina. One may suppose that such a process will take place perpendicular to the direction of the line, as if the inner movement in the retina were bound by the straight line.

It is interesting to study this problem in patterns in which parallel horizontal lines are drawn with a narrow interval. All these patterns show great restlessness. Movement takes place immediately. Bourdon and Hoffman are inclined to relate the phenomenon to astigmatism and aberrations in the refractory system of the eye. I do not think that there is any basis for this assertion. Concentration on a single line shows a pattern of autokinetic movements. The lines exhibit waves or have the appearance of a string of pearls, clearly showing that the phenomena are not due to eye movements. There is also a vertical movement, a streaming of points of light in masses perpendicular to the direction of the horizontal lines. Whatever direction the lines of the pattern may take, this movement is always perpendicular to the direction of the lines. The phenomenon is seen clearly in the afterimage. If one looks first at a horizontal pattern of parallel lines and afterwards at a white wall, one may see merely perpendicular movements, sometimes going upwards and sometimes downwards. At times it is difficult to determine whether the direction of the movement is upwards or downwards.

It is a striking fact that the horizontal pattern now seems to change into a vertical one, consisting of pearls loosely strung on vertical lines. Form would appear to be dominated by movements which form the perceptual material. These vertical lines, which have been observed by A. von Szily and myself, are not well understood. I am inclined to believe that small eye movements take place during the fixation of the original pattern. Eye movements in the direction of the lines would naturally not exert influence, and only the upward and downward movements of the eyes would matter. In other words, the eye movements would have the same effect as a horizontal pattern continually moving up and down. It is not possible to disprove this assumption unless one exposes the figure tachistoscopically. Lately I made numerous experiments and feel sure that the afterimage after tachistoscopic exposure of parallel patterns for one-fiftieth of a second shows the "perpendicular streaming phenomenon." I have not yet had the opportunity of repeating these experiments with other subjects. The experiments and afterimages of single lines make me more certain of my opinion that the pearl string phenomenon, the waving, and the perpendicular streaming are not due to ocular movements, but to processes going on in the retina which are fundamental to optic perception. The perpendicular streaming phenomenon seems to be merely a summation of the processes occurring when a single line is exposed. If this interpretation were correct one might venture an hypothesis concerning the so-called afterimages of movements. Any object seen moving provokes a series of more or less complete parallel pictures. The streaming phenomenon takes place perpendicularly to the primary movement. The shorter a single stimulation made by the moving object the more obvious it would be. The direction of the afterimage of movement is opposite to the direction of the primary movement but the direction can easily be reversed. The total situation decides whether a movement is seen in one direction or the other.

There are inner movements in the optic field. Every sensation is in itself a part of a process which expresses itself in movement. Sensations bind movements to specific directions, or rather, sensations consist of a special arrangement of movements. The field acts in its totality. The process is determined by the structure of a figure. Lines have an inner coherence in one direction to which the inner retinal movement becomes bound perpendicularly. Waves and pearls are expressions of this process. The process is stronger at the isolated end of the figure. If one deals with a system of parallel lines, the field processes increase and perpendicular movements become paramount. The binding power of an isolated stimulus is less marked. When the optic process has once started, its final configuration is dependent upon the total situation. W. S. Hunter has developed a similar theory which explains how the afterimage retains its place, although in movement. We conclude that the primitive optic impression is not static but involves movement and that this movement once started is comparatively independent of the "object" and even has a tendency to distort and to destroy the object as in the afterimage of the complicated pattern of parallel lines. With Hunter I am inclined to believe that the inner light of the retina is the expression of the same basic processes of movement which are clearly recognizable in the experiments on the fixation of points and lines. The perception of movements is only partially due to processes of a similar type, for the phenomena described are alone not sufficient to explain the phenomena of the perception of movement. For example, in experiments by F. Schumann and by M. Wertheimer,[3] the impression of a movement occurs much more quickly and decisively than in the experiences quoted above. The factor of primitive motion emphasized here is only one of the determinants of the perception of movements.

In order to have a deeper understanding of the problems involved, one can use two methods. One method is the systematic use of imagination, and the other toxic influences like mescal or hashish.

[3] When first a horizontal and immediately afterwards a vertical line are exposed to view tachistoscopically, the subjects receive the impression of a movement of the line from the one position to the other.

CHAPTER III

REPRESENTATION AND OPTIC
IMAGINATION

WHEN we think about the past or the present there are not only thoughts but also pictures in our mind. We are here primarily concerned with pictures in the optic sphere. These pictures come and go, may be complete or incomplete, may have colors, or be colorless, may be tridimensional or bidimensional. They may be a full picture of the first situation, or merely schematic, or symbolic. The pictures may appear or disappear without any particular intention of the individual to produce pictures as such. Generally speaking, we are not interested in pictures. Our meanings, tendencies, and aims, more or less definite though they may be, are certainly much more definite than these fleeting pictures. There may be particular psychic elements which are completely devoid of pictures and are "imageless thoughts" in the sense of Otto Kuelpe and Karl Buehler. (This question has in some way lost its interest since we no longer believe in "psychic elements.") But there can be no doubt that the pictures are never more than a part or, better, one aspect of the psychic functions and of the psychic situation as a whole. It is, therefore, more or less artificial to study pictures, representations, and memories in isolation. Pictures belong to the past and are in some way a continuation of perceptions, and only perceptions are immediately present. But this past is in the immediate service of the present tasks. Pictures and representations of this kind occur in the natural course of psychic life. They are not specifically intended but come as a byproduct and many persons do not actually realize that they use such pictures in the course of their psychic lives.

However there may be reasons why one would like to remember

a specific sensory experience or perceptual situation, and may therefore try by determined effort to represent this previous situation. Pictures of this kind are the result of an effort to reproduce the previous situation as clearly as possible. It is one step further when an individual is asked to produce a mental image of a specific picture. This is the procedure I followed in experiments which I shall discuss later. V. Urbantschitsch and E. R. Jaensch have shown that pictures closely following a previous sensory experience occur without any particular effort of the individual to reproduce them. The different types of representations have many things in common with each other, but they are not completely identical.

There have been many discussions as to whether percept and representation are fundamentally different or similar to each other. A difficulty in discussing these problems arises from the fact that isolation of psychic elements like perceptions and representations is artificial. There can be no doubt that our total attitude is different in representation and in perception. We certainly feel more active when representing either willfully or instinctively, and we have more of the feeling of passivity when we perceive. The percept seems more or less a gift.

However attitudes of perceiving and representing show intermediate steps. This is true, for instance, for many of the representations which V. Urbantschitsch has called "Subjecktive Anschaungsbilder" and E. R. Jaensch "eidetic images." Also, when falling asleep the so-called "hypnogogic visions" are received in an attitude intermediate between perceiving and imagining. There seem to exist two distinct attitudes with connecting links between them. The specific attitude finally decides whether we consider ourselves representing or perceiving.

Many years ago I showed that even when we have the attitude of representing, elements of perception may be combined with it. When I asked my subjects to imagine (optically) that their hands were three times their natural size, they reported *sensations* of tension and heaviness in the imagined hand. Furthermore, I have shown that an optic imagination exposed to vestibular irritation behaves in the same way as a perception. The physiologic processes underlying perceptions and representations must therefore be similar. More recently Jaensch and his school have brought forward extensive material which supports this. They produced color mixtures between representations and perceptions. Jaensch is inclined to believe that eidetic images are a particular class of experiences which stands between perception and representation. However in my opinion representations and eidetic images do not show any fundamental differences. There is no fundamental difference between the material of representations and perceptions and we probably deal with physiological processes which are fundamentally of the same order.

Leo Kanner and I [1] asked six subjects to produce optic images. The images of some objects were asked for without any preceding visualization, others were exposed for a short period of time and afterwards the subjects were instructed to imagine them with their eyes closed. First, a simple geometrical figure was imagined, such as a single straight white line, a white circle and recumbent ellipse. Second, more complicated forms were imagined, such as the outline of a rose, of a house, of a standing horse, and a boy standing on the ground. Third, balancing and moving objects were imagined such as a running dog, a boy walking (first the boy alone and then the boy in a definite setting), a man clenching his fist, stretching his arm at the elbow, a person turning his head to the extreme right and then to the extreme left, a person going through the more complicated motions of cutting bread, a ball rolling down the bowling alley, a man doing the finger–nose test. After this, the subject was told to imagine that he himself carried out certain prescribed actions or movements such as walking, stretching the arm, clenching a fist, lighting a match and performing the finger–nose test. Finally pictures were shown for a short time; then the subject was told to close his eyes and observe what happened when he tried to reproduce what had been seen. The pictures were at first shown in their natural upright position and then turned upside down. There were black and white and colored drawings; some simple and some quite complicated. The

[1] Partially reprinted from the *Journal of Nervous and Mental Disease* (November, 1930), Vol. 72, No. 5. I am indebted to Dr. Jelliffe for permission to reprint this and other articles which have appeared in this journal.

last group of experiments dealt with visualization of actual movements and the following optic reproduction. A key was dropped in front of the subject who was to observe the fall very closely and later to reproduce it in his imagination. Similarly a spool was observed rolling down a board with varying speed, and both the actual perception and optic presentation were described.

One of the protocols will be sufficient to give a general idea of the experiments. The subjects were asked to imagine a white line.

Subject A. On a black background a white line is seen, about two inches long and very narrow. The two ends roll up simultaneously towards the center, "like a carpet being rolled together," until only a dot remains in the center; this dot loses itself in the background, spreading out "like waves of water when a stone is thrown into it."

Subject B. A few seconds after closing his eyes he sees vivid movements of the imagined vertical line, especially in its lower part. They have a lashing character, and sometimes several lower ends are seen at the same time. Occasionally the entire white line swings to both sides.

Subject C. "I have to keep putting the line back. It does not stay. It runs off in the edges. It keeps getting broader and finally it is gone; it begins to disappear in the middle." In a second attempt she sees a white line in the black field before her eyes, showing sparkling movements in the edges.

Subject D. A blackboard with a white line is imagined, extending from one end of the board to the other. The line soon breaks up into several fragments which move up and down separately in front of the blackboard, often losing their contact with it. The movements of the parts exhibit a rapid flickering with considerable excursions; they are irregular, quite synchronous, but go in various directions.

Subject E. He sees a white line against a gray background. The whiteness spreads in the form of what he calls a "standing irradiation." The outline becomes gradually blurred.

Subject F. She tries to imagine a horizontal line but sees a vertical one, which immediately appears multiplied by three. The two outer lines "organize themselves in the mid-line," which is not quite straight, scintillates, and finally disappears, leaving a black spot.

We come to the following conclusions. In all the subjects examined, optic images voluntarily produced showed certain characteristic properties.

1. Fading of the picture.

2. Breaking of a line into a number of fragments.

3. Diffusion of the light of the image.

4. Movements of the image, chiefly of a waving and curling character.

5. Scintillation of the image.

6. Tendency to multiplication of the image or its essential parts.

7. Difference in the type and direction of movement corresponding to the shape of the imagined object (the motion of an imagined circle being different from the movements of an imagined line).

8. Occasional participation of the background in the changes, movements, and scintillations.

9. Changes in the size of the object.

10. Increase in the movements with the direction of the imagination.

11. Marked individual differences in the single subjects, though many trends are common to all persons examined.

12. Occurrence of the changes independent of, and not controlled by, volition, and usually not noticeably correlated with the particular meaning or trend of the imagined object.

From these findings which, so far as we know, have not been previously described, the following conclusions may be drawn.

The act of imagining may effect transformations and transpositions within the entire visual field. With every image the entire background may immediately present some alterations in color, light, and position in space, with movements and scintillations. Thus the imagination of an object and the observation of the course it may take becomes more than a strictly isolated phenomenon, being integrated in the total setting of the visual field.

The processes of fading and irradiation apparently bear a close, though at present not quite definable, relation to similar occurrences experienced in actual perception. In this respect our observations coincide with those of Jaensch and his school, but at the same time show that it is not possible to draw a sharp line between perception and representation.

Since movements of a more or less elementary nature are almost regularly present in optic imagery, movement seems to be one of the inherent qualities of the process of representation. I have repeatedly pointed out that movement is not secondary to motionlessness in either perception or in optic representation.

The phenomena observed in our experiments show a close relation to phenomena occurring in optic perceptions. E. Lindemann demonstrated definite changes in the shape and size of objects exposed tachistoscopically, consisting chiefly in expansion followed by contraction (gamma movements). The autokinetic phenomenon of Exner is characterized by the occurrence of waves in a line which has been fixed for a longer time; these waves are very similar to those described by our subjects in their optic images. The positive results of the Schumann experiments in a number of the persons examined, also speaks for the close resemblance between representative and perceptual phenomena.

The phenomena observed in our experiments were not caused by afterimages, since they were also present after spending almost a whole hour in the dark chamber; indeed, in some of the subjects the movements became even more vivid than in the bright room. The question may be raised whether there is a relation between the alterations in optic images and the "idioretinal light"; if so, they must be of a very complicated nature and cannot be defined at the present time.[2]

The alterations which take place in the optic representations of geometric figures may be divided into two parts: more elementary, primitive tendencies to motility, such as breaking, waving, or curling; and alterations which seem to be determined by the particular shape of the figure, such as expansion, contraction, or rotation. To a certain extent, one may also discern these two types of movement in the more complicated nongeometrical objects. When the more elementary movements become pronounced, they have a tendency to destroy the shape of the figure.

When objects such as flowers, houses, animals are imagined in outline, the observations remain essentially the same. One particular

[2] The investigations of this book give a definite answer to this question raised several years ago. The movements of optic images are based upon idioretinal movements which receive their form from the pictures, perceived or imagined.

phenomenon is more definitely expressed with geometric figures: very often only parts of the object could be imagined and even in those cases where the whole picture was obtained without difficulty, single portions disappeared more rapidly than the whole. The fading of parts may often be observed to be systematic; either one part vanishes after another with a more or less pronounced regularity, or the characteristic outline loses more and more of its specific and distinguishable features. It is evident that individual differences must here be taken into proper account, though they have not been followed in detail.

To the elementary or primitive movement already discussed and those determined by the shape of the figure, we must now add those determined by the objective possibility of movement in the imagined object. Experiments confirm the natural assumption that these three different forms of movement always influence one another. Wherever the elementary forms of motion are more or less completely blended into that which lies in the direction of the usual motile tendencies of the imagined object, the impression of a natural movement will be the result. But as a rule we observe a rather characteristic tendency for all motility to spread from one object or part to another and also from one form of movement to one (or both) of the others. I obtained analogous results with eidetic images. Similarly, Heinz Hartmann has proved that the primitive perception of colors ("space colors") become surface colors when brought into connection with a real object.

The blending of elementary or primitive movements into those which lie in the nature of the object was shown most clearly by Subject A, in whom we observed very vivid elementary movements in the more schematic figures, whereas living objects appeared to behave rather naturally, except that there was a gross exaggeration of these imagined natural movements.

In some subjects (see above), the imagination of movements in animated objects was of an absolutely natural character (A; C, often). The movement was two-dimensional, but often could also be visualized in three dimensions.

In others (particularly D; F, often) the representation of natural movement was entirely impossible and the images remained quiet and rigid despite real efforts to move them.

Instead of the smooth, gliding, natural movement, there was frequently the experience of jerking with several sudden interruptions, until finally motion stopped entirely (D, F, E).

The movement was often described as alien to the animated object ("mechanical," "rubber-like," displacement of joints—D, E).

The movement was, most clearly in Subject B, almost completely emancipated from the object; it was experienced as a violent, explosive motion which sooner or later destroyed the shape. The change of shape occurred, almost as a general law, in practically all subjects (with the exception, perhaps, of A).

Thus, shape and motion in optic representation were very intimately connected with each other. In any event, the final shape was always dependent on the tendencies of the movements.

The optic representation of motion was frequently accompanied by a "feeling of innervation" within the imagining person. Especially those individuals who had difficulty in visualizing motion reported the sensation of strain, effort and innervation of their own muscles. In these cases (D, F), there was a close relation between the attempt at imagining motion and their own performance of movements.

It was easier to imagine motion within the imagined setting than in a single figure only, without any setting.

In D, the incapability of imagining movements was connected with a feeling of uneasiness and "nightmare."

The imagination of abnormal or unusual movements was often accompanied by a feeling of strain and impulses in the sense of being set right referred to the imagined object, which resulted in marked distortion of shape. The imagination of a man turning his head to the extreme right and keeping it in this position brought with it a tendency to make the man follow with his whole body in the direction of the turning head and an extreme distortion of the optic representation. It may be said that motor impulses which we ourselves have in connection with such a movement were transmitted to the optic image and that there was a relation between the subject's own motor impulses and those of the imagined person.

It is remarkable that in Subject F the human shape flattened out and lost its characteristic features, partly under the influence of abnormal motility. In her optic images there was almost always the tendency of characteristic lines to lose their identity.

We may here mention that the results in freely produced images did not differ essentially from those obtained with representations produced after seeing real pictures, and with reference to the phenomena described in this paper, there is no appreciable difference between eidetic and memory images.

Imagination of movements of one's body showed little difference from that of the movements of other persons. There existed, however, an additional difficulty in that there was a vivid tactile and kinesthetic perception of the real position of the parts which were imagined as moving.

The imagined moving limb was often felt, especially by Subject B, as weightless and "ghostlike."

Kinesthetic sensations were generally stronger in this series of experiments than in the others.

From a theoretical point of view, it is especially remarkable that one has such difficulties in imagining one's own movements, particularly when one considers the great importance that has been attributed to the so-called *Bewegungsvorstellungen* in the interpretation of actual natural movements. Optic representations, as we have observed, certainly cannot be the basis for the performance of movements. We may add that all these experiments yielded practically the same results when performed in the dark chamber.

Whereas, in psychological literature, apparent movements have been very carefully studied, the phenomenology of natural movements has not found sufficient consideration. Our own experiments on this problem were only preliminary; slow motion was perceived quite adequately, but in the visualization of quick movements very often only single phases were seen, or, instead of the object, something not quite definable, vague, and shapeless was seen moving between the clearly perceived beginning and end of the movement. This experience shows that the observations made in the optic representation of movements is probably only an exaggeration of the impressions gained in the real perception of motion.

The outstanding features in the optic reproduction of previously seen movements are these.

Instead of a smooth, continuous movement, a succession of objects was perceived, either one or several at a time.

Instead of the moving object a shapeless, vague "something" was seen in motion.

Very often there was a transformation of the pathway (into a "white guiding line," or into a "rope").

An aberration of the direction of the movement was observed (the falling key described circles which grew wider and wider; the rolling spool deviated to the side or curved upward).

Macroptic and microptic changes during the movement were common.

The Schumann experiment was positive in some subjects as in real perception. Others were not capable of imagining the basic procedure; the lines were imagined in different planes and no impression of movement occurred.

We may add here that the deviation of movements as observed in the bowling alley test reminds one in many respects of Benussi's results obtained upon touching the skin with two needle points in succession. Quite frequently the subjects had the impression of a movement which was felt not as a direct one but as a curved movement going through the air.

From our observations one may draw the general conclusion that marked similarities existed between the imagination of inanimate, or living but static, objects on the one hand, and the imagination of moving objects or the reproduction of perceived movements on the other. The final result of the optic representation of a still or moving object seems to depend largely on the degree of integration of the three forms or levels of movement discussed above (elementary; dependent on the nature of the object; dependent on the natural motile tendencies of the object). Thus, the imagination of so-called natural movements appears to be the outcome of a melting or primitive motion into the entire imagined optic situation. One may suppose that this also holds true in the case of real perception; the final elaboration of the perception of a movement then would also take place under the integrative influence of the entire situation, in which the individual's motility tendencies certainly play an important part. In our experiments it appears that, just as the final integration of motion depended on the content or nature of the images, the shaping of the images was in turn dependent upon the movements.

It may seem puzzling that such conspicuous phenomena as the occurrence of unnatural changes and abnormal movements in optic images have not been observed more often. It seems to have escaped the attention of numerous investigators in the field of optic perception and representation. This may be explained by the fact that those persons who have a great tendency to imagine unnatural motion know from casual observations that, in a special task, in the constraint of a special situation, they experience, perfectly, representations natural in shape and size as well as in motion. It would seem that optic reproduction in a natural life situation is quite different from that found in the setting of the psychologic laboratory, where the test is emancipated from the more complicated and genuine psychobiologic need. The images, therefore, are no longer integrated for an ulterior purpose, but have been "ordered," and we may assume that the phenomena obtained in our experiments were the result of a disintegration of the optic images in a situation which is biologically useless.

It is of interest to outline briefly the individual differences in the optic representations of our subjects. We prefer to report each person individually and shall refrain from attempting any rigid groupings.

Subject A sees vivid, richly dramatized images with exaggerations and synesthesias, both auditory and tactile. The movements tend to become somewhat abnormal when simple geometrical figures are seen, but are natural when more complicated situations are imagined.

Subject B experiences images which show extreme motility and have a tendency to undergo destruction of shape, often of a tearing, explosive nature. His pictures are rich in detail. When picturing movements of his own body, he has the impression of a shapeless and weightless "ghostlike" structure performing the motion.

Subject C usually sees natural movements in more complicated situations. Her images show some dramatization, though to a much less extent than those of Subject A. Sometimes she experiences rigidity and abnormal movements of her representations.

Subject D notices frequent fragmentation and jerkiness of his optic images. He has a very marked inability to see movements, the effort to produce them is connected with a feeling of uneasiness and nightmares. Whenever motion is seen, it is stiff, laborious and distorted.

Subject E mostly sees stiff, jerky movements with a tendency to schematization and simplification of the images, which are usually two-dimensional. The pictures are glittering and oscillating, and the background often partakes in the movements of the imagined objects.

Subject F has great difficulty in representing movements; she exerts a great deal of effort and when she manages to obtain motion definitely she has the impression that it is her own activity that causes the imagined objects to move; these movements are jerky and quite rigid. The tendency to multiplication of the object is pronounced. She regularly experiences an annulment of the shape of the imagined object. It is remarkable that in movies she often perceives a multiplication of the objects. K. Zietz and H. Werner have also noticed that the different types of perception of motion run parallel with the types of imagination of motion.

We have refrained from placing our subjects in any of Jaensch's eidetic types (Basedowoid and tetanoid, mixed types), because we have found that, though the individual differences come out quite clearly in the analysis, there is scarcely a reaction which could not be occassionally observed in every one of the persons examined. The differentiation of the eidetic types must, after all, be evaluated in a similar way as the differences between the so-called optic, acoustic, and kinesthetic types of imagination. G. E. Mueller has demonstrated that the images depend to a very large extent upon the situation and not altogether on the individual.

In the studies of the Marburg school, it was found that the Basedowoid (B) type is capable of reproducing natural movements, whereas the tetanoid (T) type either is unable to imagine motion or else sees the behavior of the moving object as rigid and abnormal. Zietz and Werner have shown similar differences to exist in the perception of real movements and have also carried out some experiments dealing with the optic representation of motion; these experiments deserve mention because of their relation to our own observations. Of two persons asked to imagine the ocean, one saw the movements of the waves (in other experiments he imagined a cornfield and a person's face in motion), whereas the other subject was unable to see any motion. Werner's first subject had experiences similar to those of Subjects A and C in our investigations, the second one similar to those of Subjects D and F. Hans Henning distinguishes between two types of individuals with regard to the fate of their optic images. The first type, even after seeing the sea in motion, or a horse race, or a vivid street scene, cannot, with eyes closed, imagine these pictures other than motionless. And the experience of movement in optic images can be obtained only through the self-deception of successively placing the imagined object in different positions and spatial relations. The other type, when shown a picture of a mountain, a desert, or a tree, immediately sees vivid and rapid motion in the optic representation: clouds pass over the top of the mountain, a sandstorm sweeps over the desert, the tree shakes in the wind and is visited by flying birds.

Our observations regarding the imagination of movements have an unmistakable analogy to the findings obtained with mescal intoxication. There is almost no phenomenon in those experiments which could not be seen in our own tests, though, according to W. Mayer-Gross and H. Stein, two stages may be distinguished in the same individual. In the first stage of pronounced lack of motion (*ausgesprochene Bewegungsarmut*), real movements are either not recognized at all or are split off into a succession of single interrupted perceptions; imagination of motion is absolutely impossible. In the second stage of exaggerated motility (*uebertriebene Bewegungserlebnisse*), quiet objects are seen in constant motion and reproduction of previously seen objects is accompanied by various transformations, modifications and variations. Kurt Beringer, in his monograph, quotes a great number of similar observations in mescal intoxication, in which there is inability to perceive movements; instead, only the initial and the final postures are seen without a connecting motion between them, and there is a jerky, abnormal, marionettelike quality and fragmentation. As in our own observations, marked difference existed between the perception of slow movement and that of quick motion.

E. R. Jaensch has found that mescal increases the eidetic phenomena. It seems that in the intoxication both optic perception and reproduction are subject to a disintegration of the different forms of movement, similar to that produced by the special situation of the laboratory experiments. I have developed the thesis that "that which is peripheral in a normal person becomes psychic foreground under unusual or pathologic conditions."

The impossibility of imagining movements experienced by two of our subjects also occurs in certain types of dreams. It is very interesting in this connection to remember the definite "nightmare" feeling of Subject D, when he attempted to produce an optic representation of motion and found himself incapable of doing so. Henning has also called attention to the analogy between such dreams and the rigidity of optic images.

Multiplications, macropsias, micropsias, and metamorphoses, as seen in our experiments, also play an important part in hallucinations, especially those occurring in toxic psychoses.

I have pointed out that experiences obtained with eidetic images are closely related to those observed in optic agnosias. Otto Poetzl and E. Redlich, and K. Goldstein and A. Gelb found that, in lesions of the occipital lobe, movements were not perceived as such; instead of a moving object, a succession of several motionless objects was seen, or else the same object was seen sometimes in one place and sometimes in another, without being connected by motion. W. Mayer-Gross and H. Stein believe these phenomena to be in part identical with those observed by them in mescal intoxication. One should, however, be aware of the fact, confirmed in our investigations, that all these difficulties in the perception of movement may be potentially present in the normal individual: in a case of alexia reported by these authors the presence of finer difficulties in the perception of movement does not prove that the entire optic apparatus is involved when alexia is present. It would be in keeping with my thesis to venture the assumption that agnosia possibly brings to the fore what normally remains in the background and is brought out only in special circumstances such as disintegrations of the different forms of movement, as in mescal poisoning, occipital-lobe tumors, dreams, and in our laboratory experiments.

We may finally call attention to the similarity of our observations to phenomena which V. von Weizsaecker, H. Hoff and myself have described in central and peripheral lesions of the vestibular nerve. In our cases the representation of motion altered the shape and content of the optic images in all but one of the subjects (Subject A). We know that irritation of the vestibular nerve produces not only a feeling of movement in the patient's own body, but also the impression of motion in the visual field. Tonus and motility produce changes in the optic imagery as well as in actual perception. Poetzl has observed metamorphoses in parieto-occipital lesions causing changed innervation of the eye muscles. I have shown that hysterical polyopsia was produced by alterations in the innervation of the ocular muscles. Goldstein and Gelb and von Weizsaecker have described the influence of changes in the tonus on optic impressions. E. R. Jaensch observed transpositions in eidetic pictures when the subjects imagined that they themselves acted in accordance with the actions of their imagined objects. In cases of parietal-occipital lesions, reported by H. Hoff and myself, metamorphoses and polyopsias occurred in connection with increased postural and righting reflexes and spontaneous turning around the longitudinal axis. Alterations of motility and tonus may influence optic perception as well as optic hallucinatory images. According to the observations reported above, the imagined movements of one's own body and of the bodies of other persons have a quite similar effect, and it is perhaps not too far-fetched to think that possibly there is a certain relation between the vestibular impression of movement and the optic impression of movement. Hans Hoff has recently shown that such connections between the vestibular apparatus and visual perception really exist. There is a close resemblance between the optic images and their movements, on the one hand, and the changes of the optic images and perceptions under the influence of vestibular irritation, on the other. Phenomena of scintillation, and the changes of the optic background of imaginations and the sudden darkening of optic pictures, occur in the visual field of patients with labyrinthine disease, according to H. Hoff, K. Eisinger and myself.

The investigations of Leo Kanner and myself show that there is always motion in optic imagination. The motion of single parts is in intimate connection with motion in the total optic field. Motions in the optic field are interdependent. One optic imagination, filling only a small part of the field, changes the field in movement characteristics and probably also in many other qualities. In optic imagination the object binds eddies of general motion to a specific picture, which is an organization of primitive motion. Movement is another type of organization of whirlpools.

Exner pointed out that there is a directed sensory element in the perception of movement. F. L. Dimmick described movement as a gray lightning and defined the sensation of motion as a multiform gray experience of a specific temporal form. H. G. Vogt, and W. Grant, and A. Blug saw, as did Leo Kanner and I, a path connecting two outstanding points in the course of the moving object. It has been mentioned above that the exposure of one object is sufficient to set going the experience of motion and I consider this motion as the fundamental pattern for the perception of motion. Wertheimer emphasizes the fact that in the tachistoscopic exposure of two lines "Querprozessen" (transversal processes) occur with apparent movement from one line to the other and are the direct expression of a physiological process. He calls this apparent motion phi-phenomenon. But here I wish also to stress the universal importance of the perception of motion in relation to the perception of form. The perception of natural movements is relatively independent of the experience of motion.

The phi-phenomenon is merely an indicator that movement takes place. Under the influence of Exner's discovery there has been an inclination to neglect the organization of the sensation of movement, the perception of the same object in different places, or the constructive element in perception. The perception of movement is more than a sensation of movement. Only by constructive effort do we see an object moving in space. The organization of normal experiences is never complete, and experiments on the optic perception of natural quick movements show that object perception and the sensation of movement are often incompletely organized.

In optic imagination, in optic agnosias, and under the influence of drugs, disorganization in the field of movement may become more obvious. It is therefore advisable to present some material concerning optic perception under the influence of drugs.

Color vision in a case of hashish intoxication was mentioned above. Stein, using the material of Kurt Beringer on mescal intoxication, reports that color qualities disappear and everything looks like a poor reproduction where the different colors are not printed exactly upon each other and the outlines of objects are clouded by a transparent poorly colored veil. We have often observed that the colors of the objects in optic imaginations are seen as surface colors irradiating into the surrounding space and wandering with the eye movements as if the colors were dissociated from the objects, existing independently from the object, and as if the object lay behind the free floating color. Stein, after describing the spontaneous phenomena in the dark room, gives the following description of mescal experiments:

The patterns passed in an extraordinarily quick change always coming from the right side, moving in a diagonal direction and disappearing to the left and behind. This stream of colors, in connection only with geometrical figures, was gliding in a plane, whereas shortly afterwards a new space created itself before my eyes.

I see a large cylindrical hole, on the walls of which the color patterns glide toward each other from both sides and separate themselves from the wall before meeting, come towards me and lie upon each other in the middle of the space and disappear . . . a play which repeats itself in quick succession.

Different objects move before my eyes near and above each other. The filigreelike ornament develops further. In between glowing blue and yellow spots shine out. A bundle of parallel color bands suddenly starts in rapid rotation. Another one moves over the whole visual field coming quickly from the left side. The phenomena become quiet again, the filigree like ornament comes into the foreground and becomes more and more complicated and more beautiful, taking on the shape of plant ornaments. For the first time the phenomena fascinate me and excite me.

Concerning motion, Stein reports the following:

The pattern of the wallpaper and of the carpet begins to move. The wallpaper pattern was repeated three to four times, one above the other, a little transposed towards each other, richer but always strictly geometrical in shape. Movements in the different planes—one above the other—to and fro—from right to left—from above to below, become more and more polymorphous. To the movement of the planes towards each other, independent movements of single figures were added. Their lines started to run, to roll, became perspectivic, came from behind into the foreground and disappeared towards the periphery.

Stein also reports on metamorphoses (changes in the shape of the object): "Boards seem to be curved. The whole ceiling does not have its normal form. It becomes lower and higher, inclines towards me and goes back to the wall."

But during mescal intoxication, subjects very often do not see movements. Instead of a curve in which a lighted object is moved, a multiplicity of shining points is seen. H. Kluever emphasizes the following form constants in a mescal vision. One is "grating, lattice, fretwork, filigree, honeycomb and chessboard design." Related to this is the cobweb figure. A second form constant is "tunnel, funnel, alley, cone or vessel." A third important form constant is the spiral.

No special color is in the foreground. The brightness is very often intense. Unusual saturation is observed. Very frequently an illumination from behind is observed. The phenomena frequently are symmetrical. The localization of the phenomena may be difficult. Some experiences are two-dimensional and others are three-dimensional. The visionary objects may be gigantic or Lilliputian. Polyopia in visions is rather frequent. The visions are often in different systems —the one in frantic motion and the other in slow majestic movements. It seems that only at the height of the intoxication "visionary forms" such as human and animal faces, monsters, and architectural details can be viewed comfortably.

A. Knauer and W. Y. Maloney consider the following sequence as

characteristic: "labile lines, mosaics, carpets, floral designs, ornaments, wood carvings, windmills, monuments, mausoleums and
panoramic landscapes, statuesque men and animals, fiery scenes, pictures and episodes in a connected manner."

We understand the labile line, the spiral and the funnel (which is
the three-dimensional variant of the spiral) as basic forms of the
primitive visual impression. Some more remarks are necessary about
the filigree, the mosaic, the tapestry pattern. They are due to a principle of repetition. The same principle is found in polyopia. It is
wrong to believe that primitive impression is single. Primitive sensual
impression is multiplied in itself. The visual field acts as a unit which
crystallizes the same form again and again. The observers seem to
agree that at the height of the intoxication the picture becomes more
consistent and scenic. I think that we here have another instance of
the gradual development of the optic world from the primitive pattern to the object formation, and the development is connected with
a binding of movement into specific forms.

These protocols are sufficient to indicate a fundamental identity
between the phenomena observed in optic imagination and in mescal
experiments. It is true the phenomena in the mescal experiment seem
quantitatively more impressive; but the mescal intoxication brings
into the foreground in the perceptual field processes which remain
more in the background and in the field of imagination. Of course,
mescal is only one of the drugs which has such an influence. The
phenomena observed in hashish intoxication are similar in many
respects. Primitive colors play an even greater part in hashish hallucinations. "I saw different designs and lights—red, yellow, blue and
green. The lights were round or square. They all moved." Bromberg
reports more instances of this kind.

To summarize: Under the influence of specific drugs, color and
movement come into the foreground of optic perception. In imagination and under the influence of drugs, primitive perceptual qualities
make their appearance in the optic sphere.

CHAPTER IV

MOTION, FORM, AND SPATIAL RELATIONS
IN OPTIC PERCEPTION

MOTION occurring in the visual field often has a distorting influence on the form of the picture. The simplest instances are the waves appearing on lines when the autokinetic movement appears. In mescal intoxication, objects seen become changed by the movement. Optic imaginations give the clearest instances of this distorting influence. This is especially clear in experiments with geometrical figures. When the subject is asked to imagine a moving object, the distortion occurs in the moving part; legs become elongated; a stretching arm elongates; the head flattens out. These changes are particularly impressive when violent movements of another person or one's own person are imagined. There is a mild degree of change in the picture when the movements seen are described as mechanical and rubberlike. One may draw the general conclusion that optic motion has the tendency to destroy the shape unless an integrative process leads to a correct construction of the picture. Stein also has observed the distortion (metamorphoses) and destruction of the pictures by movements. However he comes to the conclusion: "The process of sensation (*Empfindungsvorgang*) does not give more than sensations. Only the process of motion makes the space and time relation in the perception possible. . . . The movements are a common basis of the so-called higher motor and sensory functions and make the connection between them." He further states that the act of perception unites two contents which are different from a phenomenological point of view; the one is the experience of quality—the sensation in the closer sense—the other the experience of the movements—which is provoked by the stimulus and the constellation of stimuli. I object to this formulation in so far as it neglects the fact that motion is not added to the primitive sensation but is one of the inherent qualities of sensation. What occurs is not a binding together of motion and sensation but a development and integration of both.

Our experiments on optic imagination hint at another problem of importance which we shall later discuss in more detail. We have stated that the optic representation of motion was frequently accompanied by a feeling of innervation in the imagining person and that there was a close relation between the attempt at imagining motion and one's own performance of movements. This leads to the hypothesis that there may be a connection between the motion one sees in the picture and the motion one performs oneself.

C. E. Ferree, in describing the streaming phenomenon, mentions that the crossing streams often cause parts of lines to disappear. The phenomenon of *Punktauchen* has been known for a long time. When several small points are looked at, one or another point may disappear and then reappear. The usual explanation of this phenomenon is that the projection of the points falls into the areas between the cones of the retina and returns after small eye movements have taken place. This interpretation cannot be true; there are difficulties arising from the anatomical distribution of the retinal elements, but the fact that parts of lines may disappear in a similar way is even more important. It is particularly interesting to stare at a system of parallel lines. At first, a flickering perpendicular to the line is seen, but very soon a part of the visual field may suddenly disappear. The disappearing parts are often in the periphery of the visual field. The phenomenon is present in monocular as well as in binocular vision, and it is remarkable that when one has a system of crossing lines only one part of the system may disappear. These phenomena are neglected in the literature and are difficult to explain. They almost seem to be a continuation of the spontaneous movements in the visual field. The phenomenon becomes more obvious when the degree of illumination decreases. I would not have given so much attention to this phenomenon if in tachistoscopic exposure parts of the picture did not disappear in a very similar way. In tachistoscopic exposures of pictures the disappearance of parts may be systematic. (Otto Poetzl, R. Allers and J. Teler.) Well-characterized parts of the situation disappear, objects may not be seen any more, or irregular pieces may be broken out.

Similar phenomena occur in eidetic images. I have a protocol of an experiment in which I myself was the subject. The picture shown is one with children. On the left side is the leader. After a little space come four boys in costume, the third of whom is carrying a drum, which is in the center of the whole group. The second boy wears a pointed green cap, the first one has a bluish-green apron, and the last boy carries a wooden sword. The eidetic images are as follows:

Above the center a red, pointed cap, a drum, wide with a red brim and a drumstick on it. The drum is too low in relation to the drumstick. A squirting movement of the drumstick, like champagne bubbles, occurs. In the right visual field there is something green which comes from the outside. It is lower than the drum. Four boys' faces, a little blurred; everything above the plane of the cartoon. A new effort to reproduce the picture lets four figures come clearly into the foreground. A green apron which is below the row of boys. Everything is in the right side of the visual field. At the same time a raised wooden sword. A clear picture coming from the previous exposure of another picture comes out. The drum is in the foreground. High above the drum a little boy marches. The movements of the legs are at first doll-like and then fantastically whirling and the legs elongate. A quick to-and-fro of the trumpet to his mouth; the last with the consciousness of an arbitrary play. The picture is quick-moving but the movement has no similarity with movement in reality.

I summarize this and other experiences in the following way:

1. The eidetic images come in parts.

2. One half of the picture may never reappear.

3. The reappearance does not occur in the original arrangement. Transpositions in space take place.

4. The transpositions may concern the shape or the color or both at the same time. Figures may turn as a whole or be transposed in space.

5. The color very often loses the character of a surface color. It appears more diffuse and disappears into space. It becomes a space color as Jaensch has already pointed out.

6. The transposed material can be elaborated and condensed in a free way. Units may be cut to pieces.

7. Transformation of movements is particularly obvious. They are transposed from the moved to the unmoved, or movements are substituted for each other.

8. The movements often take a character different from reality and do not correspond to any natural movement.

Similar instances can be found in the paper by G. Bibring-Lehner where optic images were observed during and after turning in a swivel chair. H. Kluever has studied the fragmentation of eidetic imagery in detail. According to him fragments of the following kind may appear in the eidetic image: "One eye—don't know whose eye it is"; "shovel"; "a stick with crosspieces"; "a nose upside down"; "quarter circles" (meaning curves in one row); "blades of grass"; "row of buttons"; "a jacket with black dots"; and the like. Often these eidetic fragments represent "elements" of the real picture, incorrectly named. Although the fragments may represent certain parts of the stimulus object, they are often not recognized or remembered as such by the subject: "I don't think of them, they just come." Sometimes the fragments display various degrees of similarity to elements in the real picture or do not appear at all in the picture. In summarizing Kluever states:

1. There is a splitting-up of the stimulus into details very often relatively meaningless.

2. Temporally, the fragments, after removal of the stimulus object, may appear after a relatively long period (several seconds, minutes, hours); for example, while observing a negative after-image, the head (only) of a doll which has been shown to the subject twenty minutes earlier may suddenly appear; the fragments of the image may disappear and then reappear.

3. The fragments, while not intentionally influenced by the subject, may undergo changes of various kinds: rotational displacements; translocation of shapes, colors, directions, and movements; changes in size and color; changes from "dots" to meaningful objects and vice versa.

4. Upon activation of (so-called) attention, (a) missing elements may gradually or suddenly appear, or only parts of the desired object may appear; (b) elements may appear having characteristics not found in such

a way in the stimulus object; (c) missing elements may appear, while others present in the eidetic image may disappear; (d) instead of the appearance of missing elements, only rotations or spatial displacements in the fragments present are observed.

5. "Disturbing" stimuli (noises, tuning-fork sounds, thermal stimuli, illumination or pressure on the bulbs), often lead to unexpected changes in the same sense as attention does.

6. Elements are not recognized by the subject, or only recognized after a long time as parts of the stimulus.

7. An element of the stimulus object may be absent in the eidetic image; still its correct position is indicated by an "empty" space. The "nothing" somehow exists psychologically, it has a "place-coefficient."

Kluever points out the fundamental importance of this type of reproduction. According to him it is not that the nonimportant characteristics of the stimulus are reproduced in this way but the crucial characteristics themselves suffer fragmentation. "Fragmentary reproduction must be due to an emission of the 'gestalt quanta.'" But I do not think that this conclusion is completely justified. The disappearance of one-half of a picture has nothing to do with the fragmentation of a gestalt. It is rather that in the same way as in tachistoscopic perception we deal not only with fragmentation of gestalten but with fragmentation in the total visual field.

As to the question of whether we have the right to consider fragmentation a characteristic of primitive perceptual processes or rather as a characteristic of a higher level of perception, the facts presented make it much more probable that a primitive mechanism leads to fragmentation in perception, in tachistoscopic perception, and in imagination.

In the primitive perception we find spirals, glittering waves, and vortices. Points obviously are not perceived as such in primitive optic experience. The loop, the circle, and even the star seem to be more primitive than the point. The straight line is not so primitive as the curved line, and the angle is also a later development. This latter point needs more study. It is probably pertinent that in experiments of F. B. Hoffman an obtuse angle appears as a curve when the sides of the angle are made sufficiently short and a vertical line finds a continuation in another vertical line with a small horizontal displacement. When the vertical lines are made very short, an oblique line appears instead of the two vertical lines displaced towards each other. The dent seems to disappear. If this observation is correct it would mean that there is a greater tendency to see a straight line than to see a dent. It seems difficult to interpret the results since irradiation plays some part and I cannot understand the phenomenon unless the optic picture of the dent has become blurred. The prevalence of curves, circles, ellipses, and whirls in primitive perception corresponds to the fact that similar movements prevail in primitive motor action.

Even these primitive optic experiences have some kind of shape and size. We do not know under what conditions the angle is definitely differentiated from the primitive forms. Children are not able to draw a diamond before the seventh year. One may, of course, say that this is a motor incapacity of the child. However, the sharp division between motility and perception is not justified and is a remainder of an isolating psychology. The prevalence of the curve over the straight line has been justly emphasized by gestalt psychologists. In our experiments in optic imagination, the prevalence of the curved line is clearly revealed. Sometimes, however, the curved line flattens out into a straight line and there is also a tendency of indentations to flatten out. One has the impression that forms and shapes which have distinct, sharp angles are maintained in imagination only by an effort. It also has been mentioned that in tachistoscopic exposures, figures shrink and expand. The size of an optic imagination seems to remain rather indefinite. As long as it is of primitive character a picture may become smaller or larger. We have no definite knowledge about the limits of these size variations in perception. Children are somewhat insensitive to the size of a reproduction. In general in primitive perception and imagination size is not definite; it becomes so only with further development. Primarily, optic impressions are indefinite in size. The phenomena of micropsia and macropsia have often been discussed.[1] There are increased impulses to accommodation, objects appear smaller; as for example, when we put concave glasses on our

---

[1] Compare also Chapter VIII.

eyes, or when we paralyze accommodation by atropin. If we put eserin or pilocarpin into the eye, a spasm of the accommodation muscle occurs and objects at a distance appear larger (macropsia). Definite size of an object is not dependent only on optic impression but depends also on motor mechanisms closely connected with those impulses and attitudes which Jaensch calls "attention." We do not believe that the motor impulse is merely added to the optic impression. It is a unit, deeply engraved in the total organization of the organism. It is interesting to study atropin delirium with its clear-cut microptic phenomena. We cannot explain these microptic hallucinations as merely due to the paralysis of accommodation, and the subsequent transfer of the micropsia in perception to the microptic hallucination, and it is unnecessary to assume that the mechanisms which regulate the size of hallucinations and perceptions have a deep inner connection with each other. Microptic and macroptic phenomena in hallucinations can also be found in cases in which the accommodation mechanism is not impaired. A fifty-year-old man with alcoholic hallucinosis had macroptic and microptic hallucinations:

"Yes, I drank the last few weeks before I came in. I did not take any medicine for my ulcers of the stomach. Well, the first night after I came in I was all right. The first night I saw animals like big elephants. But they were twice as high as elephants, broad and fat. They were very heavy. There were four or five of them. The room seemed to be bigger. They just moved around, walked naturally, very slowly. I did not see any other patients. There were three men in front of me. One was fat, the two others seemed to be thinner. They had scars all over their faces. As I looked at them the scars became worse, bloody and they disappeared. Then I saw little animals walking on the floor, small. There were thousands and thousands of them. They looked like sea horses. Some of them were yellow and some were red. A fellow was sitting beside me. He looked like an old tramp. I grabbed at him and nearly fell out of bed. Then I had the crazy feeling that I was on the street and everybody I touched would explode. There was an awful crash in my head like an explosion. I touched everybody I passed. I remember a little fellow came up to me on crutches and I touched him and he exploded three or four times. I could see nothing but light. It was an awful crash, like a bomb and then I ran into a bus full of people and when I ran into it the whole thing exploded. There were about ten people in it.

In such cases there is no relation to peripheral disturbances in accommodation.

A case of Otto Kauders is of special interest. He showed spontaneous turning around the longitudinal axis with increase in the postural and righting reflexes, in which microptic hallucinations played a very great part. It is probable that in cases of this type primitive motor impulses have an influence on the microptic hallucinations. In the optic experiments quoted above, objects were imagined in different sizes. An imagined fist becomes bigger and bigger while coming nearer; a hand seems to be unusually long; circle spreads out to its periphery; circle narrows down; wall gets smaller and smaller. There seems to be a tendency to see objects in different sizes. Within wide limits children are not sensitive to variations in the size of drawings which are shown to them. It is necessary to differentiate between optic representation and its perceived size and the size of the object to which the optic representation points. We know that small imaginations may easily point to large objects and vice versa; but we are primarily interested in the changing size of the imaginations. It is very probable that we deal with a spontaneous tendency in the image to expand and contract, and in addition a tendency to imagine objects in various sizes. I am inclined to believe that the expanding and contracting tendencies are basic for the imaginations in the various sizes.

Motor tendencies add new stimuli to changes in the size of the object. In addition to motor tendencies, in the proper sense, there are also emotional tendencies which act in the same direction. It is probably on this basis that children and primitive people draw important persons as larger than unimportant ones. G. E. Mueller has written about the effect of affective changes which alter the size of imaginations. The motor impulses which change the size of the object are probably of a very different kind and include not only the motor impulses in the proper sense but also the tonic impulses which are due to the righting reflexes and those which are associated with the vestibular irritation. Another factor of great importance, referred to before, are the impulses to see an object either near at hand or at a distance, impulses which are connected with accommodation and convergence. There is a close relation between the perceived size of an object and the distance at which we place it. F. B. Hoffman has discussed this question in detail. Jaensch has emphasized the role of plasticity in the perception of size. He has the opinion, especially in regard to the depth perception, that perceptual constancy is only gradually developed in the individual. We return to this point later. It is probable that the primary mechanisms underlying the changes in size in the optic sphere are aided by motor mechanisms tending in the same direction and, finally, that our whole psychophysiological organization tends towards perceptions, fantasies, imaginations in the various sizes (as I have already emphasized in *The Image and Appearance of the Human Body*). This insight may help us to understand ideas in psychotic states. One patient who suffered from an atypical depression saw an elephant of normal size in a normal-sized bathtub. Another patient believed that horses could be found in her bowel movement. Concerning anxiety states of children the following observations are pertinent: one patient reports that she was afraid as a child that lions might jump full size out of the toilet bowl; another child was afraid of being sucked into the drain of the bathtub and washed away. In these hallucinations and fears the infantile disregard of size comes into appearance.

It is obvious that in imaginations and perceptions variations in size are closely connected with the problem of multiplicity. That it is possible to have double vision with only one eye is shown by the famous observation of Bielschowsky in which monocular double vision occurred after the strabismic eye was brought into the normal position. The patient saw the object not only with the then functioning fovea but also with the other one. Similar observations have been made by W. Fuchs on monocular diplopia in hemianopic patients who had developed a pseudofovea. The patient then saw the object both according to its original and to its newly acquired localization in space.

Besides this retinal polyopia, there exists another type, in which the quality of the ocular motor impulses is responsible for the polyopic experience as in hysterical polyopia. A discussion of the problem has been made by D. M. Purdy, who rightly stresses the importance of motility. Schumann observed that the optic picture may be redoubled when an object is fixated and the attention is directed towards another part of the visual field. Monocular diplopia in organic lesions of the brain has been discussed by J. Gerstmann and A. Kestenbaum, H. Hoff, O. Poetzl, and K. Goldstein. Motor impulses in the usual sense, as well as impulses which lead to a nystagmus and tonic impulses, may have the same effect. The experiments of Leo Kanner and myself on optic imaginations show that there is a tendency to multiplication in the imagination itself. The tendency to multiply perceptions is probably a primitive tendency connected with the optic perception as such, which finds increased expression in optic imagination. This primary tendency to multiplication can then be brought into the foreground by the motion of the object, by movement of the eye muscles, or by tonic influences of any other kind.

It is quite probable that similar mechanisms can be found to determine directional orientation. In optic imaginations, optic images are occasionally turned around at an angle of 180 degrees. We found this particularly in Subject F, who also has a great tendency to spontaneous multiplication. In reading, this subject, who is left-handed, experienced some difficulties of the congenital dislexia type. S. Orton has especially emphasized that when we perceive optically there is one impression present and also its mirror image, deposited symmetrically in the nondominant hemisphere. Without discussing this hypothesis from the point of view of anatomical localization, psychologically it is true that pictures are very often experienced as turned around in an angle of 180 degrees in the horizontal plane. Otto Poetzl has emphasized similar phenomena in cases of optic agnosia. He has also given special attention to changes of direction in reading and writing. The relation of the bilaterally symmetrical motility of the body to this phenomenon is obvious. It is indeed very difficult to discuss optic phenomena isolated from motor phenomena. Whereas left-right disorientation of 180 degrees is a very common phenomenon, below and above are less often changed in optic imagination. This is probably because orientation in the gravitational field is of outstanding importance for the organism. However, such phenomena occur. Otto Poetzl has seen in lesions of the occipital lobe that optic pictures and impressions are turned around so that the person standing is now seen upside down. In migraine, similar phenomena have been observed. I have observed such a change in directions in a hypnogogic state of unknown etiology. (See Chapter VIII.) Front and back are rarely substituted for each other. Gerstmann has published an observation of this kind in a case with organic brain lesion. There exists a large field of vestibular optics in which changes and directions play a very important part. In this field as in the other fields discussed, the tendencies which are present in optic perception and related motility can only be artificially separated from the phenomena of phasic and tonic motility. Pick reported cases of epileptic disorder in which the patients saw objects and persons turned upside down. Hyslop reported a case who saw as upside down some but not all of the objects seen at one time. W. Stern found that children may perceive objects rotated 90 to 180 degrees from their position. Children, more readily than adults, recognize objects which are turned around, upside down, or from left to right. Paula Meyer also found that children commit more mistakes concerning position than adults. Mistakes in right and left are much more common than mistakes in above and below. Figures which were not symmetrical were reproduced as symmetrical. The investigations of Lauretta Bender on gestalt figures, which will be discussed later in detail, offer further material illustrating these points. A. LeMaitre reports an adolescent who had attacks twice a month, in which he had the impression that he had experienced the present situation in a dream, but in the dream everything was upside down so that human beings had their feet up and their heads down. Pierre Janet reports a case in which the patient had the feeling of moving in the direction opposite to that in which he was actually moving. G. E. Mueller says that the mistake between right and left and upside down arises from the fact that the total appearance of the figures is similar even in these opposite directions. People who were born blind and have been operated on have difficulty in distinguishing, in two-colored discs, which color is above and which color is below. Mueller has seen that a figure of a series appears in the position of the nearer image during the reproduction. Urbantschitsch found that words which were presented in mirror writing appeared in images in the correct position. G. E. Mueller emphasizes that the position in which a person turns his head is of importance for the localization of images. There is no question that, in the cases discussed here, not only optic but also postural and vestibular influences play an important part. The localization of an image or a perception is primarily given with a tendency to arrangements in a system of six primary coördinates: left and right, below and above, before and behind, and that only with the further development of the perception is there elaborated a definite orientation in space concerning direction and localization. Furthermore, a primary impression has to be brought into the system of coördinates. Six positions are particularly outstanding; but primarily the object is given in all possible positions. Careful observation reveals that individuals are continually experimenting with the various positions, until finally, under the influence of forces which are not merely optic, a specific direction and localization is given to a perception or an image.

I shall not go into a detailed discussion of the problem of the perception of depth, a problem which has occupied the attention of psychologists for a long time. Two main lines of thought can be distinguished. E. Hering is of the opinion that the binocular perception of depth is due to the inborn organization of the retinal apparatus. Helmholtz emphasizes empirical factors and experience. The depth values of the single retina are, according to Hering, inefficient. Complete depth perception depends on binocular vision and the so-called "Querdisparition." E. R. Jaensch has tried to show that the perception of depth is in a great measure dependent upon the influence of attention and that eidetic images show this phenomenon particularly clearly, and he also emphasizes the influence of emotions concerning the localization in depth. He concludes that relative constancy in depth values is secondary and is built up later, whereas in the earliest stages of development there is a great plasticity in depth values. Even if the experimental proofs of Jaensch concerning the depth perception of juveniles and children should be reliable, there is still the question why we find in adults a relative constancy, comparatively little influenced by the factor of attention. Even if this takes place by development, it must lie in the basic qualities of the organism, and even if the retina should get its constant depth values only after puberty, there are many qualities which are apparently inborn but make their appearance only at a later stage of development. One must follow Hoffman's opinion that there are innate tendencies for perception of depth which are continually modified by empirical forces and forces of attention and motility.

M. von Senden has collected material to show that those who were born blind did not have space perception. He concludes that every optic experience acquired after the operation is something new to the previously blind man and is completely different from a tactile experience. The operated patient does not use the knowledge acquired from tactile impressions but gets completely new impressions. Von Senden draws the conclusion that the patients did not have spatial experiences before the operations. They could not imagine previously that another human being could have knowledge of him without touching him.

From the reports of others, Von Senden cites the following observations on similar cases of sight restored by operation. Fialla says that a person born blind does not have an exact representation of his own body. Albertotti had a patient who had no idea of depth and substituted roundness for it. A patient of Chesselden knew that the room was a part of the house but could not understand why the whole house should be larger than the room. Uthoff's patient did not know what was round, quadrangular, or triangular. One of Fialla's patients could not recognize her old friends until she heard their voices. A four-year-old patient of Von Hippel could not distinguish between a cube and a sphere, and could not describe their shape; it is even doubtful whether she saw them differently. F. Fisher's patient did not know simple objects. Francke's case did not recognize scissors although she could draw them before the operation. Grafe says that operated patients do not localize their impressions; they do not bring them into relation with their eyes or with any other plane; nothing has shape or distance. Franz's patient said that three days after the operation he saw an extended field of light in which everything was dark, turned over, mixed together, and in motion; the movement later appeared as flying circles. He could not distinguish objects. The pain caused by light forced him to close his eyes immediately. The patient of Schnabel did not have any interest in vision. Marc-Monnier's patient described a grape in the following way: "It is blue, it glitters, it is so smooth, it has elevations and depressions." It is characteristic that newly operated patients do not want to see and have no interest in seeing. La Prince reports that a patient merely saw a succession of dark and light instead of a movement. Hirschberg and Dufour and Wederop report that the patients perceived colors at a time when they had no ideas about form. Uthoff says that a patient of his was at first apathetic to visual impressions and did not do anything on her own initiative. The operated patients had to study objects from an optic point of view with the help of touch. One of Chesselden's patients said that the objects seemed to touch his eyes, and other patients also did not have a correct appreciation of depth. According to Von Senden, the operated patient at first sees a colored surface separated from his own person. This surface has some indistinct depth.

Raehlman and Uthoff said that a teaspoon and a tablespoon of the same shape but of different distance were considered equal in size. Beer said that patients using vision alone saw only the outlines of solid geometrical figures; for example, a sphere appeared as a circular disc, lighted more or less by single points. Tactile sensation, and the direction of the movement of their hands teaches them that the sphere is curved in three dimensions, and so they learn eventually to recognize the shape of these bodies by the light which is sent from them into the eye.

It is hard to understand why Von Senden believes there is no primary tactile perception of shape and spatial relations and that real spatial relations are given only by optic impression. He goes even further than Goldstein and Gelb who at least believe in the kinesthetic genesis of spatial perception. Without prejudice the conclusion may be drawn that primitive optic perception contains no reliable data concerning space.

Movement is often one of the first optic experiences of the operated case. The movements are experienced as occurrences in the visual field. Actual movements in the outside world are at the same time often not fully perceived. Primitive optic perception seems also to be, according to these experiences, a loop and a circle of indefinite spatial characteristics, from which more organized gestalten develop. The reports stress the importance of interest and action but say little of spontaneous maturation. It is not clear whether the operated person really sees the object touching his eyes. However, there must be some psychological truth in such statements since we ourselves have often the feeling that the visual experiences wander directly into our eyes. The theory of Epicurus that during vision pictures leave the objects and wander into our eyes is based upon this psychological experience.

Furthermore, space colors seem to reach the eye and we have reason to believe that the primary color perception is space color. According to the reports collected by Von Senden, color is often perceived before form in the operated blind. I. Wechsler has observed a case in which color perception was preserved in a lesion of the central nervous system due to carbon monoxide poisoning. In a patient in Bellevue Hospital, form perception was completely destroyed after carbon monoxide poisoning, whereas color perception was almost intact.

It is interesting that Von Senden could develop such an atomistic thory of space perception at the time when psychologists speak so persistently of the unity of the senses. The term perception or impression means that something is going on in space. There is no sensory experience which lacks spatial qualities. Every sense has its part in space perception. Effort and experimentation lead to a more unified space experience. Behind the variety of different spaces of the various senses the unified space of all senses is a given experience. The experiences of all senses lead to actions by the same motor system. The reactions of the operated blind are interesting is so far as they point to a relative independence of the spatial experiences of the various senses. The blind person has to rely at first and primarily on his tactile experiences to master space. The new spatial qualities which come from the newly acquired optic sphere have to be incorporated in the space continuum of the other senses. In spite of the fact that the operated congenitally blind is afraid of his new task, there is an urge to constructive efforts which sooner or later creates a unified space continuum which fits optic as well as tactile experiences. The urge to such a construction is imperative since actions are directed toward objects in space which offer themselves through all senses.

CHAPTER V

OPTIC PERCEPTION AND TYPOLOGY

THERE seems to be great fascination in the idea that human beings are not only equal but also different. There is an inclination to group human beings into different types, and to assume that basic functions operate differently in different human beings. Carl G. Jung has separated human beings into extraverts and introverts and is inclined to believe that one deals with basic differences. It is characteristic of all endeavors in typology that the first clear systematization must soon be turned into something much more complicated. The extravert can be turned outward to the world in perceptions, emotions, feelings, and diverse subgroups arise which finally show just the opposite of their original intention, namely, that it is very difficult to arrive at a satisfactory typology. E. Kretschmer's attempt, primarily devised to account for the basic differences in the psychology of the manic depressive and schizophrenic group, divides humanity into groups of the asthenically built schizoid and schizophrenic and into the cyclothymic, cycloid, and circular psychotic who have a pyknic (rotund) body structure. This conception, although based upon excellent intuition, covers only a part of the possible facts; the attempt to erect an inclusive typology was not successful. But Kretschmer's attempt certainly has the advantage of filling the rather empty schemes of Jungian typology with actual experiences. Too many facts, however, are not accounted for by his theory, and according to Jaensch it runs into difficulties when one tries to use it for the differentiation of form and color perception.

Scientists interested in typology usually like to overrate the typological differences between different human beings. They consider such differences as more or less absolute. One of the first attempts at typological differentiation—Charcot's system of separating human

beings into optic, acoustic, and motor types according to the predominance of imaginations in the one or the other sensory field—
was certainly an interesting beginning. G. E. Mueller has shown that
there are no rigid types, but that individuals use one or another type
of imagination according to the needs of the situation. One should
not underrate the human capacity. Many of these capacities are not
used because the situation does not call for them. Beside psychological reasons which prevent the display of a specific quality, organic differences exist, which are not fundamental. Potentialities
of this type may be brought forward by drugs; as for example, optic
imagination by mescal. Indeed one may suppose that human beings
are at least potentially quite similar to each other. For this reason
comparatively little will be said in this volume about typological differences. We are more interested in the basic problems common to
all of us than in the differences one may find in different human beings. This is also the reason why in the remarks of Kanner and
myself no attempt was made to use the material for the distinction
of specific types. Human beings are here considered to show the same
basic principles in a great number of variations which can be enjoyed
without being pressed into definite groups.

Jaensch has developed a particularly complicated psychology. He
started with a study of eidetic pictures as mentioned above. Human
beings were divided into two groups. One group comprised persons
with a strong tendency to see a great variety of changing images.
A correlation of this type of eidetic imagery with exophthalmic goitre
was surmised and the type was called Basedowoid (B). It was con-
trasted with another type in which the eidetic images were few and
rigid. Because of a surmised relation to tetany, this type was called
tetanoid (T). Unquestionably these types, as such, exist but it is very
doubtful whether they are in any way fixed, and the somatic correlations have not been found by other investigators. Later on, Jaensch
extended this typology. He is inclined to substitute the terms integrated and disintegrated for Basedowoid (B) and tetanoid (T). In the
integrated type (I), all functions are interwoven. In the disintegrated
type they are isolated. The integrated type can be chiefly integrated

outward (I^1). The I^2 type is chiefly integrated inwards—the I^3 type shows an integration, especially in the sphere of will and action. Akin to the integrated types are the synesthetic types (S). S^1 shows the synesthetic attitude, especially concerning outside impressions. Whereas S^2 has the synesthetic tendency chiefly in the sphere of thinking, the I^1 type is receptive and the S type projective. The B type is now considered as an exaggeration of the integrated type.

The artificiality of such division and subdivision is obvious. Whenever Jaensch discusses single problems his conclusions become more and more contradictory in spite of the interesting material he submits. The factual material of his investigations on the Purkinje phenomenon is of importance and is therefore reviewed here.

The distribution of brightness in the colors of the spectrum is different when the eye is adapted to light or to darkness. When the light intensity is diminished and the eye becomes adapted to dark, the brightness of green, blue, and violet (these are the shorter wave lengths of the spectrum) is less diminished than the brightness of red, and yellow, and other colors of longer wave length. If one works with a red and blue color field of the same brightness at a given intensity level and diminishes the light intensity in the room, the blue appears brighter than the red. But the greater brightness of the blue is immediately diminished if one puts before the colored field objects which must be seen as distinct forms. To see distinct forms, the light function of seeing predominates and the dark function undergoes relative suppression. Jaensch draws the conclusion that the light function and the integrated seeing of forms are closely connected with each other. Blue objects appear less clear than red. Red light has a greater affinity to the light-vision function of the eye; blue has a closer relation to dark-vision. The seeing of motion has closer affinity to the dark function of the eye. Movements appear more rapid in the dark. The seeing of movements has more to do with the subjective side of life; it only shows a relation between object and subject. All elementary tasks of self-assertion are dependent upon the perception of movement and on seeing whether inimical or friendly objects approach. The dark-adapted eye has the greatest sensitivity to colors in the atmosphere. It makes the best possible use of minimal light, for the organ. The eye adapted to brightness is particularly sensitive to red, which helps in the clear perception of objects and forms. The eye adapted for brightness is more integrated than the dark-adapted organ. Jaensch thinks that integrated persons are adapted to direct sunlight and the disintegrated to diffuse skylight. Jaensch thinks that the light function plays a greater part in those individuals whom he calls integrated and in whom the faculty of seeing eidetic pictures is pronounced. It is not possible to discuss Jaensch's opinion in detail here. However his calling the dark function of the eye disintegrated and simultaneoulsy emphasizing that the dark function has a close relation to perception of movement does not fit into his total system. Kanner and I have shown that the integrated type (the type with vivid optic imagination) shows strong motion perception. According to Jaensch, the integrated type is the more primitive type; and, according to our whole discussion, there cannot be any doubt that motion belongs to the most primitive parts of perception.

Whether or not the experimental results of Jaensch are correct, it is still impossible to follow his conclusions. Motion is, for instance, an important part of every perception, and is, according to Kanner's and my investigations, marked in the integrated type. Jaensch's conception that the integrated type is primitive and the disintegrated type belongs to a later stage of development is very difficult to prove. His investigations do not help us in the search for primitive experiences since he has confused the problems by a very doubtful typology. His observation of a connection between the seeing of distinct objects and the function of the eye light-adapted for the perception of red and yellow seems interesting. These colors lead to action and to the object, whereas the dark colors invite contemplation, inaction, and neglect of the object. The investigations of Jaensch may help us to understand the relation of specific colors to form perception and action. They are of no use, however, for the distinction of definite types.

In general, primitive optic perception is closely connected with movement and with primitive forms in which the spiral, the vortex and the circle play the outstanding part; various colors are of special importance; and all these primitive optic experiences are paralleled by emotional and tonic attitudes. In the development of perception, the more definite object emerges and the motion becomes better organized, parallel to the better perception of form.

CHAPTER VI

TACTILE PERCEPTION

WHEREAS the literature on optic imaginations and perceptions is very extensive, less is known about tactile perception. Bromberg and I have studied the aftereffects of touch. The results are here reported.[1]

In almost all the subjects, the aftereffects of a single touch were associated with a spreading of the touch and this diffusion was distinctly rhythmic. Very often the touched spot seemed to wander. Usually the touch was connected with the optic images, which latter were pictures of the touching object rather than images of the subject's hand. The elaboration of the tactual sensations continued almost automatically without interference from the optic images, although in one subject the optic images played a greater part. The tactual feelings were generally accompanied by impressions of warmth or cold. We were unable to ascertain the exact time relations of the aftereffects from our protocols, because of the difficulty in deciding when the image had appeared and when the aftereffect had disappeared. It was noted that imaginations interfere with and provoke the tactual sensations again and again. Thus even when the aftereffects had passed off, after lasting several minutes, the feeling of general tension in the skin remains. As we have noted, this can be removed by rubbing the skin. In one case the feeling of tension was localized beneath the skin.

When two spots are touched simultaneously, the two spots merge together in the aftereffects as well as in the imagination. There is a marked difference between the aftereffects of a single touch and those of two simultaneous touches. However, when the two spots

<hr>

[1] Reprinted in part from the *Journal of Nervous and Mental Diseases.* LXXVI (1932), 1–24, 133–56. (See footnote, p. 23.)

are touched in succession there is difficulty in retaining one of these touches. There is often a sense of movement between the two spots, especially when the succession is rapid. In that case "something passes through the air," or one point moves to the other. The movement is not that of a straight line, but of a curve. Since our results confirm the well-known and accredited experiments of V. Benussi, we shall not go farther in this aspect of the problem. When the touches are made in succession but less rapidly, there are movements of the sensations on the skin which tend to unify the two spots. Experimental results in all our subjects are practically identical on this point. Often only one point is perceived at a time, because of the effacing of the first one. This results from a sort of repression which is exerted when the second point is felt. Sometimes the points attain the quality of deep burning or of deep pressure. It is clear that enlargements and diffusions are similar processes. If more than two spots are touched, the same principles of movement, diffusions, and effacements hold good.

In the experiments on the aftereffects of a line, the same general tendencies were noted. The beginning and the end of the lines were influenced in a peculiar way. Often the line contracted in the middle, or it shrank from both ends. The tendency to broadening and tingling is remarkable; and even more extensive transformations were effected.

In the aftereffects of triangles, the angles are not felt, and the sides do not touch each other. One line may be clearer than another, or one line may be effaced partially or completely. Apparently no influence is exerted by the direction in which the lines of the triangle are drawn. The sides may disappear, with only the center space remaining as an irradiation area. Although none of the subjects perceived the angles, the apex of the triangle was felt by some as a diffuse but definite point.

In the aftereffects of the circle the same principles are illustrated. One portion of the circumference may drop out. There are serious discrepancies between the optic picture and the tactile impression.

Thus there may be a concentric shrinking of the circle, but since the first tactual impression remains present, there may also be a multiplication of impressions.

Of especial interest are the experiments performed by making a cross on the skin. The point where the crossing takes place is most often absent; one-half of the cross may be absent, or the four ends of the lines forming the cross may be united, forming two diagonal lines. A common result is that the ends of the lines swell into a diffuse bulb. One line is usually more intense than the other line. The intensity of the afterimage in this group was remarkable. In general we may say that the afterimages have a tingling character and a tendency to motility, and that the areas of sensation change in several ways, as by diffusing and broadening.

One may of course say that the results described are products of disintegration and have nothing to do with the fundamentals of tactile perceptions. "Tachistohaptic" experiments which would allow a study of the development of tactile perception have never been performed. Conclusions concerning primitive touch experience may be reached only by inference. M. Frey and Goldman conclude that a simple touch experience disappears very quickly if the stimulus is unmoved. The important experiments of V. Benussi have shown that successive stimulation of two points of the skin provokes the impression that the object is moving from one place to another. One immediately sees that this result is closely related to our experiments on aftereffects. We at once reach the conclusion that as in vision the simple touch has a quality of movement in itself and that the primitive perception is not static but in motion. It has often been emphasized that even a light touch with a fine hair does not provoke the impression of a point but of a small disc. As in the optic sphere, the primitive perception is certainly not the perception of a point but is that of a disc in movement with irregular surroundings. A close analogy exists between autokinetic movements on the skin and in the optic field. Movement is also inherent in the primitive tactile perception. When the stimulus is applied with a very low pressure, one sometimes has the impression that the skin is coming towards the stimulus and is bulging. In our aftereffect experiments the impression sometimes goes deeper than the surface.

We expect of course an exaggeration of this phenomenon in mescal intoxication. H. Stein writes that in mescal intoxication one finds an analogy to the optic illusion of movements in the multiplicity of haptic illusory movements. When stimulating with the Frey-Paulis lever apparatus (successive stimulation by two stimuli in different places) the impression of streaming through the skin takes place. The stimulus seems to pierce deeply into the skin. The stronger the intensity of the pressure the deeper the stimulus seems to penetrate. If there is successive stimulation of one spot there is either a localization of the stimuli in different spots or the impression of a movement going into the skin.

Paradoxically, the phenomenal quantity of these movements into depth may be more extensive than the objective arm diameter. The end point of the movements into depth is then away from the body. The phenomenal movement is continued into space. The intensity of the stimulus and the number of stimuli applied to the same point in a given time have an influence on the length of the movement. It is clear that more than merely strength of stimulus determines the intensity of the sensation. In the quoted experience the dynamic factor expresses itself as movement. This is the dissolution of the normal experience of intensity. If the same spot were stimulated successively with stimuli barely over the threshold, the subject felt as though something were dancing on the skin or as if a fine particle fell on the skin and jumped back again. This jumping back was experienced in the same way as movement without images (*unanschaulich*) as in the experiments of V. Benussi and W. Scholz.

H. Stein also is of the opinion that the movement present in a successive excitation of two points is inherently present in the single touch. There is further confirmation of this opinion in the results obtained in the method of willful imagination applied by Bromberg and myself.

In the majority of our subjects we got tactual imaginations when we requested imagination of a sensation on the skin. In all our subjects optic images were produced first. These optic images were partly of objects approaching the skin and partly of lines drawn on the skin. In one subject no tactual imaginations were available. The experiments show that the tactual imagination has two parts: one part (which the subject called a memory) corresponds closely to the actual sensation expected; and another part, which consists of a tingling or itching, has the character of an actual sensation rather than a memory. In the majority of these subjects these two parts combined, but they could be kept distinct and separate.

The visual picture of the hand was frequently perceived in a schematic way or as an indefinite surface. Even if a single touch were imagined there was a general change in a broader tactual field. In two cases the whole hand was affected.

There is no correspondence between the optic pictures and the tactual imaginations: there may even be an independent elaboration of the optic pictures. At the same time the tactual feelings develop a functional independence from the optic pictures.

The feelings are sometimes on the surface and sometimes below the surface of the skin, while in some subjects the feelings are those of tension in the tendons; a feeling of penetration through the hand was noted. In the main, subjects reported not only sensations of touch but also of burning or of coolness.

No particular effect was noted in the results when the subject tried voluntarily to exclude optic pictures. It is interesting to note that one subject had to make use of eye movements to imagine a line tactually.

The surface on which the imagination takes place need not be on the body but may be placed before the body on an external surface, but these surfaces are definitely related to the subject.

In the imagination of a point, diffusion of the sensation along the surface occurred in almost all the subjects but irradiation occurred in one, and wandering of the point in two subjects.

Tingling was frequently felt as a rhythmic phenomenon in the single touch imagination. In some instances, if the subject were not careful in his reporting of results, it could be felt as part of a succeeding experiment.

When we asked for the imagination of two points, it is remarkable that, among the subjects who could keep one spot in the imagination without difficulty, none was able to imagine two spots at the same time. In addition, there is a marked difference, apparently, in the imagination of several points simultaneously or only one point at a time. When two spots are imagined simultaneously, the difficulty is either in imagining the second point, or in a tendency of the second point to move away. When a greater number of points are imagined, the last point moves or the last two points may join together. This part of the experiment proves that imagination of two spots is far from being merely the sum of the imagination of two different touches. This principle also holds true for imagination of lines and geometric figures.

One subject reported that only one part of a line was imagined and that the other parts faded away irregularly. In the figure of a triangle the angles were often absent and the shape of the triangle changed. In the imagination of an oval and a circle, parts of the tactual picture faded out. In the imagination of a cross, instead of the crossing lines being sharply felt as angles, only a diffuse spot was felt at the crossing point. In general, we always see that tactile imagination of angles and crossing points is especially difficult. Since tactual imaginations may shrink and expand, it becomes apparent that several imaginations may be present at the same time. Of special interest is the experiment in which one touch follows another in immediate succession. In such cases the points extend toward each other; something seems to connect them. Either a feeling of actual movement takes place or the touches are connected by a visual image and by a sense of tactual connection, as with the subject who had a sensation of "something" passing between the points.

It makes no great difference in the final result whether a tactual imagination is preceded by real sensations or not. Although the experiments were made on the back of the hand, the forehead, and the fingertips, there were no significant differences in these various locations. Experiments on the fingertips have given the same results as mentioned above and for that reason the protocols will not be presented here.

The aftereffects of touch and the imagination of touch show the same basic qualities. I want especially to refer to the rhythmic quality. It is also noteworthy that we never deal merely with isolated sensations; we deal with a definite figure on a definite background. We also found that the irregular oval disc is one of the primitive units of tactile perception. But it is furthermore of utmost importance that there exists a definite tendency against the perception of sharp angles and straight lines. Also the perception of lines crossing is decidedly difficult. The analogy with optic experiences is decidedly marked. We again come to the opinion that the curve belongs to the essentials of primitive perception.

We may summarize as follows the result of experimentation on tactile imagination in normal subjects:

1. Tactual images have an objective and subjective part. The subjective aspect is partly a memory image and partly a sensation on the skin.

2. There are tactual images without subjective components.

3. Persons with strong objective images have very unsatisfactory subjective images and sensations. In our experiments we deal chiefly with the subjective part of imagination.

4. In every subject the tactual sensations and images follow the optic pictures, in spite of the fact that tactual imagination soon progresses along its own line of development and becomes widely independent of the optic imagination. The optic imagination can also elaborate independently of the tactual imagination.

5. The optic picture of the touched area of the skin is often vague and indistinct, having a rather symbolic character.

6. Imagined sensations are partly on the skin and sometimes under it. They are frequently mixed with sensations of temperature—warmth or cold.

7. The tactual imagination which is in the foreground creates in association with it a tactual background.

8. The dissociation between the optic and tactual imagination becomes more evident when the subject is turned in the turning chair.

9. The tactual subjective imagination has a tendency to irradiate to remote parts of the body. In two subjects there were sensations on symmetrical parts of the body.

10. These general rules are valid for any area of the skin on the body.

11. Tactual imagination often has a rhythmic character.

12. In every tactual imagination there is a quality of movement which is inherent in the imagination as embodied in its tingling character; in addition, there are movements of the image as a whole.

13. Vestibular irritation increases the tendency of movement in the image. In general, there is a consistent relationship between the direction of turning and the movements of the image. However, there are many exceptions. In addition, there exists a definite nonspecific increase of movements in the images.

14. Several simultaneous imaginations of touches form a unit (gestalt). Imagination of successive points provokes curved connecting lines between the points, sometimes through the air. More distant points are connected by slow movement along the skin.

15. In the imagination of lines and geometric figures the result is incomplete because parts of the lines disappear.

16. A distinct tendency towards curving of lines is noted. There is a marked difficulty in imagining angles and crossing points of lines; with only three exceptions, angles were not imagined in all the experiments attempted.

17. Spontaneous multiplication of tactual images may occur, but not so frequently nor so intensively as in optic images.

18. By the method of noting the subjective aspect of the aftereffect of touch on the skin, we find that slight touches have a distinct aftereffect of rhythmic character, lasting roughly up to three minutes; and the duration of the aftereffect varies in different individuals.

19. The tactual aftereffect is independent of the optic images. The tactual aftereffect may provoke optic images, but even then each series (i. e., optic and tactual) develops independently.

20. In the aftereffect the foreground of the perceptual field stands out more sharply from the background than in tactual imagination. Transference of aftereffect from one side of the body to the other has not been observed.

21. The effects of vestibular irritation can be well studied in tactual aftereffects, which show an increased rhythmic tendency, elongations, curvings, and a general nonspecific increase in the tendency to movement. With a more careful technique the specific influence of turning was: movements of sensations in a direction opposite to the turning, during the turnings; and movements in the direction of turning, after stopping. The nonspecific effect consisted of a slow wandering in the direction of turning, occurring some time after the turning stopped.

22. The general tendencies to irradiation, to the formation of a background, to the effacement of certain parts of the images, to the building up and destruction of forms (gestalten), to movements, to curving of lines, and the tendency against perception of angles, are identical in the aftereffects with the tendencies noted in imagination.

The influence of the vestibular apparatus on tactile imagination will be discussed later. But the remarks reproduced here show the close interrelation between different senses and show also that discussion of the senses as if isolated from each other is artificial. It is not surprising that, in pathological cases, primitive ways of tactual perception are present. W. Bromberg and I have shown that we may establish a closer relationship between the phenomena observed by us and the phenomena of the so-called lability of the threshold of H. Stein and V. von Weizsaecker. These authors have observed in spinal cord lesions, especially in lesions of the posterior columns, that after irritation of one point by M. Frey's method, the irritability changes very quickly. Soon the point may become unexcitable. They associate this change with the lesions in the posterior column and their cortical connections. There is an irradiation of this lability of the threshold to nearby areas, but especially towards the distal parts. Iterations are present, especially concerning temperature (G. Cohen). These phenomena are partly identical with the phenomena already known to exist in cases of tabes. These alloesthetic and polyesthetic phenomena have been studied in the last few years, especially by myself and by Stein and Guenther. In such cases one also finds that touch with a single point is changed into a movement. There is a tendency to perceive straight lines as curves. A cross may be felt as two parallel lines. There is a general tendency against angles and straight lines. E. Stengel observed these changes clearly in an operated case of tumor of the spinal cord.

We may say that the phenomenon of tactile imagination and the phenomena observed in spinal cord lesions, especially of the posterior column, are to a great degree identical. But I have seen marked polyesthesia and wandering of impressions in a case of probable parietal lobe lesion in which there was also an allochiria, but allochiria has also been present in our experiments on imaginations. The borderline between the phenomena in normals and the phenomena in pathological cases is certainly not sharply drawn. We may note, in this connection, that E. Stransky and E. F. ten Cate found a symmetrical hyperesthesia in normals in whom anesthesia was produced. My patient observed that a tactile sensation is felt as a movement in a joint, an observation likewise made by Head in organic cases. This phenomenon was observed in two of our subjects. Furthermore, disintegration phenomena after spinal-cord and more central lesions are identical with the phenomena in aftereffects and in the imaginations of normal subjects.

The question of whether similar phenomena play a part in toxic psychoses is of interest. In the optic experiments there was a close relationship to the results of mescaline intoxication described by Kurt Beringer. The protocols of Beringer do not contain much material about touch. His experiments are chiefly directed at touch experiences and not at touch sensations. In a previous article I have pointed out the possibility that some of the symptomatology in alcoholic psychoses may be associated with vestibular influence on the tactile sphere. One of his patients felt a multiplicity of tactile impressions. Some alcoholics felt dust and other multiplied impressions on the skin. The phenomena are of the same structure as in our normal subjects, but magnified. One protocol of a thirty-year-old alcoholic who was slightly delirious follows:

Two spots were touched on patient's right hand. "I feel the two main spots with many spots between them. I feel a long line going down to the wrist connecting the two main spots. Now the first spot has disappeared but the second spot is moving to the left side. I cannot get rid of them even if I wave my hand. [Patient was instructed to rub his hands.] The spots have gone now."

The patient had no tactual hallucinations. Buerger reports a case of alcoholic psychosis in which every touch provoked a feeling of being sprinkled on. This certainly belongs to the range of phenomena described here.

We think that these phenomena are very often the basis for psychic elaboration in hallucinations. In order to show this, we will give here the protocols of a boy who was hypnotized. In the aftereffects he sometimes felt as if dust were coming out of his skin. Instead of the imagination of a cross, he felt a circle in one of the quadrants.

M.S., a boy aged thirteen, was admitted on August 8, 1930, with a history of fainting spells. He had become quarrelsome and was somewhat of a disciplinary problem at home. The past history was essentially negative. The falling seizures were described as occurring most often at night, when the patient would fall out of bed. He rarely hurt himself. He would become unconscious, but had no clonic or tonic movements. In the hospital the seizures were observed and considered to be psychogenic in nature. Physical findings were negative. During residence in the hospital hypnosis was tried for its therapeutic effect, and it was at this time that the experiments detailed below were done. While under light hypnosis the patient was given the commands, without further suggestion, except where noted:

A cross was drawn on the left hand. "I feel the cross. It feels as if something were coming out of my hand. Now only the left upper corner is left. I feel something coming out of my hand, like when the room is darkened and sunshine comes through a crack in the window. Now I feel a tickling over the whole hand, over the wrist, like a strip."

A line was drawn on patient's hand. "It feels like a 'J' and the turn of the 'J' is all gone. Now it is starting to chip away at the top and now it is all gone."

M.S. was asked to imagine a cross on his hand. "I feel it well. Now it has gone away. My hand itches and I feel an incomplete circle in the upper right corner quadrant of the cross. Now the cross and the circle fade away, but I feel all kinds of things mixed up where the cross was—squares, circles, and all of them are moving into each other very fast. [The suggestion was made that the patient pick out the square and feel it.] I only feel two sides of the square but not the angle. Now the ends of the line chip off and everything is very faint, and it all goes away."

With phenomena observed in pathological cases, A. Buch correlated results from normal persons under special experimental conditions. H. Ahringsmann moved a punctate object under minimum pressure and slow speed over the healthy skin. The subjects did not perceive a line but points distant from each other. There was a movement, the direction of which could not be stated. Buch found similar phenomena in a case of transverse myelitis.

It is necessary to investigate more fully the manner in which the tactile hallucinations in alcoholics are related to the results given here. E. Bleuler believes that they are connected with the paraesthesia due to polyneuritic symptoms. Although, as experiments of E. Lindemann in our clinic show, similar phenomena also occur in neuritis, we believe that in the majority of cases we deal with normal perception. We have also observed a case with a parietal lesion in which the phenomena described here were increased on the affected side.

Effects arising in the course of the imagination and aftereffects in the tactual sphere can also be observed in intoxications of the central nervous system. All these products of disintegration are connected with very vivid impressions of movements. Tactile hallucinations are probably very often based on the products of disintegration of perception. But these products of disintegration are elaborated according to the psychic situation of the individual and his particular state of mind. In the toxic psychosis the factor of confusion will certainly influence the way in which these disintegration products are finally elaborated.

W. Bromberg has studied the problems of alcoholic hallucinosis in more detail. In these alcoholic patients the duration of the aftereffects was prolonged. A rapid diminution and multiplication of the spots of sensation, rapid rotary movement, fragmentation of lines, and diffusion, fading, and disintegration of tactual impressions were perceived by the patient. Tactual experiences were often referred to pivotal parts of the body, the knuckles, arms, and fingers, which are outstanding points in the image of the body. Sensations were often perceived below the skin level and were associated with movements from the level upward into the air.

W. Bromberg points out that the aftereffects and the changed perception very often are the basis for further elaboration. It is also particularly remarkable in this experiment that there is not only movement on the skin but also a vertical movement from below the skin to above it. We meet with a great number of phenomena of motion in the tactile sphere. There is also definite proof that this motion on the skin depends to a great extent on vestibular influences. The conclusion is that primitive tactile experiences also are in motion and that the primitive units are not points but discs, with irregular borderlines, and not the straight line but the curved line. Perception of the angle and the crossing is particularly late in developing. Studies about temperature perceptions from a similar point of view have not been made. We have no definite knowledge about the primitive perception of posture. It is remarkable that, in parietal cases, movements on the skin are occasionally perceived as movements in the joints.

In the sphere of pain we find practically the same phenomena as in the sphere of touch, when the pain is not strong enough to make the objective side unimportant.

It has not been emphasized sufficiently in our previous remarks that the building up of the optic impression is to a large extent dependent on the movements of the eyes and of the head, although the extent to which these movements participate in the development of the perceptive sphere has not been definitely determined. Whereas W. M. Wundt put an enormous emphasis on the eye movements, the later development in psychology has considerably restricted this importance. In the tactile sphere the importance of motion and motility is uncontested for movement on the skin, and successive stimulation facilitates clear perception. M. von Frey and Metzger showed that the successive stimulation of pressure points can be distinguished when the simultaneous stimulation does not allow a distinction and that the threshold for successive stimulation is much lower than for simultaneous stimulation. V. von Weizsaecker and his co-workers obtained interesting results by successive stimulation of one point. D. Katz emphasizes the fact that active movement is a creative power in the tactile sphere. All modifications in the tactile experiences of surfaces such as smoothness or roughness, can only be perceived by movement. He remarks that the kinematic form of the stimulus is transformed into a static quality of an object. The same is true of the perception of soft and hard, and of the impression of elasticity. Katz states that there is general tendency in sensory perception to transformation from kinematic to static perception.

Tactile sensation is more purely subjective than any other experience; it immediately points to something going on in our own body. To a much greater extent hearing, seeing, smell, and taste are directed toward the outer world. Tactile, temperature, and pain sensations are the only sensations in which the relation to one's own body is constantly in the foreground of experience. In no other sense is movement by active innervation so important in reaching an objective perception of the outside world. It is true, as pointed out in *The Image and Appearance of the Human Body,* that, even for the experience of one's own body, motility is ultimately indispensable. In the tactile sphere the tendency to move one's limbs is almost imperative. One can really speak of an urge to move. One can see this most clearly when one uses the clinical method of testing the perception of the posture of the fingers. In order to perceive finger positions the subjects regularly make movements, especially if sensibility is impaired.

CHAPTER VII

HEARING, SMELL, TASTE: INTERSENSORY
ANALOGIES

HEARING

THE nature of primitive hearing is difficult to understand. Most of the experimental evidence brought forward in this field concerns tones, whereas our world of hearing consists chiefly of noises of all kinds. Speech to a great extent belongs also in this category. Judging from the motor performance of children as they sing, it is improbable that tones as such play a very important part in childlife. The pleasure derived from noises of various kinds, especially rhythmic noises, is at least as great as the pleasure of singing. Karl Buehler writes justly that a child enjoys the terrible screeching of an unoiled carriage axle as much as the most beautiful lullaby. Buehler also emphasizes the importance of rhythm. Buehler and Alfred Gross describe vividly the pleasure children have in the production of noises. It is difficult to imagine what the outstanding factors in this acoustic world are. Noises certainly have the qualities of brightness and darkness, even if the character of pitch is not clearly expressed. Charles Hartshorne puts particular emphasis on the auditory volume, which he differentiates from pitch.

Without entering into the detail of theories of hearing, one should remember that pitch is most important for tone, whereas density, loudness, volume, vocal character, brightness play the outstanding part in the more important world of noise. It is doubtful whether E. G. Boring is correct in considering noises as combinations of incompletely established tones. Hartshorne is particularly interested in the problem of brightness, since he feels that brightness is a universal attribute of all senses. He thinks that in this dimension color and sound are qualitatively alike. The findings of pathology concerning the primitive acoustic world are rather unsatisfactory. M. Silbermann and M. Tamari found that, when the third temporal convolution in humans was frozen by ethyl chloride, the intensity of hearing was increased, and they also report that these patients complained of spontaneous noises which hindered their hearing. If these findings are correct, a part of the temporal lobe is necessary to prevent our being overwhelmed by noises. In a case with a skull defect over the temporal convolution, the patient complained of being too sensitive to every noise. This was most obvious when the exposed part of the brain was sprayed with ethyl chloride. Some of the patients with similar conditions complained of depersonalization of their voices. These investigations indicate that in the primitive world noises play a more important part than in the developed acoustic world. Hans Henning, Sam Parker and I studied acoustic imaginations. Whereas Henning's subjects were able to hold acoustic imaginations for a longer time, the subjects of Parker and myself held these imaginations only if there was a continual acoustic movement present; as for instance, when the imagination included a crowd and noises coming from it. Otherwise, the acoustic image faded out and disappeared, or it had to be renewed or came back rhythmically. It was not possible for our subjects to keep tones in the imagination for a long time. The tones generally did not change in quality or pitch. Henning obtained slightly different results but even according to his results changes in acoustic images were negligible in comparison with the changes observed in optic images. It is important to recognize that a sound does not remain stabilized. It travels in a double direction into space, which it fills, and also directly towards the hearer. There is no question that this motion is inherent in the perception, but it is also clearly shown in the imagination. In every sound there is a restlessness of spatial localization which surpasses even the restlessness in the optic experience. The high-pitched tones go into the air, the low ones seem to roll on the earth. Sound has inherently the quality of wandering in space. These spatial characteristics are as primary as the spatial characteristics of vision. E. G. Boring writes, "Nobody has ever argued

that tones have form or shape. What they have is position and size."
I think that tones nad noises have shape. They expand and travel in
definite ways. I do not think that there is any question that tones have
size and volume.

In our experiments on acoustic imagination the subjects very often
felt as if they executed the imagined sound or noise themselves. The
imagination of the human voice was regularly connected with the
perception of the subject's own movements and with his own tendencies to formulate words. In experiments on imagination the motility which is connected with hearing did not appear. There is a
tendency to turn towards the acoustic stimulus and there are concomitant tonic changes. This is seen particularly in cases of cerebellar
lesions with increased postural reflexes, such as the case observed by
H. Hoff and myself. This case also showed tonic changes in connection with an acoustic imagination. The study of hallucinations
does not lead us much further. In cases of alcoholic hallucinosis we
found a tendency to rhythm and repetition in the majority of cases.
Only five out of twenty patients heard tones and only one of them
heard musical sounds only. When voices were heard they were usually not single but multiple voices, against a continuous, irregular,
auditory background. The tendency to repeat the voices oneself, which
occurs in schizophrenic cases, was not observed. Some of our cases
did not have the feeling that they themselves were speaking, but
nevertheless felt that the voices heard were their own. In the acoustic
world there is definite motion, in the image and in the percepts, and
threefold motility—a tonic answer to sound; a movement towards
the sound; and finally a motor tendency or even a movement to produce the sound oneself. I am inclined to believe that this latter quality
is particularly characteristic for the acoustic sense. The acoustic sense
has, therefore, a motility which corresponds most closely to the identification concept. It is important that this identification is especially
noted with the human voice, which forms such a close bond between
different human beings. In optic imagination only the imagined
movement of another person occasionally provokes a tendency to an
identical movement of the self.

SMELL [1]

In the mechanism of smell sensation another form of motor activity is important. Most investigators do not place sufficient emphasis on the importance of the motor components of smell. W. Boernstein, for one, denied (erroneously, we think) that smell has any motility. In our experiments motor activity finds outspoken expression in the sensations. On smelling coffee, subject M. said: "I have a feeling of movement, originating in the bottle and going to the nostrils, with visual images of streams of coffee going into the nose." As von Skranlik showed, a stream of air is necessary to convey impressions of smell. It is a peculiarity of the sense of smell that it requires motor activity for its presentation for perception. This is seen in the reflex (automatic) respiratory movements of smelling, but even here some regulation of breathing is necessary for smelling activities; i.e., one has to sniff in order to get a sufficient quantity of the object-smell for perception. The object-smell, then, is partially determined by these activities, since the smell going from the object in any other direction than the nose is obviously no longer destined to be an olfactory sensation. What one perceives as an odor is therefore partially the expression of motor acts connected with smell. The object-smell is, therefore, the expression of direct linear relationship between the smelling object and the subject. Subject Sc. after holding coffee under his nose for twenty seconds noted: "Without breathing, the warm air in the nose seems to be connected directly by smell to where the object is." This relation is a particularly intimate one in psychologic experience. It probably has to do with the fact that part of the object-smell is in the nose. The object-smell is carried on a prolongation of air extending from the object to the nasal air: the smell is conveyed, so to speak, from the atmosphere of the object into the atmosphere of the nasal cavity, and there anywhere along the course of this extension it is perceived as smell. The subject then knows of the smell, because he has perceived it outside and inside the nose. He has no immediate feeling (unless he sniffs) that he exerts any special activity in perceiving smell; there is not, in the common sense, an immediate sensation of smell. The sensation of smell is objectivized and has to do almost exclusively with the object-smell. Even though an important part of the object-smell is in the nose, it is objective, because the inside of our nose belongs physically and psychologically to the external world. The object of smell thus does not come into such intimate contact with the

---

[1] This passage and later ones are quoted from Walter Bromberg and Paul Schilder, "Olfactory Imagination and Olfactory Hallucinations," *Archives for Neurology and Psychology*, XXXII (Sept., 1934).

subject as, for instance, the object of touch sensation. It is remarkable that there is no directly mediated sensation of smell, whereas there is a direct sensation of touch. Smell, like hearing and vision, is an objective sense; it is much more objective than touch.

In the foregoing description it has become clear that objectivity is characteristic of the perception of smell. We realize that smell is perceived around the object, surrounding it, but we do not know from our own experiments what smell clearly is. It is not essentially a sensation but an experience belonging to the object. It is an indefinite quality of an object and as such is something objective in the outside world attached to the solid object or more or less independent of it.

In the world of smell there is again a clear-cut motion, and motility which is absolutely specific for smell is closely correlated with breathing and sniffing. The vegetative repercussions and interrelations are remarkable; strong emotional factors are also involved. In the imaginations of smell, basically the same phenomena come into appearance. Changes in the image do not take place. When the olfactory representation does come to sensory experience it stays unchanged and soon disappears. The imaginations of smell are either placed in the head, in space, or in the nose. They are more vivid when smell is imagined in the nose. Hallucinations of smell in both schizophrenic and alcoholic patients are alike in the character of real and immediate perception. It is interesting that in these hallucinations smells connected with the body are outstanding.

Careful analysis bears out the fact that the smell is of something organic, such as is found in decayed substances or feces. It is opium which smells like dead bodies, or it is like meat which has been too long in the box. Dead spirits smell like rotten meat. There are smells like halitosis and carcinoma; smells of decayed cabbage; stenches like stool, urine, or vomiting, musty smells, a smell of dead mice; and a terrible smell like gas or ether may be present. A strong odor connected with sexual intercourse is noted. There are smells like stale, offensive urine and water coming from the sewer, or like bilge water; smells like rotten egg or decomposing foul bodies; odors coming from the stomach and from the genitals; or sweat odors, like urine inside the underwear; bad odors coming from the hair, or from the back; a smell like refuse of dogs or chickens; a urinary smell akin to sulphur; smells coming from a carcinomatous uterus; a smell like ammonia and compound solution of cresol, comparable to urine;

odor coming from the mouth; attacks of odor coming from the body; odors of wet laundry; a swamplike odor coming from the body, and an odor of burned flesh.

The experience of smell appears very closely related to a self-protective attitude towards decay and death. It is true that children derive pleasure from anal smells as from anality in general. During later development these primitive pleasures are denied. These self-protective mechanisms of the ego may well be a factor in helping the strong repression of anal impressions. It is very difficult to discuss the physiology of olfaction without going deeply into emotional problems. This is not accidental since vegetative responses are strongly involved in olfaction. Henry Head's patients did not hallucinate agreeable smells. Raoul Mourgue comes to the conclusion that all of Head's subjects with hallucinations also showed hyperactivity of the vegetative system. Henry Head observed seventeen cases with hallucinations of sulphuric hydrogen, nine cases with the odor of something burning, odors of the earth or of stale water, of gas and of feces. Nausea almost always accompanies these hallucinations. It is doubtful whether these cases of Head's had real hallucinations; it is more probable that one deals here with paraesthesias in persons with somatic illnesses and nausea and the hyperesthesia connected with a nauseated feeling. At any rate the analogy to our findings is remarkable.

TASTE

Reports on the psychology of taste in the literature are rather meager. In the few experiments we made, the following points were outstanding: When an edible object is imagined, the individual experiences the optically imagined object outside of the body and at the same time inside the mouth; vivid taste imaginations occur in connection with salivation, chewing and swallowing. The vegetative reaction is even more obvious than in imaginations of smell. The subjects always imagine an object in the mouth and not on the tongue or on the mucous membrane. Taste and smell deal with objects which are decidedly separated from one's own body. There is a strong vegetative response to the perception as well as to the imagination. This is stronger in taste; also the motility is rather energetic.

Charles Hartshorne emphasizes that one should not exaggerate the qualitative differences in the senses. Julius Pikler believes that it is possible to understand the sensory qualities as products of a continuous process of adaptation in the organism. As mentioned above, he stresses that brightness is a factor common in hearing as well as in vision. He quotes the investigations of E. M. von Hornbostel who claimed to have shown that brightness could be translated from one sensory modality to another. Unfortunately, Von Hornbostel's results are now generally considered somewhat equivocal. Hartshorne believes that expressions like "the silver needle notes of a fife" or "the moon, a tinkle of ice in a cool blue glass" really indicate basic qualities which are common to all senses and are transferable from one sense to the other. In regard to synesthesia, he thinks that the structure of the color system runs parallel to that of the sound system. K. Zietz shows that color and sound sensations, when simultaneously evoked, may modify each other so that the color will alter the pitch of the sound or the sound the hue of the color, but that supposedly heterogeneous elements frequently blend together in an experience to such an extent that they are given as one and the same thing. He draws the conclusion that tone and color must be something identical on a deeper level. Hartshorne is of the opinion that there is no radical qualitative gulf between sensation and affection. He believes that the color of biologically important objects indicates the biologic meaning of colors. Green is the color of the vegetables and of the normal foreground. Blue is the background, and should therefore not be too glamorous or lively. Red stands for the dramatic crisis in life. It is the color of blood. He emphasizes that qualities are universally understandable and have the same meaning for different species. Hartshorne calls this theory the dimensional theory of experience. He speaks of an effective continuum and uses the adaptation theory of Pikler freely.

One cannot help but feel that Hartshorne's experimental evidence is insufficient. It is true that there are similarities in all experiences of the senses. There is, after all, one human being who is experiencing through all the senses. Hartshorne is unquestionably justified in saying that the subjectivity of feeling has been exaggerated. There is a quality (physiognomic quality of K. Koffka) in the object to which we respond with feeling and this quality is as objective as the sensation. But the distance from this to Hartshorne's conclusions is great. It is very difficult to explain the impression of red merely as a tragic crisis. And one must confess that the difference between a tragic crisis and an attitude of contemplation is a qualitative type, and cannot be so easily bridged. Although the sound of a trumpet has some red and yellow qualities, there is a gulf between those and the perception of the color red. One cannot doubt that all senses come from a common ground and that they still bear signs of their common origin. On the other hand, it is true that the anatomy of the ear and of the eye are very different from each other and that we no longer have common skin sensibility. One must remember that the intersense analogies are often neither convincing nor generally accepted. They are merely vague impressions and hints and cannot compare with the definite perceptions which are so specific for the different sense organs.

CHAPTER VIII

THE VESTIBULAR APPARATUS

INTERSENSORY RELATIONS

IN studying the vestibular apparatus we may most closely approach problems of intersensory relations.[1] Through P. Flourens, J. Breuer, N. Mach and others, we have learned that the vestibular apparatus is responsible for the phenomena which occur after turning and for the perception of accelerations. It consists of two different parts, each with a different function. The semicircular canals are organs which help us in the perception of movements. There is some question as to whether they serve for perception of circular movement only or of progressive movement also. Disease of the vestibular organ provokes dizziness. In the labyrinth there is evidently another organ which helps us to perceive gravity. We are not quite sure whether this is the sacculus-utriculus, but there are many facts which point in this direction. There is little doubt that the labyrinth is not the only graviceptor; skin and muscle sensitivity also play a part in the perception of gravity. S. Garten denies the importance of the labyrinth in this regard. M. H. Fischer, however, has collected material which disproves Garten's radical opinion. The semicircular canals are the organ for the perception of the circular movement, and

[1] The following discussions are taken from my article, "The Vestibular Apparatus in Neurosis and Psychosis," *Journal of Nervous and Mental Diseases*, LXXVIII (July 1933). The article uses much so-called pathological material, but one should not draw a borderline between normal and abnormal from the point of view of psychology. The so-called abnormal is merely another manifestation of the life processes. It is inevitable that some of the ideas and facts expressed in my book, *The Image and Appearance of the Human Body*, and even parts of other chapters of the present study, had to be repeated. The vestibular apparatus has a special position as uniting factor among the senses and as a general organ of tone and motility. Such material naturally has to be repeated in various places in a work which stresses the inner connections of psychic experiences.

probably they also help in the perception of progressive movements of the body. However, the otoliths are the most important organs for this function.

The vestibular apparatus is not only an organ of perception; it is an organ which gives rise to very important reflexes which are caused in part by the semicircular canals. These are reflexes to turning and progressive movement. There are also reflexes which are determined by the position of the labyrinth in space. These are postural reflexes probably related to the function of the otoliths. The labyrinth is, therefore, an organ which influences the muscle tone of the body. Certainly it is only one of the many organs responsible for tone, motor attitude, and posture. The vestibular apparatus is the means for bringing into clearest focus the sensory impulses which influence our system of attitude and tone. It is a great system for orienting ourselves in the world. This system is, of course, not isolated but coöperates with the other systems of orientation, especially that of the optic perceptions. It is more closely related to primitive motility than is vision. We no longer believe that there are isolated senses. Impressions of the tactile and auditory sphere are always connected with our optic impressions; synesthesia is not an exceptional occurrence but is one of the basic principles of perception. After all, we never have optic impressions alone, but perceive objects by sight, hearing, or touch. These visual objects are also objects for all the senses.

Whenever we perceive an object we already have basic knowledge of our body and of the attitude of our body. A perception always belongs to an individual with a body. The perceiving individual gets knowledge of an object and the object as such immediately provokes certain attitudes in him. These attitudes make a complete perception possible. Such an attitude does not exist in the psychic sphere alone; it is always an attitude of the body as well. Investigations by Goldstein, Hoff, and myself have proved that there is always a tonic component in such an attitude. The muscle tone of the body changes according to our impressions. At the same time there arise tendencies to actions, and more or less purposeful movements. Even these preliminary remarks show that the vestibular apparatus with its influence on the muscle tone plays a part in every perception. We may also expect that every change in the vestibular apparatus must have an immediate effect on all our senses. F. B. Hoffman and Fruboese have shown that the optic perception of the vertical direction is dependent on the vestibular organ.

These few remarks only indicate the importance of the vestibular organ. Our impressions concerning our attitudes, the posture and the motility of the body (moving or stationary), form a continuous background for our experiences. That this background is not in the full light of our consciousness does not impair its importance. We know that experiences which are in the full light of self-perception very often do not have a strong influence on the vegetative system. Indeed we know, on the other hand, that whatever is outside the field of immediate consciousness has a strong influence on the somatic vegetative sphere.

We know that the labyrinth has a strong physiological influence on the vegetative nervous system. T. D. Demetriades has collected what is known about this topic. Labyrinthine irritation is connected with pallor of the face, nausea, and vomiting. The breathing is changed and the tone of the blood vessels is influenced.

We would expect that such a sensory organ, receiving only half-conscious impressions and leading to a motility of an instinctual and primitive type, would be very sensitive to emotions and would therefore play an important part in neuroses and psychoses. It will react strongly, and we may even expect that changes in the psyche will immediately express themselves in vestibular sensations and in tonus. Organic changes in the vestibular apparatus will be reflected in the psychic structures. They will not only influence the tone, the vegetative system, and the attitudes of the body, but they must also change our whole perceptive apparatus and even our consciousness. These general considerations make it possible that the study of the vestibular apparatus may have great importance for the understanding of psychotic and neurotic states.

The vestibular apparatus has, as peripheral sense organs, sacculus, ventriculus, and the semicircular canals. From there the vestibular nerve goes to the nuclei of Deiters, Bechterew, and of the triangularis. It is more than probable that Deiters' nucleus, which has a more lateral position, has more to do with the motor function of the vestibular nerve. The other nuclei, situated nearer to the median line, probably have more to do with the vegetative functions of this nerve.

Spitzer has differentiated between idiotropic and oikotropic functions in the nervous system. The idiotropic system has, according to him, the task of correlating the single parts of the body and of guaranteeing the unity of one's own body. The oikotropic nervous system correlates the body with the outer world. In the medulla oblongata the oikotropic sensory zone is more lateral, in the idiotropic more medial. The acoustic nuclei, which serve in the perception of the outside world, have a more lateral position than the vestibular nuclei, which get their impressions from the body itself but have some relation to the outside world. The functions of the lateral nuclei of the vestibular nerve lie between the oikotropic and the idiotropic. The median nuclei are idiotropic only. We do not know very much about the further pathways of the vestibular impulses. There is no doubt that the nucleus of Deiters is connected with the oculomotor nuclei, via the fasciculus longitudinalis inferior, but it is at least probable that the path of the vestibular impulses is via the median fillet to the cortical region. E. A. Spiegel poisoned localized parts of the sensory cortex (from the region between the temporal and parietal lobe) with strychnine and he got specific epileptiform reactions to the turning of animals.[2]

After these theoretical remarks we may begin the discussion of an interesting group of cases to which Von Weizsaecker has drawn attention.

Rudolf Allers, A. Lenz and Guenther had previously made similar observations. In V. von Weizsaecker's first case a patient with Menière syndrome saw distortions of optic space with monocular as well as binocular vision, and he also had similar impressions in the haptic sphere. It was remarkable that these distortions were syste-

---

[2] E. A. Spiegel has since increased the range of his experimentations on the action currents of the cortex under labyrinthine irritation. The new experiments confirm his belief that labyrinthine impulses enter the temporal lobe near to the parietal lobe.

matic, straight lines giving the impression of being oblique. In his second patient the disturbance was confined to the right eye only. When the left eye was covered he saw everything very well, but the floor and ceiling and objects in the room appeared oblique and he felt uneasy. Every vertical and horizontal line appeared slanted to the left; on the other hand, he saw every line slanted from the vertical 10 to 20 degrees to right or left as vertical, and every line slanted upward or downward from the horizontal was seen as horizontal. Circles appeared as ellipses; ellipses, slanted to the left or right side, appeared as circles. Many angles were not seen as angles but as parallels. Vision and perception with the left eye were absolutely normal. The patient also showed many aberrations in his posture, which according to Von Weizsaecker are due to an erroneous haptic orientation. Von Weizsaecker does not go into the local diagnosis of his cases, although in his first case the diagnosis of a lesion of the inferior cerebellar artery is at least probable. In the discussion of a third observation, recently published, he speaks against a vestibular localization of the disturbance. He points out that most of the cases observed gave evidence of a more diffuse lesion.

Hans Hoff and I have observed a very similar case (K.L.) in which the autopsy gave definite evidence. This patient had an accident in the year 1909. He lost consciousness and vomited. A few months later a slight paresis of the left side of the face and of the body occurred. There was also a loss of sensation on this side. The patient had fits three or four times a year, which lasted between five or ten minutes and were accompanied by a complete loss of consciousness. During these attacks he often saw black buttons flying around. When he came for an examination in 1928, there was a vertical nystagmus. Other symptoms found were facial paralysis, cerebellar asynergia, and flexion combinée. There was a hemianesthesia on the left side. The strength on the left side was diminished, and the hearing in the left ear was also diminished. The left vestibular nerve reacted less to turning and irrigation. The otologist made the diagnosis of a traumatic lesion of the peripheral vestibular apparatus. Several times loss of consciousness had been observed, with a pulse rate of 54. The patient showed a constant dizziness. Objects turned around him in the frontal plane from the right side to the left. The phenomenon was always present when he looked with both eyes. The object moved more and more rapidly and was finally replaced by a revolving disc. The revolving remained, even when the object was removed. When the patient looked with the right eye, the apparent movement was either absent or very limited. When he looked with his left eye alone, very often the object appeared doubled. Objects seemed to rotate 360 degrees in the frontal plane, with the lower end fixed, and then returned into the upright position. Beside these phenomena of movement, the left eye saw directions changed. All objects shown to the left eye were seen in an oblique line, which in an angle of about 30 degrees went from the right above to the left below.

It was of no consequence whether the objects exposed were horizontal, vertical, or inclined outside or inside. The patient saw only a line, irrespective of whatever object was shown to him. Instead of a cross he saw only one line. The patient had occasional disturbances of the right eye. But even during these disturbances he saw crosses and angles which he could not see with the other eye. At times he could not see at all with the left eye, and the disturbances varied on different days. Even when he saw well and no amblyopia was present, the visual field became spiral. Besides these sensory phenomena, the patient showed a persistent disturbance in equilibrium. He swayed and deviated to the left side, with the left shoulder pushed forward. Sometimes he turned to the right side (in a clockwise direction) during this deviation to the left side. He had marked anomalies of the postural and righting reflexes. It is remarkable that the left arm behaved differently when the patient was lying and when he was sitting. We came to the conclusion that there was a lesion in the cerebellum and the medulla oblongata. A disturbance of more proximal parts appeared probable, considering the disturbances in the sensibility. An organic lesion of the vestibular system was proved by the nystagmus. This disturbance was a central one. From the history, we believed at first that there were real epileptic attacks, but a further study led us to the conclusion that the attacks were not epileptic but probably due to an immediate influence on the centers of consciousness in the medulla oblongata. Autopsy showed an extradural abscess which descended from the end of the pyramidal bone to the medulla oblongata (Hans Hoff). At the microscopic examination, the left pyramidal tract showed small infiltrations. From the nucleus of Deiters on the left side, to the hypoglossal nerve were many infiltrations. Without question this was a central vestibular lesion. Von Weizsaecker doubted whether such cases were vestibular, but the evidence in the case reported is convincing.

At this point important conclusions can be drawn.

1. The vestibular apparatus has an influence on the visual field. This influence can be a homolateral one. Its irritation provokes darkening or concentric narrowing of the visual field. The patient observed had a lesion in the region of the nucleus of Deiters. There is a question of whether purely peripheral lesions can provoke the same disturbance. It is a well-known fact that almost every patient with labyrinthine disease complains of darkening of the visual field. K. Eisinger and I have observed it almost regularly in our cases of labyrinthine fistula. We have never observed peripheral cases with unilateral darkening of the visual field, but further observation on the subject is necessary. H. Brunner and H. Hoff have studied many patients who complained that while their ears were being irrigated, they saw everything in a mist. They had the impression that the vestibular apparatus influences the optic sphere in cases in which the optic sphere is not properly protected or in which the vestibular irritation is increased by a lesion of the vestibular nuclei. My own experiences with peripheral labyrinthine cases make it probable that also a purely peripheral increase of impulses may provoke the phenomenon.

Cases in which there is no darkening of the visual field when there is a labyrinthine fistula are very rare. It should be remembered that in most cases there is not simple darkening or mist but rather scintillation in the optic field. Sometimes small circles appear, usually glittering. Eisinger and I have observed that even in dreams this trouble is present. Patients may report that there was darkness, complain of mist or smoke, or report that rain seemed to fall. One may ask whether this darkening of the visual field may not be due to a vasomotor disturbance in some cases. This is not very probable in view of the scintillation. The unilateral character in the case of K.L. points clearly against this theory. In one of the dreams reported by K. Eisinger and the writer, the glittering plane of a skating rink changed into the glitter of a movie screen.

2. In the case of K.L., there was apparent movement in the visual field, homolateral to the side of the vestibular lesion. This movement was present even when the eye was closed. But the movement was chiefly a movement of objects seen with this eye. There is little doubt that vestibular irritation provokes apparent movement of objects. It is a well-known fact that during turning, objects seem to move in a direction opposite to the direction of the turning. When the movement is stopped, objects move in the direction of the turning. This movement is not a continuous one; the objects move, and then suddenly return to their original positions. As R. Bárány and M. H. Fischer have shown, this movement is partially dependent on the *nystagmic* movements of the eyes.

Probably the rhythmic impulses, which are at the basis of nystagmus, also influence the perception of movement in a direct way. It is quite apparent that in the case of K.L. the vertical nystagmus cannot explain the complicated apparent movement. One may of course hypothesize that the posterior semicircular canal could be made responsible for the apparent movement, as well as for the vertical nystagmus. Are these apparent movements due to a purely peripheral or to a central disturbance of the vestibular apparatus? The unilaterality, unknown in peripheral lesions, points clearly to a central lesion. However, the symptomatology of the apparent movements in peripheral disease of the vestibular apparatus has not as yet been sufficiently studied. I have observed a great number of patients with peripheral lesions who complained of something going around in their heads but they were unable to give a clear description.

We also know very little as to why the speed of the apparent movement is so different in different cases. It is noteworthy that in our patient the speed rapidly increased. In experimental vestibular irritation, the speed was generally moderate, and did not change when the irritation continued. In our case the object itself made a rotation of 360 degrees around its base. It seemed as if there were many different impulses to apparent movement. One must consider that vestibular movement apparently does not have a very definite direction. After rotation, some subjects see objects move in a direction opposite to the direction of the turning. The vestibular movement can be transformed into a movement of opposite direction, but the possible extent of such transformation has not been sufficiently studied. In the dreams of labyrinthine-fistula patients, these transformations play an enormous part. Some of the dreams run as follows:

The patient was on a skating rink, and there were many people skating. They came from the background towards her and then turned to the right side. Two children were especially clear. The skating rink was very large. She wished to go nearer and then suddenly stood before the vertical plane of a glittering screen. She dreamt about a white stain. Then it was a scarf. She wanted to pick it up. Then it was a heap of guinea pigs which scattered in all directions. They ran up her legs. She screamed, pushed them away, and awoke with disgust.

Another patient dreamt that she was running after a train. The train stopped. There was a funeral, but all the people ran very quickly and the music also played very quickly. She walked on a small path near an abyss. She felt dizzy and swayed to the left side. She saw many people at a rather great distance. They moved in the crowd in an irregular way. All of them were killed. They started to run and it began to rain. She was killed and fell backwards. She was in a performance of a play. She had to climb some stairs. She crawled up a pole and slid down quickly. There was a hearse with a big glass box, as big as a room. The carriage moved very slowly.

Other patients dreamt about many couples dancing in a dance hall. Finally all the couples fell down. In other dreams there were crowds garbed in light dresses, in vivid movement with tapes and banners fluttering.

One immediately sees the enormous variety of transformations. The movement in the horizontal plane, and even the horizontal plane itself, can be transformed into movements in the vertical plane.

Vestibular movement appears as an irregular and broken movement. It can appear as an upward and downward movement. The speeding-up of the movement is seen very clearly in some of the dreams. Paradoxically, movement can appear particularly slow. One may say that the change in the consciousness of the dreamer may be responsible for all these transformations, but the fact remains that such transformations seem to occur easily. The dreams of vestibular patients lead to the conclusion that the important primary phenomena are (1) movement and (2) speed. It seems to be more or less secondary which movement and which speed occur, and even the plane of the movement is changeable. One must remember, of course, that in most of these cases the lateral semicircular canal is affected. It is difficult to say whether influences are present on the other semicircular canals, and it is not clear how the sacculus and utriculus are affected. It appears that in some cases the otoliths can provoke apparent movements. I have observed the following case of a medical student, and reproduce his own description:

This is an attempt to describe in writing, as correctly as I can, the syndrome which I have been experiencing since May 26, 1930. My first experience was that I was dizzy. The room seemed to be turning around. The ground and floor were rising up and down, and chairs, tables, and desks seemed to be revolving. I felt this dizzy sensation on two occasions during the prodromal period, when I did not feel up to par. I ran a temperature of 101 with a pulse rate of 125. The diagnosis of grippe had been made. The dizziness became permanent and has remained so till the present time.

Were I now to experience this sensation for the first time in my life, I would describe it exactly as I have done above, but having had the unfortunate opportunity of living with it for a year and a half, my description can be more detailed. The focus of the trouble seems to be in the region of the left inner ear, a point midway between the ear and the occiput, several inches within the skull. I feel something about every second, but sometimes the feeling is more irregular. It seems to be an impulse travelling across the left side of the head to about the midline. The body swings with it, in the manner of a pendulum, simultaneously in the direction it takes to the left side. The greatest swing is in the legs and the least in the head. The impulse sometimes does not travel to the midline, but in a lateral and anterior direction. The body swinging follows this direction. In between, the impulse travels perpendicularly downward, causing a sensation of falling into the earth, and in between all these sensations, the body always comes back to the normal position. The sum total gives the sensation of an up and down movement, with the left side swinging to the left, right, backwards and forwards. The head tends to swing rhythmically from the midline to the left side, and there right itself. But I can't control it, and no actual movements take place. Also in walking, the left foot, due to these bizarre sensations, does not strike the ground normally as does the right one, for these sensations give it the appearance of being elsewhere. The ocular impressions in some way conform to those impulses. The usual thing is that the room shifts to the left and dips downward on the left side. While fastening my gaze upon an object, the object moves slightly from the center to the left, to the right, and back to the center. There is little movement in either direction. These sensations are continuous all the time, and I only get relief when I sleep or ride in a moving vehicle. In the latter case I feel normal once again, until the vehicle stops. I also get relief for a while when my mind is intensely engrossed in some problem, until the sensation forms itself back on my consciousness. Jerking my head up and down to the left, raising my head about 45 degrees above the horizontal, cause a slight increase in the swings. At the same time I feel vibrations in the drums of both ears. Sudden turning to the left provokes stronger impulses, and a feeling in my stomach like one gets when riding in an elevator and it comes to a sudden stop. Outside of this dizziness, my health is unimpaired. The right side of my body participates slightly, if at all, in any of these manoeuvres.

We shall later discuss these observations more carefully, when we discuss apparent movement of the body. I might point out the continuous downward movement of the objects. It is very difficult to explain such apparent movement by disturbances in the semicircular apparatus. It is much more probable that we also deal with a change in the otolithic apparatus. There is the additional question of whether changes in the cortical vestibular apparatus can provoke changes in planes as reported in the dreams.

3. This leads us to a discussion of the problem of changes in the

perception of directions by vestibular dysfunction. K.L. sees every object as oblique, and always inclined 30 degrees to the right side. The patient does not see any horizontal lines. The seriousness of the disturbance in this case did not allow more precise analysis. But such an analysis was possible in Von Weizsaecker's cases, which have been reported above. The perception of space is changed in a characteristic way. Parallel lines very often appear instead of crosses and angles. A triangle is seen as two parallel lines. There is, of course, again the question of whether these changes in the perception of directions are due to the semicircular or to the otolothic apparatus; we do not know the differences in the central representation of semicircular canals and otoliths. According to investigations by Mach, eccentric rotation provokes the feeling that the subject is sitting in a position slanting away from the center of rotation. A pendulum slanted from 10 to 20 degrees appeared vertical, probably because of influence of gravity on the otoliths. I am therefore inclined to believe that the disturbance in the otolithic function, mentioned above and in the cases of Von Weizsaecker, is due to a lesion of the central apparatus of the otoliths.

We are accustomed to consider that peripheral otolith irritation leads to one-sided motor disturbance (F. H. Quix). However, one-sided optic disturbances are never seen in peripheral lesions. Whatever interpretation regarding localization one may prefer, the facts that in Von Weizsaecker's case triangles could not be seen and that in our case (K.L.) only one or two slanted lines came to perception, offer great difficulties for interpretation. In lesions of the spinal cord, angles drawn on the skin are often felt as parallels (compare Erwin Stengel). Seeing straight lines as oblique may doubtless be a vestibular phenomenon; it can also be provoked by many other causes. J. Wilder is inclined to believe that in all these cases, peripheral and central factors participate. He stresses the importance of disturbances in the eye muscles, but believes that a cortical lesion is also necessary. Hans Hoff and I do not believe that oblique vision is caused only by vestibular lesions. Paralysis of the eye muscles can provoke similar disturbances. In Lenz's patient A., a lesion in the optical sphere seems probable, but the vestibular apparatus is only one of the many systems for orientation in space. Usually we do not expect to find that any important function of the body is mediated by one apparatus only. Julius Bauer speaks of the principle of manifold insurance of important functions in the organism, particularly in regard to metabolic and glandular disturbances. What is true in the somatic sphere is especially true for the central nervous system. Hoff has taken a very similar point of view. I have mentioned that apparent movement in the vestibular lesions is partially dependent on the nystagmic movements of the eyes. The oculostatic factor has a great importance, but there are also important relations between the innervation of the eye muscles and the vestibular apparatus. The case of K.L. does not show one symptom which is very often coexistent with oblique vision, namely, seeing in the opposite direction. It is A. Pick's opinion that the feeling, which one often has in trains, of riding in a direction opposite to the real direction is due to vestibular influences. Joseph Gerstmann has described a case in which the patient saw objects behind him which actually were in front of him. In one of Wilder's cases there was a tumor in the parieto-occipital region. Otto Poetzl has observed a case of purely occipital lesion, in which the patient saw the ceiling as below and the floor as above. People seemed to walk with their heads downward. Similar phenomena have been reported in migraine. In my material I have a rather remarkable case belonging to this group.

The patient was an alcoholic with emotional deterioration but unimpaired intellectual capacity. He writes as follows:

Due to the length of time that has elapsed, it is difficult to recall vividly the details of the mental picture I described for you, but I find that I am able to visualize them so that I can give an analysis. During the afternoon preceding the night in question, there was a snowstorm that had left the ground covered with a blanket of snow, against which the bare trees stood out very prominently. I recollect noticing especially this background of the first heavy snow of the winter. The first scene, after I retired a night, consisted of a mental picture of a similar type of scenery, although not recognizable as identical. There were invariably landscapes of a serene and restful nature, but they grew very tiresome as they continuously presented themselves. Apparently, too, this was what caused my wakefulness, as I was not conscious of any other sensation at the time, except a lack of ability to relax as night approached. These scenes changed from time to time, as if one merged into another, rather than with an abrupt shift, and in this manner went on and on in a sort of connected sequence, disappearing only temporarily, as they took on some new definite form. Each individual picture stood out sharply and was very distinct to the eye before it faded away, to be replaced by another. After these pictures had persisted for a while, I would open my eyes and they would cease to appear. This went on until I could think of nothing else but these scenes.

The first pictures consisted of many tall trees with bare limbs, standing in a deep snow with an upward slant toward the distance. So much land was visible that there was barely any sky and just the suspicion of an horizon. This was succeeded by a similar type, that was identical, except that instead of snow there was bright green grass in each view. The trees were the same and had no leaves. I arose several times and walked about the bedroom but the scenes always returned as soon as I returned to bed and shut my eyes. Gradually some of the trees disappeared and a little water crept into the pictures. Finally, for a short time, a small pond with a winding creek appeared at one side in the picture; first the creek and then the pond. Both creek and pond had sloping banks which were very grassy. This was the only time that I recognized anything that looked at all familiar, except for the lack of foliage. It resembles the locality I know. I was certainly surprised to see the trees upside down. During the time they were inverted, I do not recall any change in the scenery except that the trees were more prominent than ever. At this point I tried hard to visualize the scene right-side-up, with the result that the trees grew sideways, what would normally be parallel to the ground instead of perpendicular. I would immediately fall asleep when they stopped.

One may ask whether these phenomena have anything to do with the vestibular apparatus. The vestibular apparatus influences the perception of directions, and it is more than probable that the parietal lobes give the final shape to direction.

Transformation from one plane to another is also one of the most important functions of this part of the brain according to Poetzl and Hermann. Transformations from the right side to the left side take place in the cases of agraphia and alexia. The parieto-occipital lobe arranges directions into definite planes. Movement and direction are at first indefinite, and need to be brought into connection with a system of coördinates. It seems that below, above, right, and left can very easily change into each other. We shall later discuss the way in which this system of coördinates is dependent on motor impulses and on the tone of the body. Similar disturbances in perception are not uncommon immediately after awakening, when this final synthesis of the directions is still incomplete. The vestibular dreams reported above are in some way proof that the mechanisms indicated have indeed a deep relation to the vestibular apparatus.

4. When, in our example, apparent movements start, the object very often appears smaller. In other words, we deal with a micropsia. There is no doubt that normal function of the vestibular apparatus is necessary in order to give us the right appreciation of the size of objects. It is very difficult to judge what part tonic impulses play in this phenomenon. In another of our cases, the patient had a micropsia on one side. In vestibular dreams objects appear very small when they move rapidly. There are people dancing and the figures appear very small. In the parieto-occipital lobe lesions, which disturb the central portion of the vestibular apparatus, hallucinations of small figures have been observed (Otto Kauders). Rudolf Allers has already pointed to the relation of micropsia to the vestibular apparatus.

5. When our patient looks at an object with his left eye, there is also a marked polyopia. This polyopia is a monocular disturbance. When nystagmus is provoked by peripheral irritation, some patients see objects double in the direction of the nystagmus. It is as if nystagmus tore optic impressions asunder. J. Gerstmann and A. Kestenbaum have discussed this phenomenon. It is probable that the muscular change in the eye muscles is partly responsible for this phenomenon. Peripheral lesions provoke this disturbance in both eyes. Monocular polyopia gives evidence of a more central lesion. In the case of K.L., no relation exists between nystagmus and polyopia, while in O. Kauders' case multiple microptic hallucinations are present. H. Stein and Urbantschitsch have reported monocular polyopia in labyrinthine lesions. In central lesions, nystagmus and monocular polyopia are seen as coördinated phenomena; the more central the lesion, the more closely they are related. An analysis of a case of hysterical polyopia has led me to the conclusion that changes in the

distribution of the impulses to the eye muscles is responsible for the polyopia. The actual movement of the eye muscles may have some important influence; but, as the dreams of the labyrinthine-fistula patients show, change in the distribution of the impulses is sufficient to provoke the phenomenon. When we move the head or the eyes, we undoubtedly get a multiplicity of optic impressions. That they are shaped into single objects, moving or standing still, is a purely organic synthetic function, in which the vestibular apparatus participates. Vestibular lesions allow the appearance of fragments in the synthetic process.

6. Micropsia and polyopia are generally accompanied by metamorphopsias (object-distortions). V. von Weizsaecker's patient saw objects as incomplete and distorted. Metamorphopsias were also present in Otto Kauders' case. In one case of atropine delirium, vestibular irritation provoked distortion of the pictures. It is quite possible that metamorphopsia only sums up disturbances provoked by change in the perception of directions. The patient in atropine delirium was unable to see horizontal lines. Poetzl, who has analyzed similar disturbances in parieto-occipital lesion patients, emphasizes the importance of the oculomotor processes. Apparently, we deal not only with a purely sensory factor, but also with tonic and oculomotor influences in the genesis of metamorphopsia. Micropsia, polyopia, and dysmetamorphopsia have often been interpreted by reference to changes in accommodation. I do not deny that disturbances in the peripheral or central mechanism of accommodation may provoke similar phenomena; but in all the cases reported there are no disturbances in accommodation. It is doubtful that the vestibular apparatus has any influence on accommodation. However it is not difficult to prove that tone, motility, and especially motor impulses, have an important influence on the phenomena mentioned. Central lesions of the cutaneous sensibility system can provoke phenomena corresponding to polyopsia and metamorphopsia. H. Stein, E. Stengel, and P. Schilder have shown that under certain conditions, a straight line drawn on the skin is perceived as a curve. We have also observed that in spinal and parietal lesions, parallel lines are perceived instead

of angles. Distortions are, therefore, phenomena which are not peculiar to the lesions of the vestibular apparatus, but may occur in all modalities in lesions of the cerebral nervous system. It seems that distortions of perception occur most often in cortical lesions. I may point to the phenomena observed in optic agnosias (compare Otto Poetzl). All senses follow the same basic principles. Some of them are more clearly seen in vestibular disturbances, since the vestibular apparatus is a coördinating apparatus for sensory functions. Its close relations to tone and motility are of special importance.

In every sensory perception, motility and tone play an important part. There is a part of motility which has special importance for the elaboration of perceptions (the sensory movement of H. Stein). Motor mechanisms, akin to vestibular ones, are involved in perception, so that disintegration of the perception leads to phenomena similar to disturbances of the vestibular apparatus. It seems probable that the tonic components of motility are of special importance. From this point of view the special importance of the vestibular apparatus, with its close access to the tonic apparatus, is obvious.

7. Although K.L. did not show obvious changes in tactile perception, the phenomenon of tactile dizziness (*Takschwindel*) in vestibular lesions is very well known. When, during rotation, the foot touches the ground, after the turning has stopped the ground seems to turn around the foot in the opposite direction to the rotation. In von Weizsaecker's case, the apparent vertical seemed to be inclined in space to the left side and away from the patient. The patient also made mistakes in haptic localization. It is difficult to say in this case which components are secondary to tonic disturbances, since the description of the tonic disturbances is not very clear. Disturbances in spatial perceptions provoked by changes in tone were not well known at the time von Weizsaecker published his observation. In the experiments of W. Bromberg and P. Schilder on the vestibular influence on cutaneous afterimages, the influence of vestibular irritation was obvious. After stopping, the sensation moved in the direction of the turning, and during the turning it went in the opposite direction.

8. Our patient showed considerable weakness, homolateral to the

optic disturbances. I have also noticed this in another patient. I do not think that this is a psychogenic disturbance, but the organic character of the weakness cannot be definitely demonstrated. Proof of vestibular influence on the strength of the same side is therefore lacking.

9. The patient also showed disturbances in the sensibility on the same side. In other cases similar observations have been made. There is in some cases a suspicion that the impairment of sensibility may be psychogenic, but there is still no doubt that the vestibular nerve exerts an influence on the homolateral sensibility. Guettich reports homolateral disturbances in the perception of temperature in vestibular irritation.

10. It is impossible here to discuss fully the influence of the vestibular apparatus on motility and tone. M. H. Fischer has often pointed to a reaction which they term the "fall-reaction." When a subject, after rotation in a swivel chair, changes the position of his head in space, he falls quickly and with great strength in a special direction. Severe nausea is present. The direction of falling depends on the direction of the turning and the position of the head. There are close relations between the direction of turning and the sensation of turning which one gets by a change in the position of the head. The falling occurs in the direction opposite to the sensation of turning, and is connected with a feeling of falling to the other side. M. H. Fischer considers the "fall-reaction" an answer to the sensation of turning. It is an unconscious counterreaction. Hans Hoff and I have shown that, in cases in which the apparent movement occurs in the frontal plane, falling is not uncommon. We relate it to changes in the posterior vertical canal. Besides this reaction of sudden falling, there are the well-known tonic deviations which Bárány, M. H. Fischer, and E. Wodack and others have carefully studied. We do not yet know the different motor reactions which follow a change in otolith function. F. H. Quix has developed an elaborate system based on past-pointing, but it has not yet been proven. We know very little about otolith reflexes in normal human beings, except through the experimental work of R. Magnus and A. de Kleijn (see the study by H. Hoff and P. Schilder). The problem becomes still more complicated when we

consider the more central lesions of the vestibular apparatus. The close anatomical relation of the vestibular centers to other tonic centers makes solution of this problem almost impossible. In our patient, disturbances in equilibrium are permanent. He sways to the left side and deviates to the left side. The left shoulder is pushed forward and sometimes even turning to the right side is present. There are anomalies of the postural reflexes and of the righting reflexes. The left arm deviates to the left in different ways depending on the position of the head in space. This points to abnormal otolith reflexes. H. Hoff and I have pointed out that there exist cases of lesion in the parieto-occipital lobe with considerable changes in the postural reflexes. It is probable that these changes are partially related to the central representation of the vestibular nerve. These changes in the posture have great importance for our problems, since every change in the tonic apparatus also has an influence on the perception of the body. H. Hoff and I have hypothesized that vestibular tone and the tone of the postural reflexes let us feel the part of the body on which the tone is acting transposed into a direction which is opposite to the direction of the pull of the tone. Or in other words, the vestibular influence distorts the postural model of the body, the knowledge and perception of the body-image.

11. Before discussing this part of the problem, it is necessary to make some remarks concerning the perception of the body. H. Hartmann and P. Schilder have shown that the perception of the inside of the body is chiefly a perception of heavy mass, and that the body and limbs are perceived in the same way as other heavy substances. When there is a pull in a special direction due to tonus, the amount of this pull is added to or subtracted from the gravity of the body. Spontaneously, a rising extremity is light and a sinking extremity is heavy. Objects put on a rising arm seem lighter. We know now that an important element in every dizziness is that the body as a whole or in part appears lighter. This change in the weight of the body may be referred only to the head, but it may also be referred to any other part of the body. The pull of tone is, paradoxically, identical with any other pull on the body. Since an irritation of the semicircular canals

provokes considerable changes in the tone, the impression of the weight of the body will change immediately. M. H. Fischer and E. Wodak have shown that vestibular irritation with cold water makes the right arm fall and the left arm rise. At the same time the right arm feels heavier than the left. Cerebral and cerebellar lesions cause changes in the appreciation of weight according to the changes in rising or sinking tendencies. When we are under the influence of centrifugal forces, we immediately feel changes in the weight of the body. Every pressure, every pull, and every change in the outward force of gravity, will immediately change the impression of the weight of our body according to the physical forces.

When ascending in an airplane, the weight of the body seems immediately to increase. It is remarkable that the apparent weight of the body increases more in the part of the body which is supported. When we are sitting, the lower part of the trunk increases its weight. S. Parker and P. Schilder have studied changes in the postural model of the body in an elevator. When one goes up the legs become heavier, and when the arms are stretched forward they are also heavier. This feeling is only present during acceleration. After stopping, the arms go higher and the body becomes lighter. In these results we deal with the influence of inertia, which acts like an additional weight or a loss of weight. When the elevator stops, one feels as if the body were still going upward, becoming lighter and becoming elongated. When one goes downwards the arms rise and become lighter. There is an elongation of the body. When one stops, the feet are heavier but the other part of the body seems to go further down, so that there are two lighter phantom feet under the real feet. At the same time the body appears to be shorter. There can be a further aftersensation. A phantom, a mass, goes down and the body appears to be shorter.

It is very important to notice that during the going down of the elevator the body is not only lighter but also longer. It is as if a part of the head did not go down with the rest of the body; that is, the aftereffect of the position of the head in space is stronger than the actual sensation. One sees this very clearly when the elevator stops. The head then goes further down, and at the same time there exists

an impression of the actual position of the body. The tactile, kinesthetic, and optic images of the body do not influence our perception
of the position of the head, but the soles, touching the ground, give
us a clear and definite perception. There is also a dissociation of the
postural model of the body when there is accelerated movement, and
a part of the substance of the body seems to step out of the body (in
the sense of the positive aftersensation). The substance of the head
stepping out of the actual head has a special importance. This emanat-
ing substance is the carrier of the localization of the ego. E. Claparède
has shown that we generally localize the ego at the base of the forehead, between the eyes. Vestibular aftersensation influences this
localization. We estimate the length of the body according to the actual sensation of the sole of our feet and the localization of the ego,
which is dependent on the vestibular aftersensation. The body may
therefore appear longer and shorter. The positive aftersensation can
persist for a long time. The shortening and lengthening of the body
is particularly clear then, according to the dissociations between
"vestibular head and real legs."

One may ask whether these sensations are really due to the vestibular apparatus, or whether they are due to tactile and muscular
graviceptors. There is no basis for the latter assumption, especially
if one considers the part the head plays in this phenomenon. That
vestibular irritation results from the movement of the elevator is
proved by the fact that strong dizziness may occur in sensitive persons. This dizziness is connected with swaying. When it occurs,
some substance seems to emanate from and enshroud the head. The
head then appears larger. This is, by the way, the well-known phenomenon of the increase of the apparent size of the head after alcoholic
intoxication. It is difficult to say which part of the vestibular apparatus
is affected in these experiments. Probably it is the otolithic apparatus.

In general, irritation of the otoliths dissociates the postural model
of the body. The vestibular irritation described here dissociates the
vestibular impulses from the other senses. Along with vestibular
sensation, there goes a part of the heavy substance of the body. Its
quantity may vary. It is like a phantom of indefinite borderlines. It

contains the head. In a person standing, the center of the other perception of gravity is in the legs. The body is lighter when the vestibular substance is subtracted from the body. The body seems emptied.
The vestibular irritation dissociates the heavy substance of the body,
and with it, the body itself. Dissociations of this kind take place not
only in accelerated perpendicular movements but also in accelerated
movements of all types, which influence the vestibular apparatus.
Normal function of the labyrinth in all its parts is necessary for a
unified postural model of the body. Heaviness and lightness of the
body, in their subjective sense, are also largely dependent upon the
vestibular apparatus.

P. Bonnier's patients had the impression of being divided into two
persons during attacks of dizziness. It is probable that vestibular
irritations, of the type described here, are responsible for such phenomena. Since the perception of the weight of one's own body has an
influence on the perception of heaviness of objects, we must expect
that objects will appear heavier and lighter according to function. In
an observation by R. Allers, objects appeared larger and smaller,
heavier and lighter. In cases of this kind, the tactile perception of
objects is also changed. Heveroch has observed hemistereodysmetria
in two cases.

12. We are now prepared to study changes in the postural model
of the body (body image) caused by vestibular influence. The postural model of the body is built up of optic impressions, as well as of
tactile and kinesthetic impressions. It will therefore change with
vestibular changes of vision. Metamorphopsias necessarily change the
perception of the body. Changes in the perception of the heaviness of
the body will add an additional difference. One of our patients felt her
neck swell up and her extremities become larger during dizziness. In
an old observation of M. H. Romberg's, the hands became larger and
moved in different directions. H. Stein reports a case in which the feet
of the patient seemed to elongate. Another patient felt as if her neck
became longer and longer and her head were flying. However, only
a minority of patients have similar sensations. In our case, reported
above, no such observation has been made.

13. Besides changes in the perceptual field and in the field of motility, vegetative symptoms are very constant. Nausea is one of these symptoms. Vestibular irritation and disease are often accompanied by feelings of heat and cold. I have already referred to the observations of T. D. Demetriades.

14. Changes in consciousness are present in these cases. In the case reported, every long and lasting fixation leads not only to nausea and increasing dizziness, but also to changes in the consciousness. (The patient believes he is on a boat and is very confused.) Since H. Hoff and I have observed several cases of this type, we have come to the conclusion that the vestibular apparatus has an immediate influence on consciousness. This change in consciousness is not only an answer to the disagreeable sensations of the dizziness, but also the expression of an immediate change in the function of the apparatus for consciousness. In certain types of Menière syndrome, loss of consciousness may occur. Other material leads to the conclusion that an apparent movement in the frontal plane has a stronger relation to the consciousness than other apparent movements.

These apparent movements seem to destroy the important biological relation of the body to gravitation; the apparatus which orients us to "above and below" is especially closely related to the apparatus of consciousness. Deep clouding of the consciousness makes an upright position impossible. The relation of the vestibular apparatus to motility must also be considered in this respect. We know that every change in motility which is sufficiently extensive, changes the attitudes of consciousness. In the cases of K. Goldstein, H. Hoff, and P. Schilder, changes in consciousness were connected with an increase in the postural reflexes. J. Wilder has observed similar clouding of the consciousness in some of his patients, but he relates the disturbances of consciousness to vasomotor disturbances. We have often seen these disturbances of the consciousness, in patients in which there were no vasomotor disturbances present. We have good reason to believe that there is a direct relation between the vestibular apparatus and consciousness. K.L. sometimes had a deep loss of consciousness. It is difficult to determine whether we deal here with the influence of the vestibular irritation or with the immediate influence of the process on the vagus. At any rate such an occurrence proves the close neighborhood of these two apparatuses. The hallucinatory pictures connected with vestibular loss of consciousness will be discussed in detail below.

VESTIBULAR INFLUENCE ON IMAGES

In the following remarks, we shall try to understand the vestibular influence on images, especially optic and tactile. It is first necessary to consider the influence of vestibular irritation on the optic afterimage. When the individual is rotated passively to the left, a deviation of the afterimage to the right occurs. This deviation is not continual, but there are quick movements back towards the apparent median. If the rotation continues regularly, the deviation of the afterimage to the side remains continuous, then diminishes and finally disappears. If one stops the rotation to the left, the afterimage deviates slowly to the left side and makes quick jerks to the right and slow movements to the left side. The slow movement is more impressive. As long as the sensation of turning persists, the afterimage seems to turn around in the same direction as the body is turning. Fischer points out that the slow deviation parallels the slow component of the nystagmus and the jerky movements parallel the quick movements of the nystagmus. Fischer believes that nystagmus changes the "local-values" in the retina for the perception of space. Dittler and Koellner differ from this opinion. Optic representations also show changes under vestibular irritation. In one of my subjects a cold irrigation of the right ear provoked the feeling of an empty cylinder turning to the right side. An imagined line in this empty cylinder also seemed to turn. When nystagmus is increased by movements of the eyes, several shorter lines seem to turn to the left side. As I have not experimented sufficiently with this particular subject, I cannot say what the typical movements of the optic images are during vestibular irritations.

G. Bibring-Lehner has made experiments on subjects in whom eidetic images were provoked. Eidetic images stand between optic representations and optic perceptions, and have many qualities of perceptions. At the beginning of the turning, most subjects see details turn in a direction opposite to that of the turning. During the turning details return toward the midline. After stopping, the details go toward the direction of the original turning. There is a close relation between the movement of afterimages and of the eidetic pictures. Very often in the eidetic picture details only, and not the whole picture, participate in the movements described. W. Bromberg and P. Schilder have made similar observations on aftereffects of tactile sensations and tactile imaginations. These also showed definite deviations corresponding to the slow component of the nystagmus. It is of general psychological importance that imaginations follow the same laws as perceptions and afterimages, and are under the immediate influence of vestibular irritation. (My experiments also show that the tendency to movement in a special direction in images, is sometimes used in a rather free way.)

Bibring-Lehner reports important material bearing on this problem. In one of the experiments, a child is imagined while the subject is turning. The child seems to turn in the same direction as the subject. Here we deal with the projection of one's own movement into the eidetic picture. I have already mentioned that during turning it is sometimes difficult for subjects to maintain optic images. In the optic eidetic images as well, parts of the picture tend to become very unclear. Sometimes one-half of the picture disappears, and very often the colors become gray during the turning. One of the most remarkable features is multiplication. Two stilts may change into a wooden fence. Instead of one dog, several dogs jump over a rope. The doubled and multiplied details very often become smaller and appear farther away. This is very important because it shows that turning induces the same changes in optic images as in optic vision. It seems as if free transformations of movements come out in eidetic images with special clarity.

These facts gain still greater importance if we study the quality of optic and eidetic images, when they are retained for a longer time. They disintegrate in a similar way as under vestibular irritation, except that disintegration under vestibular irritation is more complete and more rapid. There are continuous tendencies to movement in optic and tactile images. It is remarkable that almost every detail described by G. Bibring-Lehner has some analogies in retained eidetic images.

H. Kluever has demonstrated fragmentary eidetic images in which parts disappear completely. There is a continuous tendency to movement in every eidetic image. Vestibular irritation enormously increases tendency to movement, very often in an unspecific rather than in a directed way. The mechanism by which the vestibular apparatus produces the changes in optic pictures is probably partly due to the influence of nystagmus and it is quite probable that the quick component in the nystagmus has an especially important influence on phenomena of multiplication. But it is not the actual movement that provokes a change; more probably this is caused by the impulses. Vestibular dreams have much in common with the changes provoked by vestibular irritation in eidetic images. We deal partially with specific and partially with undirected apparent movements. We do not know whether the vestibular influence on the eye muscles is the only cause of the changes described. We do know that there are many changes in the tone of the whole body and that these probably have a similar influence. H. Hoff has pointed out that the dreams of persons forced to fall asleep in an unaccustomed position have a character very similar to vestibular dreams. This brings us close to an understanding of vestibular hallucinations.

Many years ago I described a case of hallucinatory psychosis in which the patient complained that airplanes were flying around his head. The patient showed an horizontal and rotatory nystagmus. He showed past-pointing to the right side in both arms. Later I studied the influence of vestibular irritations on hallucinations. When the hallucinations are produced under hypnosis, the objects seem to begin to move around. Sometimes one gets a typical turning movement, and the impression changes according to the vestibular irritation. One of the patients, in referring to an hallucinated tree, said that the tree was hewn. In cases of delirium tremens, the hallucinations begin to move much more vividly, and the movement has a turning character. The objects are multiplied when the vestibular irritation takes place and the hallucinations also become microptic. Results were especially clear in a case of belladonna intoxication. In the same way as in the vestibular dreams, the patient showed the influence of vestibular irritation in her hallucinations. During the irritation she saw the *Titanic* sinking, with many passengers moving on the deck. The hallucinations showed metamorphopsia; the face of a woman showed distortions, until finally her jaw disappeared. I may again mention Kauders' observation that turning the head causes increased postural reflexes and optic hallucinations consisting chiefly of many small figures in active movement. Again we see the close relation between vestibular influences and changes in the postural tone. It is not probable that all hallucinations can be influenced in the same way; further investigations should determine which hallucinations can be influenced and which cannot.

These remarks open the way to an understanding of the spontaneous hallucinations in delirium tremens. Hallucinations in acute alcoholic intoxication, as well as in delirium tremens, are connected with considerable changes in the peripheral and central vestibular apparatus. Multiple hallucinations, often microptic and macroptic, are partially based on the vestibular factor, but certainly not on the vestibular factor alone. Changes in the consciousness and in the sensory fields are present, as W. Bromberg has demonstrated by his examination of the aftereffects of tactile impressions in alcoholics. We generally say that multiplication of optic impressions, micropsia, macropsia, metamorphopsia, and vivid movement in hallucinations are signs of vestibular influence. The movements need not be circular, but very often are progressive. Circular and progressive movements can very easily be transformed into each other, as experiences with vestibular dreams show. In alcoholic hallucinosis one may also observe vestibular phenomena.

One of my patients, reporting about his hallucinations said:

Sometimes I saw three or four people on the street instead of one. I saw three faces in glaring white; faces of Negroes and whites. They moved forwards and backwards and when I saw them they started to chase me. I felt them behind me. They said that I had raped a white woman. They wanted to kill me, and talked to each other. Once I saw a very tall figure standing against a wall. It had a red coat and had something in its hand which became bigger and bigger and then collapsed. Then I saw very small figures in red dresses. A little woman wore a green dress. Some danced. Dancing figures came out of the windows. Voices said, "Run away, get out of the way."

The patient was a thirty-four-year-old Negro who was admitted to the hospital because he climbed over roofs and fire escapes. Very similar symptoms are seen in acute cocaine intoxication. The following case shows that the vestibular influence in psychosis does not affect the optic sphere exclusively.

Katherine M., thirty-seven years old, was admitted to Bellevue Hospital on the 17th of April, 1930, in acute alcoholic hallucinosis. The next day she was clear and oriented and gave the following report:

Eight days ago I stopped drinking. I couldn't eat as long as I drank. Yesterday I told my husband that my nerves were shattered. When I awoke I saw dust everywhere. Suddenly the single little particles started to jump. They moved upwards and downwards. The flowers in the vase began to move. Also the patterns in the curtains moved like dolls. Then I felt pain in the stomach and felt that they would have to operate on me. A great number of small worms crawled on the bedcover. A mouse ran through the house. A small doll danced around the piano and shook itself. People made grimaces. Worms and dust had a gray color. The patterns in the curtains were red. When I was in bed I heard footsteps coming and going. They were before me. I had pain in my head, and thought that I had lost my intestines. My uterus was crushed. Something was not in order. I felt numerous small pinpricks on my skin. I felt them close to each other. Somebody said, "Make her ready for the operating table." I thought he wanted to cut me into pieces. I read in the newspapers that bodies are dissected for medical purposes. At first I felt my stomach heavier. I thought I had a tumor. Then my intestines fell down. I thought it was the stomach. When I drank water, it took a long time till it arrived in the stomach. I felt that my intestines were bound in a knot. I did not feel my sex parts. I felt as if everything was shrunk. Then I felt heaviness, which I considered as a tumor, the bladder or the kidney. I thought they would cut me and throw me into a basket when the study was finished. The lower part of my body suddenly disappeared. [When questioned, she said] It did not come into my head whether there was a connection between my legs and the upper part of my body. The whole thing did not last longer than a day. When I drank, my sexual desire stopped. When I am drunk, I hear people talking about me, that I am a drunkard. I heard my little son in the hospital. I thought that I would go into heaven. My body was lighter. I felt happy and prayed to God that He should send me to heaven.

In this case there are unmistakable signs of vestibular dysfunction in the optic sphere, and in addition a marked change in the feeling of the body. I have already mentioned that lightness and heaviness are dependent on vestibular functions, and that gravitation gives the most important impressions concerning the inside of the body.

The inside of our body is perceived as a heavy mass. We do not wonder therefore that the vestibular apparatus, with its tonic influence, is so important in the perception of the body. Feelings of heaviness and lightness of the body are also dependent on the vestibular apparatus. In many instances we are not able to say what part the vestibular apparatus plays. When we are elated we feel lighter, and when depressed, heavier. On the one hand, when we feel very happy we say that we feel so light that we could fly, and on the other hand, we know that the flying sensation in a dream is an expression of processes in the vestibular field. One sees such flying dreams in vestibular diseases; but one also sees similar phenomena in neurosis, in which a conversion influence on the vestibular apparatus can be demonstrated. I shall later discuss the vestibular apparatus as an organ which attracts conversion. In the case reported above, changes in the heaviness and lightness in the body are partially localized, and lead to the feeling of disease, to the fear of being cut to pieces, to the dismembering motive or, in psychoanalytic terms, to the castration complex. Organic vestibular irritation can lead to a disruption of the postural model of the body and can give an organic basis for the castration complex.

According to the investigation of W. Bromberg and myself, dismembering motives are typical of alcoholic hallucinosis. The final formulation and elaboration of the dismembering motive is, however, dependent on psychic motives. In a case of severe anxiety neurosis, the patient complained that she was melting away. She said: "I am completely in pieces. When I am melting I have no hands. I go into a doorway in order not to be trampled upon. Everything is flying away from me. In the doorway I gather together the pieces of my body." She complained that her skull once fell from her neck, and lay before her feet. She was in danger of stepping on it. She felt some pulling in her body, and upper and lower parts were separated from each other. At the same time the patient had hallucinations of vestibular type. She saw five big heads, and also had many flying dreams. From a psychological point of view, the patient showed increased sadism and many compulsions and obsessions. This observation helps us to understand the influence of the vestibular apparatus on the perception of the body.

Since there exists such a close relation between the optic and vestibular sphere, it is very often difficult to say whether a particular hallucination of movement is due to a change in the vestibular or in the optic influence. Movement and the impression of movement are certainly common to both the optic and vestibular sense.

I have discussed several cases in which hallucinations of movement, connected with hallucinations of space colors, were probably due to changes in the optic sphere. Arnold Pick has noted the importance of oculomotor impulses for the perception of movement and for the hallucination of movement. On the other hand, every movement of one's body can give the quality of movement to hallucination. I have shown that choreiform restlessness can appear in moving optic hallucinations. Perception of movement can also be based upon motor impulses and kinesthetic sensations.

Vestibular influence on hallucinations is not present in alcoholic psychosis alone. In a psychosis of cortical encephalitis, in which nystagmus was also present, the patient saw animals which ran quickly. Vestibular influences are seen in other intoxications. In experimental mescal intoxication there may be many little red and green points which move. Moving hallucinations are common, according to K. Zucker, J. Zádor, and Kurt Beringer. C. Stein reports the following hallucinations: The pattern of the tapestry began to move. The patterns were repeated three and four times, one above the other, but still in geometrical shape. Movements in different planes took place, to and fro, from right to left, and from above to below. Single figures made movements independent from the movement in the planes. The lines began to roll, to be in perspective, and to move from the background to the foreground.

The vestibular apparatus must have some importance in these hallucinations of movements. There are changes in the postural model of the body in mescal intoxication. E. Forster reports that he felt as if his left side were very thin and his right side were five times as thick and heavy. He felt as if the limbs did not fit each other. V. Zador reports that a patient felt smaller and felt as if his legs were shorter, as if he were shrinking. When he closed his eyes, he felt as if he could go into a mouse hole. When there is a vestibular factor in such hallucinations it is certainly of a much more central character than the vestibular factor in the hallucinations discussed thus far. Under the influence of mescal, subjects see a room as smaller and the ceiling as lower, like a narrow cell. Another patient said that the floor seemed oblique and came down to him, or he felt as if his chair were going up and down. According to V. Zador, a blind patient often had the feeling that the sofa on which he was sitting was inclined. He heard the voice of the physician from above. Another blind patient said that the distance from one wall to the other was diminished. R. Allers has described changes in tactile space perception under vestibular influence. According to Mayer-Gross, it is not yet clear whether the vestibular apparatus has any part in the phenomenon of movement in mescal intoxication.

The vestibular influence on perceptual changes under mescal intoxication must be very central. There is a relation between the remark of one of W. Mayer-Gross' subjects who said that he always tried to find the true horizontal line in the position of his body and could not find it, and the observations of Von Weizsaecker, Hans

Hoff, and P. Schilder on the changes in the perception of horizontal lines. Kurt Beringer quotes the case of a schizophrenic in whom similar perceptual disturbances were present:

A matchbox took the size of a shoe box, so that the patient had to laugh. When she looked upward at a chest it increased in size and even reached the ceiling. Human beings were two or three heads taller. When the patient read the newspaper the print was oblique. A candy box one meter distant, suddenly became small, remained so momentarily and was suddenly big again, and this change was repeated two or three times. A table suddenly seemed to be far away and appeared small as if in a doll house. The movements of her relatives appeared slower, but they were also awkward and stiff like marionettes. The speech of her relatives very often seemed rapid, so that patient could not understand it. The people on the street moved more quickly and often looked around. Traffic was generally more rapid and it seemed as though an accident might result. Suddenly everything was slow again. At the same time there was slowness of the street cars and automobiles. Objects multiplied; instead of one crystal tumbler she saw several varying in number and size like organ pipes. There was a feeling of dizziness which came from the left side. Sometimes it looked as if one or another object would fall down. She had the feeling that her arms were shortening and lengthening. She reported feeling as if there were no borderline in the left occiput. There were changes in the persons around her. The shape of the noses and the positions of the mouth and teeth were different.

All these remarks are identical with those reported in mescal and hashish intoxication. A subject of F. Kant and E. Krapf remarked, "I see you now much squarer and you now have a pointed chin. Now you have long shoulders." The same subject reported a change in visual movement. The importance of ocular movements in the genesis of metamorphopsias has been noted. Arnold Pick considers oculostatic influences important in their genesis. The vestibular apparatus is only one link in the chain of the tonic apparatus. Impulses to movements or attempts to imagine optically one's arm, would change immediately the optic picture of the arm, which tends to become very long. This shows clearly the close relation between optic impressions and motor impulses. Every sense-modality involves motor tendencies and thus changes in optic appearance. In the

"Mickey Mouse" films, motor impulses as well as impressions from other senses change the appearance of the animated objects.

According to her husband, Irma G., fifty years old, was always nervous. Her nervousness increased after her husband lost a lot of money in Wall Street. She developed the idea that she had cancer and that her finger nails were falling off, and she often expressed a wish to die. She worried about every little thing. Two or three months prior to admission, she became very restless and was unable to sleep and took sleeping medicine. On November 24, 1931, she took sixteen tablets of barbital and mixed them with bichloride. She was admitted to Bellevue Hospital on November 25, 1931, in a comatose condition. On November 28, 1931, she came out of the coma and was admitted to the Psychiatric Division. Two days later she said:

I have intense pain across my stomach. I had trouble—so much trouble that I didn't think I could stand it. I took barbital and mixed bichloride, sixteen tablets, but I don't know if I took it or not. Whether I took the baribital or not I don't know. We lost over a million dollars and then the blows came one after another and Saturday night came another blow and Monday came another blow. We had everything in railroads. I just was desperate. I didn't care what happened. (Did you want to commit suicide?) That's what I had in mind. I haven't harbored any idea of it but I have always been a cynical sort of person. Now I feel as though I have made a great fool of myself. It doesn't help matters. I have only impaired myself physically. I feel better but I have frequent urination and pain in my abdomen. This morning I had intense pain but it has passed away. (Is your head clear?) Yes, it is clearing. I have been seeing geometrical forms. I just felt as though heavy black trains were coming down on me. The thing that has ruined us has been my husband's investments in railroads. Just great, black, crushing trains which seemed to be crushing me, coming at one side and at the other side. My husband's face always appeared just sympathetic, but not that I could really visualize his expression. I did not feel the crushing. They felt as though they were coming on, but never at any time could I say that I felt they had reached me. Then I felt myself sinking down in black caves and black earth. After that night almost everything I have ever seen in my travels has come in some form, but never a fixed time and place. Some of the scenes were natural. Some of the geometrical figures were natural. Some of the vegetation in the gardens seemed to be rather normal, but most of these figures seemed to be sinking down in the earth. Forms of animal life and plant life were drawn into a geometric form. It is getting less but I feel it to a certain extent. The last things I have been seeing were flowers and shrubbery. I saw animals. (Were they pleasant or vicious?) Never vicious. (What did this mean to you?) I could not interpret it. The thing that stood out plainly was death. I was conscious that they were dreams I was experiencing. (Do you feel that you will be able to face the future?) I hope so. (Have you lost all your money?) I don't feel there is much left to lose. I have my jewelry, which is not worth much now. We can practically say we are wiped out.

At this time the patient was oriented. She frequently closed her eyes as though she were drowsy and complained of being confused but was coöperative and appeared in a pretty good mood and was objective in the description of her troubles and present condition. She discussed vividly the optic hallucinations which were beginning to disappear.

December 1, 1931. (How do you feel to-day?) I feel much better to-day. I felt bladder pains yesterday but I have not so much to-day. (What have you been seeing?) Many geometrical forms. I just seemed to be sinking down into the earth. On one side was my husband's face, very dim, and on the other side were two great iron trains. They did not move but they always seemed to be over an abyss. My husband had everything invested in railroad stocks. Then I saw figures similar to the figures in the catacombs in Palermo. I was surrounded by them. I saw a great deal of wrought iron. I saw many beautiful scenes almost like Earl Carroll's *Vanities,* only without the beautiful girls. Things did not move. I also saw a great many tree trunks and roots. A great many roots—never in natural color but always in a very dull color. A sort of dull yellow. (Did you see yourself?) No. The only time I saw myself was the night I was sinking into the earth. Everything instilled me with the feeling of sorrow. (How long did the whole thing last?) About four nights, but always growing less. I also saw it any time I closed my eyes. (What do you think about this whole situation?) We have lost practically everything. We just have to meet the world. My husband is sixty-two. We have lived very happily together. There are no children. I intend to go and live with my sister for a while.

In this case we deal with barbital intoxication. The patient had the feeling of sinking into the earth. At the same time there were geometrical figures. The impression of wrought iron was probably related to the optic vestibular phenomena described above. Most remarkable were the great iron trains in the foreground of the psychological picture. They were not moving but were very big and near an abyss. This was the transformation of a vestibular movement into a macropsia and into an optic picture which fit the situation. The tree trunks and roots were the expression of distortions in the optic spheres under a vestibular influence which was also shown by a nystagmus. The choice of the optic picture is dependent not only on the vestibular background but also on the life experiences of the patient.

Louise, twenty-nine, was admitted on October 7, 1931. On September 22 she had developed convulsions in the course of an otherwise normal pregnancy. There was a large amount of albumin and pus cells in the urine, with a systolic blood pressure of 190. On September 26, labor was induced and on September 27 she gave birth to an infant weighing little more than two pounds, which died two days later. On October 3 she became restless, singing and crying alternately. Symptoms of a puerperal psychosis persisted from that time on.

Patient's husband confirmed this history obtained from the physician and stated that on October 2 she rang the bell continually for the nurse, and talked irrationally, continually reproaching the doctor for allowing her to get sick. He said that she was a brilliant girl, a teacher of languages, and always very lively and active, and that she worried about the baby.

The patient came into the hospital in an excited condition and threw herself on the floor. With the exception of a slight anemia there was no evidence of a somatic disease. There were no signs of nephritis. The lochia was normal as was the neurological examination and examination of the internal organs. During her residence at the hospital, the patient gave the following protocols:

October 8, 1931. I want my husband. You wouldn't lie to me, would you? I am a nervous wreck. I am crying for my husband. (Has anybody done you any harm?) Yes, Elia—Elia—I want Elia, my husband. Elia wouldn't lie to me. Oh, can that stuff. Oh, I am dead. I wish Elia would kill me. I hate to leave him. (Anybody talking about you?) Oh, you ought to hear them—all kinds of things. I'll say they call me bad names. If you would shut up a second I'd tell you. People say I always get everything backwards. I guess I am talking in my sleep. (Where's your husband anyway?) I wish you would listen—you are always arguing with me. These people that are always laughing—ha! ha! ha! The voices say, "Needles and pins." Oh, forget it—forget it. "Oh, Lord—oh, Lord!"—that's what she said.

She was wildly excited, noisy, assaultive, resistive, clutching at everyone near her. She tore up the bed clothes and laughed and cried in turn. She made rhythmic movements of the hands, verbigerated, spit, buried her head in the pillow, covered up her face and would not allow herself to be examined. She gave evidence of vague disagreeable auditory hallucinations at which she laughed wildly.

October 10, 1931. I have been sicker than I thought I was. I dreamed that I lost all my insides. I dreamed that my heart dropped out and I dreamed that I lost my lungs. I dreamed that I cracked my skull and that I was all over like a boil. I dreamed that I had a hot-water bottle inside of me and every time somebody punched me gas came out. I thought I was empty-headed. I felt like I was a doll and I cracked my skull open and I scattered all over the house. All this was in connection with losing my baby. First I dreamed I had a baby girl and my baby girl died. Afterwards I dreamed I had twins. I raved like a maniac. I remember I swore at anybody. I knew I was out of my head. Then I prayed for two boys, twins, for my house. I dreamed I was murdered and being cut open. That was when they put the straitjacket on me. Then I thought I was in heaven and I saw all my ancestors up there. Then I dreamed I was in a morgue and they were taking a post-mortem on me. The night that the baby came I remember I kept ringing and ringing that bell until my husband told them to disconnect it and that's when I got the idea that they were kidding me. I thought they had cut off my toes. I thought I had double pneumonia because one minute I was hot and one minute I was cold. I wouldn't eat any of the food because I thought they put medicine in it. I did have clear intervals and then I dreamed I got another hypo and off I would go. I thought I heard somebody say I was dead and they would do a post-mortem on me.

She was extremely talkative all morning, describing in full detail dreamlike experiences which she had had for the past week. These included markedly bizarre hypochondriacal ideas, feelings of being dead, of being empty and brittle, of being inflated with gas like a balloon. She was a little euphoric. She said she had several lucid intervals. Present episode has lasted only half an hour. She has a strong feeling of well-being, is quiet, composed and well oriented.

October 10, 1931. I dreamed I lost my insides. I imagined my ovaries dropped out. I also dreamt that I lost my legs. I dreamed that I had double pneumonia and that I had a terrible, terrible cold. I dreamed that all those little bugs were coming out of me; that I had taken so much medicine that they were just crawling out of me. I think I dreamed I had a tapeworm. In 1928 I had a nervous breakdown when I went to see my father in Sweden and I had wild hallucinations there. I had suffered from insomnia. I had hallucinations of seeing a snake. When I had my first breakdown in 1921 I had no hallucinations but there was always something like a pendulum moving in me. I felt it first in my head, then in my stomach and this last time all over my body. It is a circular movement. Sometimes I feel it in my brain. If I lie on my stomach I feel it there. This last time it is mostly in the lower part of my body. I thought it was a pendulum. I kept asking for the time. I kept feeling my pulse and they said, "How do you know what time it was that this happened?" and I said, "Well, I heard the kitchen clock." I thought the kitchen clock was in my room. I thought I knew everything that was going on around me.

October 13, 1931. I have been sick. I thought I had twins and I can't get anybody to tell me whether I did have twins. (Why were you drawing pictures with saliva?) I was trying to amuse myself. I kept myself from going nutty. I will go nutty if I can't find out the truth about something. I want to know if I had twin boys. I hear something telling me that I did have twins. Here goes the bug again. I just imagined I saw a bug around me. I imagine I see something go round and round. When I open my eyes I see funny things and also do funny things. See how crazy my eyes are? They feel cross-eyed. You all think I committed suicide because I wiggle so. I think that you think that I committed suicide. I have been fooled so often that I won't believe anything until I see it with my own eyes. I was born in San Antonio, Texas, in 1901. My father was a lawyer. I am the youngest child. I have two older brothers. I went through Texas State College and graduated with honors at nineteen. I had some puppy loves. At least I thought I was in love. It was a ticklish feeling. No, I never necked with the boys. I was kissed once or twice. I never thought about sexual intercourse then. My mother always told me things that she thought I ought to know. She told me how babies were born. She told me how to take care of myself. I was my father's favorite and he was my pet. He never saw much of me and I never saw much of him because he wasn't home much. My parents didn't have normal relations. My mother was very irritable and my father was, too. They tried to use birth control methods and they didn't know much about it. I suppose my mother ruined her health trying to prevent having more children. They were both very emotional and highstrung and they quarreled quite a bit. As a child I always took my father's part but when I grew up I saw my mother's viewpoint and I turned against my father. We always had to do as my father said. He was a very brilliant man but my mother had more common sense. She didn't have much education. She was very musical. We always had to do as my father said. I rebelled against that. My father was a Free Mason and a Free Thinker. I did a lot of reading. I read a lot of H. G. Wells. I read Thomas Hardy's poetry. Of the Russians I read Tolstoi. I read some Russian fairy-tales. I read *Crime and Punishment* by Dostoevski. I read the *Woman's Home Companion, Delineator*, and *Current History*. I read the *World-Telegram*. I don't know much about art. I like pretty pictures—landscapes. I like Norwegian art. I like classical music and jazz if I want to dance. I like Victor Herbert of the modern composers.

October 14, 1931. I read an awful lot in college. I don't think I was very popular. I didn't have to bother. I had two brothers who would take me anywhere. We had lots of fun. I was so busy I didn't have time for dates. I went out for athletics. I spent at least three hours a day in the gymnasium. I enjoyed working in the reformatory except that the work was very strenuous. No boys or love affairs. After that I went to California and stayed there till the fall of 1924. I had the best time of my life there. I had no worries. I was rather popular there. I was engaged to a fellow there. I was mad about him but I broke it up because I thought the fellow was too old. My mother died the next year. She committed suicide. She left no note. She had been physically sick. It was an accumulation of emotions. She said before she died that she was sorry for it. She said she was unhappy about the death of a grandchild. She was having her change of life then. At the time, I didn't know she had committed suicide. My father told me later. I had a hunch that he had a mistress while in Europe. I got a job teaching in 1925. I was at that time madly in love with my present husband, who was an electrical engineering student. He had been a White Army officer and was compelled to leave Russia. He went to Sumatra for a while and then returned to Russia to fight the Bolsheviki. He spent a lot of time in jail. He interested me very much. He was the first man who did not bore me. I helped him in his work and we got on nicely together. At that time he was engaged to a girl in Russia and it was very hard for him to break the engagement. It was a point of honor for him to stick to it. Finally she broke it. We married last year. We hadn't seen each other in six years and happened to meet up here. I wasn't in a hurry to get married. We had been corresponding all along. It was just a matter of chance.

October 15, 1931. I woke up at five o'clock this morning. I had a nightmare. I dreamed there was a whole collection of earthworms and scorpions at the foot of my bed, taking a bite at my toes and I just shot out of bed as though I had been shot. I see all kinds of things. I think my eyes are weak. They feel like they are crossed. I remember you stuck me with a needle and you took some blood out of my arm and it amused me. It seemed very funny. I thought there was poison in my finger and I thought this whole forearm was poisoned. I got that idea when I was ten years old and I had erysipelas in my arm. When you took the blood out of my arm I thought I was going to have erysipelas in that arm. I remember throwing an apple at somebody but I didn't think it hit you. I thought I punched you in the arms.

October 21, 1931. They promised me they would give me what I wanted if I kept quiet. I wanted a German Jew. I felt drowsy and I was almost ready to relax and go to sleep and they gave me too much of something. It was a pill. I messed up the bed like a baby three months old. Then I said I wanted a German Jew. It took them so long to give me what I wanted. I wanted to go to the toilet and I didn't want to go with anyone but a German Jew. I thought I could control myself and when I wanted to go to the bathroom nobody would take me and I yelled like a three-months-old baby.

October 28, 1931. You lousy bum. You're from Vienna. Such a stench! I suppose all you ever do is read Freud—F-r-e-u-d. I would like to go to the Tombs—T-o-m-b-s. You are an American and I recognize the breed. If you don't recognize the breed you recognize the creed. You thought I had a complex, didn't you? You are quite right—I had one. I had one— h-a-d. I bet they think I fell off the Alps. Yes, I did fall off the Alps. Did you ever dream you fell off the Alps?

October 30, 1931. At one time I felt I was in a play. At one stage of the game they seemed to be having a trial of some kind. I was a double to this man up in Ossining who is the double of this Two-gun Crowley. He was the fellow who was accused of robbing a drug store and I think that Crowley had said that it was not this other boy who did it but he himself and the question was whether it was not a question of mistaken identity. The opinion seemed to be that he was taking the crime on himself to free the other fellow. I was taking the part of this other fellow. The judge was asking me questions but I didn't answer and when I did answer I did so insultingly. I must have been frothing at the mouth and I must have been spitting at the radiator. (Who was the Judge?) Seabury. (Were the nurses there?) We were all there. I saw it very clearly in my mind. (Doctor there?) The doctors took the Judge's stand occasionally at the same desk and occasionally I would order the Judge out. I said I wanted to go home. I think if I could think about it long enough I could tell what each person said. I remember seeing Doctor R. there. He was a school teacher or social worker.

This remarkable patient developed her symptoms after eclamptic fits. She felt that she had lost her insides. Her ovaries dropped out and she lost both her legs. She also had the feeling that something was going "round and round." She also felt that wheels were going "round and round." She felt cross-eyed. We are dealing here with vestibular phenomena in a psychosis with an organic origin. The subsequent development suggested a schizophrenic psychosis. She already had a mental disorder in 1921 in which she felt a pendulum moving with a circular movement inside her, in her head and in her stomach and often in the lower part of the body. This observation shows how vestibular changes can determine the symptomatology of a psychosis of a seemingly very different type. As in the foregoing case in which the big trains were connected with the losses in railroad stock as well as with vestibular impulses, in the latter case the losing of the intestines is also not due to the vestibular influence alone. I cannot discuss in detail the expression of the castration complex, provoked by the birth and death of a baby. The vestibular influence and the organic background of the psychosis will always be shaped by the life experiences which are at the basis of the psychosis. These give the vestibular impulse its final form. We also should not forget that the vestibular apparatus is under the strong influence of psychic attitudes. Psychic influences not only give material for the content of the psychosis but also contribute more or less to the change in the vestibular function.

Wherever optic distortions, macropsias, micropsias, and changes in the perception of directions occur in a psychosis, one is justified in thinking of vestibular influences. The vestibular change may depend on a central psychic influence. But it may also be due to the peripheral apparatus (first level), to a lesion of the vestibular nuclei (second level), to a lesion of the cortical vestibular apparatus in the parietal region (third level), to lesions of the parieto-occipital elaboration (fourth level), or to the utilization and elaboration of the vestibular impulses in connection with the activities of the whole brain, or psychologically speaking, to problems of the total personality (fifth level). After all, our life experiences go through the medium of the senses. Every sense is involved in them. According to the particular problems of the individual, sensory impulses of one or the other kind will be preferred. The vestibular apparatus has its particular position among the senses and must therefore react in a particular way to specific sets of experiences. I often have emphasized that the function of the vestibular apparatus is very closely related to the function of the oculostatic apparatus and to tonic activities in general. In psychosis, we find many feelings concerning the weight of the body. The flying sensation is connected with the feeling that the weight of the body has diminished. But the impression of the weight of the body is often connected with the acknowledgment of the body in its sexual aspect. The dream of flying, in which the weight of the body is changed, may help us to understand the changes in the experiences of the weight of the body in psychosis. Flying dreams have, in part, sexual desires as their basis and are an attempt to sublimate them.

One of my schizophrenic patients developed the fantasy that she was soaring to heaven with anxiety. The soaring means that she overcame a heaviness of the earth by loss of sexuality. It is a substitute and satisfaction for the removal of her sex organs. The same patient had two visions. God was on a throne in the air and she was kneeling before Him as an angel. Then she had the vision of a black eagle which flew high in the air. Both visions were in the air at the same time. The patient said: "I saw myself very often in a vision; I saw myself in the air, shrouded in veils." The phenomena I have described as occurring in elevators are the psychological basis for the phenomena which occurred in this patient. It is impossible to say whether an irritation of the vestibular apparatus projects itself into pictures of the type I have mentioned, or whether the particular psychic conflict chooses expression in the vestibular field. Particular conflicts express themselves in a vestibular language, but I do not think that this vestibular language is in the psychic sphere alone. Specific conflicts have an influence on the vestibular apparatus as such. It is probable that even the peripheral vestibular apparatus reacts to emotions. One may ask whether the conception of ghosts in folklore and in psychosis is not closely allied to vestibular phenomena. One of the characteristics of the ghost is that he has a weightless body. The conception of heaven is based upon an upward movement. God is in heaven and heaven is above. Angels fly. It is the negation of gravity, and especially of the gravity of the body. The flying dream of the neurosis and the flying dream of the patient with peripheral or central vestibular disease, shows either the individual flying or flying objects all around him. They may be angels or they may be airplanes. The urgent need of instincts blends with the heavy substance of the body. The sexless angel is out of the reach of gravitation.

THE OCULOSTATIC APPARATUS

One organic phenomenon which needs special discussion is the oculogyric crisis in postencephalitis. Changes in caloric irritabilitv of the vestibular apparatus are very common according to E. Stengel. Feelings of dizziness seem to be diminished. Some of the patients show changes in consciousness. Symptoms of depersonalization are common. Robert Stern has reported anxiety states connected with the oculogyric crises. Obsessional trends are also observed. The function of the oculostatic apparatus has an effect similar to that of changes in the innervation of the vestibular apparatus. Complicated relations between these two systems exist.

The patient, aged 51, came to the psychiatric clinic in Vienna in March, 1927. Since 1921, she had had attacks of a few seconds' duration during which her left side felt numb and she could not speak. Since 1926, she often became excited and nauseated, and her attacks had increased in frequency. Objective examination showed a vertical nystagmus when the patient looked upward, and the corneal reflex was absent on the right side and almost absent on the left side. The vestibular apparatus showed a slight hyperexcitability. Smell was impaired on both sides, but a little more on the left side. Otherwise there were no somatic changes. During observation of about six weeks, the patient complained that the left side of her body felt as if it were lame. Every sensation was different on this side. She had burning sensations in the skin of the left side. Objects in the left visual field were blurred. She heard the ticking of a watch less audibly on the left side. Her left side felt heavier, and her left abdomen seemed fuller. She could not think on the left side. She felt a horizontal turning movement in clockwise direction between her eyes. When the foot of her bed was raised, objects appeared larger and her dizziness increased. During the examination there were short periods of absence. The patient said, during the first observation, that she slept the whole day but was extremely restless, noisy and excited during the night so that all the other patients were disturbed in their sleep. She urgently asked to be restrained so that she would not disturb the other patients. She said that these other patients complained about her noisiness and asked for her commitment. The patient was however objectively quiet and awake during the day, and slept quietly during the night. Toward the end of the observation period the patient sometimes had short attacks of a narcoleptic type, in the daytime.

In this case we deal with an organic lesion in the region of Deiters' nucleus; but there were also considerable changes in her consciousness, in her sleeping apparatus, and a one-sided depersonalization took place in connection with these changes in the central vestibular apparatus. This observation points to a vestibular and oculostatic genesis of some neurotic symptoms (compare P. Bonnier). An organic disease of the vestibular apparatus changes the consciousness so that many of the tendencies of the patient may express themselves in hysteriform pictures, which show a vestibular genesis in their content. This ultimately leads to the question of the relation of the vestibular apparatus to what is usually called the psychic sphere.

During the war, Julius Bauer observed cases of neurosis in which there were changes in past-pointing, abnormal reaction movements, difficulties in the appreciation of weights, and adiadochokinesis. Such symptoms sometimes persisted for a long time. I have shown that vestibulocerebellar deviation and past-pointing could be influenced in hypnosis. Bauer and I suggested to hypnotized subjects that they felt dizzy, and that everything was turning around. These suggestions caused changes in past-pointing. Not all subjects behaved like persons in which an actual irritation of the vestibular apparatus had taken place. We concluded that it is possible to change vestibulocerebellar mechanisms by suggestion. P. Loewy by later investigations tried to prove that the psychic influence of hypnosis does not change the vestibulocerebellar function, but that only the psychic representations of the static impressions have undergone changes. Loewy speaks of "Psychostatik." I do not deny that suggestion can change the entire level of static impressions, but I do think that there is an immediate influence of the psyche on the vestibular apparatus.

In their later study on dizziness in neurosis, R. Leidler and P. Loewy found cases in which the vestibular function of the first level was changed. It was their impression that this was not a vasomotor influence. It may be difficult to prove the direct influence of the psyche on the vestibular apparatus, but I do not think that the organic vestibular symptoms in neurosis can always be interpreted by reference to the vasomotor system. Probably the psyche acts on the vestibular system in a dual way, either affecting the nervous regulation directly or affecting it via the vasomotor innervation of the labyrinth. The psychic influence certainly not only influences the lower levels of cortical and psychic elaboration of vestibular data. What part do dizziness and the vestibular apparatus play in neurosis? The symptomatology of dizziness in neurosis has been carefully studied by Leidler and Loewy. They often found a spontaneous nystagmus. In only fourteen cases out of seventy-eight was it completely absent. There were also changes in equilibrium. Turning perceptions in the head and sensations referred to the head were very common. Several of the patients also saw objects turning. Many patients felt that their bodies were pulled or inclined, or that they might fall. Some felt pure progressive movements. Movements of the ground were often felt. Some felt loss of the ground. Optic apparent movement and oblique vision were not uncommon.

Leidler and Loewy stress the fact that reactive vestibular movement and apparent movement in the neuroses very often go in the same direction, whereas in organic cases the reactive movement is usually opposite to the direction of the apparent movement. They consider that no fundamental difference exists between the phenomenology of dizziness in organic diseases of the static organs and the dizziness in neurosis. Phenomenologically, both contain the same psychic material. This is especially true of subjective, statosensory phenomena, where no difference can be found. The objective static phenomena of the neurosis, the statomotor phenomena, contain the same phenomenological elements as the static phenomena so far known in organic diseases. There are qualitative differences, that is, in frequency and in intensity. "But they are different especially in a different relation between the subjective and objective symptoms, which we have called the identity of direction of apparent movement and static motility disturbance." P. Loewy believes that vestibular phenomena in neurosis are a part of the vegetative vasomotor disturbances of neurosis. He believes that vegetative attacks have a special influence on the vestibular apparatus, which is especially sensitive to general vasomotor disturbances. This formulation is related to a theory that neuroses are due to vegetative changes which overcome the individual as an attack from the body or as an attack outside of the psyche. This is a physiological theory of the neurosis. Freud in his theory of the "actual neurosis" has a somewhat similar conception, except that he attributes the somatic crisis to the change in the sex function.

Freud has noted the importance of dizziness in the picture of anxiety neurosis. In psychoanalysis the tendency to find a meaning in the special affliction of a particular organ or function in neurosis has become more and more prevalent. When dizziness occurs in neurosis, this dizziness is not only the expression of a general vegetative disturbance, but also has a more or less specific psychological meaning. In 1873 Krishaber published his observation on *Neurose cérébrocardiaque;* these are the cases which are called depersonalization in the later literature. For these patients, world, body, and ego are estranged. They observe their actions as impersonal spectators. They do not acknowledge their ego. The outward world is new and has lost its character of reality. Krishaber knew that all these patients suffer from dizziness. It is worthwhile to review the symptomatology of these cases. Many patients see objects as flat. The patients see objects as smaller, more remote. They say that they live as in a dream. The body seems dead. It is too light. They feel as if they could fly. The relation to vestibular complaints is obvious. E. Pick and R. Allers have also utilized this interpretation. The patients express their inability to coördinate their diverse impulses in the way in which the vestibular apparatus—the sense organ which has to coördinate the data of senses—is impaired in its function. Dysfunction of the vestibular apparatus would be thus the expression of two conflicting tendencies in the psyche. This formulation is, of course, too general. Conflicting tendencies are present in everybody, but not necessarily vestibular symptoms.

Conflict is, of course, increased in neuroses. We would have to expect, then, that in every neurosis, dizziness, that is, dysfunction of the vestibular apparatus, is an important factor. I am indeed inclined to believe that this is so. The dizziness is a danger signal and an admonition to the ego [3] to coördinate its effort in a better way. Organic dizziness occurs when there are discrepancies between the perception of different senses. Psychogenic dizziness occurs when conflicting tendencies endanger the unified action of the ego. This formulation, although superficial, at least indicates the deep symbolism in psychogenic symptoms of conversion type. Vestibular flying dreams and psychogenic flying dreams, studied especially by P. Federn, are identical in their roots. According to H. Hoff, lack of coördination between the habitual posture and the actual posture during sleep also provokes vestibular dreams. The sexual element in a flying dream has been well studied and is fairly easy to demonstrate. One often finds incestuous desires at its bases. We undoubtedly deal with actual changes in the vestibular apparatus.

Many patients show slight symptoms of dizziness at the end of an analytic session (S. Ferenczi). It is possible that this dizziness is

[3] Ego is used here in the psychoanalytic sense.

caused by the change in position from lying down to sitting or standing. A more important change is that from an infantile world to a real world; one finds this dizziness especially after sessions which have carried the individual into deep infantile material. In the same way, awakening from hypnosis very often leads to dizziness. P. Loewy reports spontaneous apparent movements in hypnosis. The change from the everyday life adaptation to the deeper layer of the consciousness is bound to provoke changes in the vestibular apparatus. Repression of heterosexual genital impulses frequently leads to dizziness. It seems that flying, changes in the weight of the body, and rotatory apparent movement, are the most outstanding features of this heterosexual dizziness. In the type of neurosis found especially in connection with sadistic impulses and obsessional symptoms, the different parts of the body may lose their connectedness, the body is dismembered, the parts of the body fly around, or in some way show a sadistic conversion on the vestibular apparatus. A patient with melancholia, who was under the influence of allonal and opium, had the feeling that a part of her bed was being thrown around the room with enormous force. Although she was lying quietly on the couch, she felt multiplied: "not I alone, but it was I and several editions of me. . . . These editions are light. Everything I see is terribly moved." Neurasthenics very often complain that something in their bodies has become loose. They speak of bubbles in their head and limbs, of emptiness. I may mention that normal subjects often experience the heaviness of their bodies, not as a homogeneous but as a spongy mass.

Whenever there is vestibular irritation by conversion of sadistic impulses, the integration of the body will be impaired. The concept of the destruction of the body belongs in the sadomasochistic sphere. In neurasthenia there are often vestibular changes in the postural model of the body. This is a circular process; the complexes, the psychic life, under specific conditions will influence the vestibular system, and the lesion of the vestibular system in a retroactive way will change the content of the neurosis. T. M. French found that vestibular phenomena in the dreams of a patient were the expression of a conflict between a desire for passivity and passive homosexuality, and an ego which struggled to attain a more active part. It is important for the understanding of vestibular phenomena in neurosis to realize that the child gets pleasure out of every vestibular sensation. The child likes to be rocked, tossed in the air, and swung. These excitations of the vestibular apparatus are undoubtedly connected with some more or less pronounced sexual feeling. Every quick movement downwards provides sensations, as everyone who has been on a scenic railway will recognize. The phenomenology of these sensations is not yet known and we do not know anything about the underlying finer mechanisms. A great number of phenomena are allied to function and dysfunction of the vestibular apparatus, such as dizziness at heights. We know that there is a tendency to get into a position which is in a proper relation to the optic surroundings. When we are on a steep rock the optic surroundings impel us to an attitude vertical to the base; but we are compelled to remain in a position vertical to the general direction of gravity. The discrepancy between these two motor and attitudinal impulses is probably an outstanding factor in the genesis of seasickness. From an analytic point of view dizziness is a danger signal in the sphere of the ego. It occurs when the ego cannot exercise its synthetic function in the senses, but it also occurs when conflicting motor and attitudinal impulses connected with desires and strivings cannot any longer be united. Dizziness is as important from an analytic point of view as anxiety. In connection with the function of the vestibular apparatus, dizziness occurs particularly when a violent action threatens to disrupt the unity of the body. The normal function of the vestibular apparatus insures coordination of motor actions and impulses of a unified body. We have seen that in vestibular dreams the organic lesion of the vestibular apparatus provokes symptoms and dreams which fit the general characteristics of vestibular function. We may suppose that every organic disease of the vestibular apparatus will provoke a particular set of impulses and actions. In other words, vestibular disease prepares the way for neurotic action.

The vestibular apparatus at first changes the general consciousness,

and with the change in the consciousness, unconscious material will
have the opportunity of breaking through. Those unconscious tendencies which fit the inherent qualities of the vestibular apparatus
will tend to be expressed.

V. von Weizsaecker has pointed out that every organic disease
brings with it a pattern of psychic reactions. It neuroticizes the individual, but only in a special direction. A special part of the psychic
life, a special province belongs to every organ. Diseases start either in
the psychic province and affect the organ in a secondary way, or they
start in the organ and the psychic changes are secondary. I have
formulated this problem as follows: An organic disease goes from the
periphery of the personality, from the shell of the organized body,
to the center of the personality, with its strivings and desires. The
organic disease in this respect proceeds centripetally. The psychogenic
disorder starts in the nucleus of the personality and goes to the organ
which is peripheral in the circle of our experience. The functional
disease is therefore centrifugal. I have already explained how often
centripetal and centrifugal tendencies are present at the same time,
so that the difference between psychogenic and organic disease very
often loses its sharp distinction. Studying the vestibular apparatus, one
sees this double movement very clearly.

There is some question about the factors which make the vestibular apparatus so important in the whole of the psychic structure.
C. Stein and J. Zádor have indicated the enormous importance of
movements in the genesis of all our perceptions. I have very often
emphasized that every impression has its set of tonic and phasic activities. These tonic and phasic activities, in the broader sense, are the
uniting factors in our experiences. The perception of space and time,
so basic for our whole psychic life, are closely related to the vestibular
apparatus. Elie von Cyon has come to similar conclusions, but he has
overlooked the motor factor in vestibular function, and his idea that
the perception of time is related to the cochlear apparatus does not
have sufficient foundation. He also does not recognize that the tempo
of our innervation and tone is of great importance in time and space
perception. Kurt Goldstein has developed ideas which point in sim-

ilar direction. Starting from the postural and righting reflexes, he comes to the conclusion that there are motor tendencies of the body, tendencies to disrupt the unity of the body, and he thinks the body would be disrupted by these motor impulses, if it were not for the uniting influence of the cerebellar function (and, in addition, I may add, if it were not for the uniting function of the vestibular apparatus). Here again we must emphasize that the vestibular apparatus is only one link in a chain of important apparatuses. It is the head organ of a kinesthetic function which has its representatives all over the body. And although this head organ has a special importance for the distribution of tone, it is still only one of the many organs which serve this function. It is, finally, always impossible to study an organ in isolation, especially an organ the function of which is directed against the isolation of the diverse functions of the body.

SUMMARY

The vestibular apparatus consists of two different parts, the semicircular canals and the otoliths. Both deal with the perception of accelerations, the latter also with the perception of gravity. The vestibular apparatus is not only a perceptual organ; it is also a reflex organ which reacts to movement and to the position of the head in space. There is a peripheral and a central vestibular apparatus. The central apparatus consists of the nuclei in the medulla oblongata, of primary cortical centers, and of centers which are connected with the elaboration of the primary impulses in the parieto-occipital lobe. However, the vestibular system is also under the influence of the personality, of brain function as a whole. Regarding the symptoms which occur in organic lesions of the vestibular apparatus, our findings are as follows.

The vestibular influence on the visual field; darkening of the visual field, narrowing of the visual field, and scintillation. There is a difference between peripheral and central lesions.

There is a multiplicity of apparent movements which are only partially dependent on the nystagmic movements of the eyes. The apparent movements have a great tendency to transformation.

The perception of directions may be changed by vestibular lesions. There are also transformations from one plane to another.

Micropsia and macropsia may occur.

Polyopia and metamorphopsia belong to the symptomatology of vestibular lesions. These vestibular changes may be unilateral in central lesions; they are homolateral to the side of the lesion.

The haptic sphere is changed by vestibular lesions.

Homolateral weakness and homolateral sensory disturbance belong to vestibular symptomatology.

Changes in tone and in reaction movements are well-known symptoms of vestibular lesions.

Special importance is ascribed to the changes in the postural model (body image) of the body by vestibular influence. Under vestibular influence, a part of the substance of the body may be dissociated from the rest of the body. Heaviness and lightness of the body in their subjective sense are largely dependent on the vestibular apparatus.

There are also changes in the vegetative system.

Changes in consciousness are directly due to vestibular influence.

Optic images, tactile images, tactile and optic eidetic pictures, can be influenced by vestibular irritation in a way similar to afterimages. In hallucinations, vestibular influences change the appearance and add movements to the picture. In delirium tremens the multiplicity of hallucinations is related to vestibular influence. Multiplicity of hallucinations, macropsia, micropsia, and metamorphopsia indicate a vestibular influence on hallucinations. The postural model of the body is influenced in the same way in alcoholic psychosis in which the vestibular apparatus is affected, as in organic neurological cases or in normal persons in whom the function of the vestibular apparatus is changed. Vestibular changes disrupt the unity of the postural model of the body. The symptomatology of delirium tremens and alcoholic hallucinosis are considered from this point of view.

The importance of the vestibular influence for the symptomatology of toxic psychosis is shown in a case of barbital intoxication and one of eclamptic psychosis. In psychosis, the utilization and elaboration of the vestibular impulses in connection with the activities of the whole brain is of special importance. The vestibular apparatus has a special function among the senses and is associated with particular life experiences.

Dysfunction of the vestibular apparatus is very often the expression of two conflicting psychic tendencies; dizziness occurs, therefore, in almost every neurosis. The neurosis may produce organic changes in the vestibular sphere. Dizziness is a danger signal in the sphere of the ego, and occurs when the ego cannot exercise its synthetic function in the senses, but it also occurs when conflicting motor and attitudinal impulses in connection with desires and strivings can no longer be united. Dizziness is as important from the psychoanalytic point of view as anxiety. The vestibular apparatus is an organ the function of which is directed against the isolation of the diverse functions of the body.

CHAPTER IX

THE CONSTRUCTION OF THE OBJECT
AND THE PROBLEM OF GESTALT

IN THE preceding chapters we were concerned with the impression of the senses and were especially in search of the primitive world of experiences. We used the term "sensation" to designate an experience in its relation to the self and the term "perception" to designate an experience related especially to the outer world. It is questionable whether any experiences exist which do not ultimately point to the outside world. In *The Image and Appearance of the Human Body,* I have tried to prove that in many respects one's own body is also a part of the outside world. Even the sensations coming from outside the body are referred to something within the body. In describing a disease the sufferer compares his sensations with objects in the outer world: "It is as if there were a stone in my stomach"; "Something sticks in my throat"; "I have a splitting headache"; "When I close my eyes, the darkness is not far from me." We observe the idioretinal movements as we would describe objects in the outer world. In the optic imagination of movement, we perceive movement as a movement of something, even if we cannot describe the object which is moving. The optic image has a twofold objectivity: the picture, and the object imagined. Even the space color is something outside of ourselves. The object is not very distinct but nevertheless it is an object. Even when there is a sensation within the skin we tend to say that there is something on the skin. I have discussed the objectivity of smell and taste experiences. The objectivity of hearing must be particularly emphasized. Primitive experience is therefore not a world of primitive "sensation" but a world of primitive perception. The question must arise of how primitive perception is built up into a more or less complete perception. The character of motion is much more pronounced in primitive perception. The primitive object has neither a lasting nor even a definite organization. Motion in primitive perception immediately provokes a motor response. This motor response is an integral part of the perceived motion; it appeals more strongly to the emotional side of the individual than does the fully developed perception. There is comparatively little motion in the perception of smell; but the emotional and vegetative reactions are very marked. This is also true of taste. An imagination of taste almost immediately provokes a great number of vegetative answers, salivation, "feelings" in the stomach. In preliminary investigations concerning hallucinations of taste, patients usually complain that they have been poisoned, and prove it by referring to the feelings in their stomachs. Sound comes through space, not only in the world of physics, but decidedly so in the psychological experience. In the optic sphere we have gained some understanding of how the construction of the object occurs. The space color, which is primarily without definite object, loses its vagueness when attached to a stable object. It loses its inner motion and becomes stabilized. Lesions of the occipital lobe permit the color to diffuse into space again. In H. Hartmann's case we may observe this process of space colors consolidating directly into surface colors. The transformation of space color to surface color is a part of the process of the creation of definite objects. Motion in the primitive experience leads to an action (tonic and phasic) which is the resultant of the experience of all the senses.

In the reports of several of the patients observed by me, curtains play a very important part. They are described as very beautiful, and as standing still (as in a case of alcoholic hallucinosis and one of bromide intoxication; this patient hallucinated not only curtains but also pictures by Corot). The phenomenon seems to be related to the fact that the curtain is between the object and the individual. It is semitransparent. This curtain hallucination is probably associated with film colors, or with space colors, whose distribution in objects is not completely organized. In some way the colors wander toward objects but become crystallized into curtains on the way. Very often the colors are motionless, since an attempt at crystallization has already taken place. This is one phase in the movement of the free-floating space color to the surface of the object. It is interesting that a curtain very often symbolizes the secret, the object which is not completely known, either by its very nature or because the individual does not feel clear enough in his mind. H. Silberer has called this "functional phenomenon."

Every change in the optic field is also a change in our attitudes. Different states of consciousness are reflected in different subdivisions of space. The clear consciousness sees the object clearly, not in any way hindered by films and curtains. All newer investigations show that there are elements of synesthesia in every perception. Our protocols concerning optic imaginations show this very clearly. C. Hartshorne has pointed especially to the universal character of synesthesia. K. Goldstein in a very different way has come to the same conclusion. Hartshorne stresses the character of "brightness" connecting all the senses, and believes the impression of different senses to be comparable to each other; but he does not emphasize the fundamental importance of motility as a connecting link, although its existence is easier to demonstrate than that of brightness.

There is an additional important link in the emotions and in the vegetative reactions which Raoul Mourgue accents in his book on hallucinations. Every primitive perception hints at the possibility of objects in all sensation. With progress in the stabilization of the object, the possible appeal of the object to all senses becomes stronger. I have emphasized the unifying influence of the vestibular system. This unification is partially a unification of the senses with each other. I shall later discuss in more detail the part which space and the construction of space play in this unification of the object and in the elimination of perceptual motion so that efficient action directed towards the stabilized object may become possible. In *The Image and Appearance of the Human Body* I have shown that the stabilization of the object parallels the stabilization of the impression of the body.

Every sense has its specific motion and motility. In the optic sphere, motion is vivid in perceptions of the most primitive kind, even with the eye at rest. Primitive perception, especially color perception, is connected with tonic phenomena in the body. Beside these, there are immediate phasic responses, following of the moving object by eye movements and, in further development, grasping of the moving object. In the tactile sphere, primitive tactile impressions are in motion. Experiences with blind people and with the patient of K. Goldstein and A. Gelb, show that there is an immediate tendency to move the muscles connected with a point which has been touched, a tendency to touch such a point, and tendencies to grasp the object touching the point. General tonic responses mentioned above in reference to vision are also present in the tactile sphere, as has been shown by the investigations of K. Goldstein and H. Hoff and myself. We again see motion, tonic and phasic responses belonging to tactile experiences as well as to other modalities; the phasic response is built up in different levels, which will be discussed later. In the acoustic sphere there is a definite wandering of the sound to the subject, and the sound during this wandering changes its spatial properties. Tonic tendencies connected with sound are evident, as are tendencies to repeat the sound (if it is in the range of human expression) and tendencies to move towards the sound. The tendency to action against the sounding object is less marked, because we deal here with a quality arising from a part of space outside the proximate range of action. In the sphere of taste the impression as such has no immediate tendency to motion in itself, but there is present a strong phasic activity of the chewing apparatus and an extremely strong vegetative reaction. In the sphere of smell the perception is closely dependent on the motility of breathing, of sniffing, without which smell perception is hardly possible. There is motion in the smell perception in so far as the smell itself comes from an object and moves as an object to the nose. In general, we may say that motion and motility are inherent in every perception, and that in the different senses the relation between motion in the tonic and phasic responses, and the vegetative responses, varies.

Some general remarks about the tonic phenomena are necessary. K. Goldstein has emphasized the point that every experience of the organism is connected with an orientation of the organism toward the place where the experience occurs; the whole body is directed towards the stimulus. The orientation represents a primitive reaction of reception or defense and is dependent on the state of tonus. However, the tonic state of the body is important not only for the reaction of the organism, but also for our experiences, for the construction of our world in its spatial, temporal, and qualitative relations, for our conscious actions, and for our thinking. These tonic reactions come out very clearly in cerebellar cases in which postural and righting reflexes are increased. In a case of cerebellar lesion observed by H. Hoff and myself, an optic stimulus in the lateral visual field of the patient provoked a turning of the eyes to this side; the head and the trunk followed and the patient occasionally fell in the same direction. The outstretched arms deviated in the direction of the stimulus. Acoustic stimuli have the same influence. According to the point from which the acoustic stimulus acts, inclination of the trunk towards the stimulus, deviation of the arm, turning of the trunk are provoked. Tactile stimuli applied on one side of the face provoke deviation of the arms and inclination of the trunk on the same side. Optic imagination and eidetic images produce the same reaction as optic impressions. Pictures, therefore, influence tone. On the other hand, the tone produced in this way influences the perception. If a normal subject looks toward an object in the lateral visual field, a sound heard at the same time is transposed to the side on which the object is seen.

The final elaboration of the world of perception is dependent upon the motor impulses. The tone of the postural and righting reflexes ("induced tone" in K. Goldstein's terminology) is only a small sector of motor possibilities of the organism. Beside these mass reactions which usually involve at least one half of the body, there are more specific ones which are based upon these more primitive functions. To this class belong the reactions of groping, of grasping, and of incorporating into the body, which appear especially in the primitive grasp reflexes. Here too belongs the sucking reflex which reappears after certain lesions of the brain. Many primitive defense reactions also belong to this group. One is entitled to say that with every perception a double series of kinetic and tonic motor phenomena is coördinated; the tonic phenomena seem more primitive. Tonic and phasic influences affect perception. In one patient who showed the syndrome of spontaneously turning around on his longitudinal axis with an increase in postural and righting reflexes, a macropsia and polyopsia occurred. This phenomenon might be due to an occipital lesion, but the more probable explanation is the effect of motor impulses on the optic perception. This seems more probable since according to my findings, hysterical polyopsia is closely related to oculomotor impulses. Otto Poetzl has shown that oculomotor impulses are responsible for the mistakes in halving lines which patients with hemianopsia commit. The eye muscles are only a specific part of the total motility, which in principle has the same importance for the elaboration of our perceptions. To Otto Kauders' patient with parietal occipital spontaneous turning around the longitudinal axis, a glass seemed to become alternately smaller and larger. The patient saw the face of the physician at first as very small, then as long, and finally, the doctor had no face at all. Also, his own hand seemed swollen; the thumb was squeezed together. Queer sensations followed, in which he felt his own face changed and squeezed together. This patient also had multiple microptic hallucinations. In discussing the vestibular apparatus, I emphasized the influence of vestibular tonic impulses on perception. There exists a formative influence of the motility on the perception. It is difficult to determine how inner motion in perception and the motor impulses elicited by perception and influencing perception work together. F. Stein hypothesizes that the inner motion of perception, which he calls "sensory movement," is the factor which creates sensation and perception; but his point of view is difficult to justify. I have tried to show primitive perception in a state of motion. Motion is not something independent and separate from the perception, but is of its very essence. The inner motion of the perception is not creative but a part of the primary experience. Development is in the direction of the elimination of the inner motion of the perception. Motility is one of the important factors in this process of the stabilization of perception. On the other hand, we know that moving objects have a particular influence on the motility; they are, so to speak, the prime mover of actions. The consolidation of the perception therefore depends on motility. By this very fact the impression gets its spatial localization.

The close relation between motor tendencies and inner perceptual motion is particularly emphasized in vestibular disturbances, which prove that we deal with an apparatus which can act exclusively upon one side of the body. In observations by H. Hoff and myself, distortion of the optic picture was connected with a very vivid movement. In V. von Weizsaecker's instructive observations, distortion of the optic picture was seen without accompanying motion. The disturbance was present in only one eye and could be summarized as follows: "Angles smaller than a certain acute angle are seen as parallels. Circles appear as ellipses of specific direction. Curves which are not closed are seen as horizontal and vertical lines." V. von Weizsaecker's patient undoubtedly had tonic disturbances, but the relation of these tonic disturbances to the distortions is not clear. The vestibular apparatus (in its broadest sense) has a threefold influence: on the perceptual world directly; on the motion in usual pictures; and on tonus (which again influences perception and its inner motion). The unifying tendencies of the vestibular apparatus influence all these spheres. K. Goldstein and A. Gelb believe that the tonic influences upon the perception take place outside of the psychic sphere, and they are inclined to believe that psychological factors do not play any part in the transitions and distortions which have been discussed. E. R. Jaensch, who has seen similar phenomena in eidetic images, stresses the factor of attention. Attention is a direction of an individual towards a stimulus. This direction is psychic as well as physiological. It may originate in the psychic sphere, it may originate in the physiological sphere, but there is always something in common between the psychological and the physiological direction of the organism.

The unified object which gives a specific orientation for action is not an isolated experience but is related to the attitudes and actions of an individual. Primitive optic experience consists of colors, movements, spirals, and vortices that are only incompletely differentiated from the background. Whenever the beginnings of figure-background differentiation appear, the differentiation is increased by forces involving the organism as a whole. The figure becomes the rallying point in a background composed of all other sense perceptions and of vegetative influences. This is followed by tonic and phasic impulses which lead to development of clearer perception. This clearer articulation prepares the way for directed organismic action, resulting in even clearer definition and articulation of the object and its properties, and is therefore a new unification which involves the perceptual data of other senses and creates a synesthesia, which may be considered a concordance of senses of the second degree. Further manipulation of the objects reveals new properties in the optic and tactile sphere, gives a more distinct shape for the spatial relations and may lead, by bringing the object to the mouth, to new data concerning the olfactory and gustatory qualities of the object, adding in this way to the completeness of perceptual data regarding the object. It is therefore of special importance that groping, grasping, sucking, and bringing the object to the mouth belong to the most primitive organic reactions.

I have emphasized that rhythmic qualities are important in primitive perception. Optic images and optic afterimages come and go. Sound and tactile impressions have definite rhythmic qualities. In smell and taste, however, there is no definite hint of rhythmic tendencies. Rhythm is ingrained in the motor structure of the organism. The experiments of Sir Charles Sherrington have shown rhythmic qualities in simple spinal reflexes like the scratch reflex. T. Graham Brown has shown that the rhythm of gait is a central rhythm independent of outside influences. Proprioceptive and extraceptive stimuli merely modify the rhythm of the central nervous system. Physiologically it seems, therefore, that the rhythmical impulses become the definite isolated impulses under the influence of closer relations to the object. The same conditions which increase postural and righting reflexes also increase the tendency to rhythmic movements, as for instance in the cerebellar patient of Hoff and myself cited above. In the case of decerebrate rigidity in an idiot recently observed, turning of the head provoked rhythmic gait movements. It is interesting that stimuli applied to the sole may provoke rhythmic movements of crawling and creeping, as was observed by J. Bauer in a normal suckling and by H. Zingerle [1] in his cases of automatosis (increased postural and righting reflexes.) M. H. Fischer and E. Wodak have shown that vestibular phenomena of the motor type as well as of the sensory type show an exquisite rhythmic character. It seems in the sensory field, that in the development from the primitive perception to organized perception, rhythm becomes subordinated to the impression of a stabilized object. The suppression of rhythm in perceptual development is as important a step as is the suppression of motion.

We always speak of unchanging objects. However, objects are continually changing and still they remain the same objects (E. G. Boring).   Not only do objects change, but there is a continuous change in the sensory impulse which is the basis for the perceptual object. The static object is a product of late development. The primitive object is in motion internally and externally. In pathological cases the tendency of change inherent in all our experiences comes out in an intensified form. I have already mentioned the patient of Otto Kauders, who is particularly instructive in regard to metamorphoptic changes clearly related to movement. When, because of the inner structure of the perception and also because of tonic and kinetic influences, the experience of motion is not sufficient to disrupt the object completely or to move it as a whole, distortion takes place, which is experienced as change. In some cases the change seems to be independent of the movement, and in other cases movement and change are present at the same time. In a severe case of paralysis agitans, reported by N. Ross, the patient saw everything as changing. The features of people changed; objects changed; sometimes the room changed into another apartment; pillow cases on the bed were blown up and were altered in design. The protocols on mescal intoxication and toxic psychosis show the same characteristics. In an atropine delirium,

[1] See the bibliography in H. Hoff and P. Schilder, *Die Lagereflexe des Menschen* (Vienna, 1927).

changes could be produced in the optic hallucination by vestibular irritation. The experience of change is closely related to the primitive experience of motion and is exaggerated by the dissociation of motor impulses. The impression of a static object is dependent on the suppression of the inner motion of the perception and on the coördination of motor impulses. This does not remove the question of how we reach the perception of a stabilized object. I do not believe that primitive perception does not point to an objective world. With the exception of tactile experiences, which belong decisively to the sphere of the body, every sensation not only points to the body but also predominantly to the outside world, and this primitive outside world has more motion, more rhythm, more color and less sharply distinguished spatial relations than the developed perceptual world. Its synesthetic character is different from that met in the fully developed experience. Some definite characteristics belong to this primitive world, such as the tendency against sharp angles, the preference for curves, vortices, circles, the prevalence of movement and rhythm, the tonic mass reaction and the rhythmic phasic reaction. This problem must be exemplified in the important field of gestalt and its developments.

We cannot understand the development of the primitive perception without acquiring better insight into the problem of configuration. The Berlin gestalt psychologists, Max Wertheimer, Kurt Koffka, and Wolfgang Koehler, claim that a structuralized configuration is immediately perceived in such a way that it corresponds with the external stimulating world. The pattern is the result of a dynamic interaction between the sensory field (internal organizing forces) and the stimulus (external organizing forces); or, as Koehler puts it, the sensory field is organized by the relative properties of stimulation. Max Wertheimer used figures (see Plate I) for visual perception, asking normal persons what they experienced as they perceived them. From this data he derived his laws of good gestalten, namely, that we tend to perceive things in certain patterns because of the proximity of their parts, the continuity of the structure, similarity of the parts,

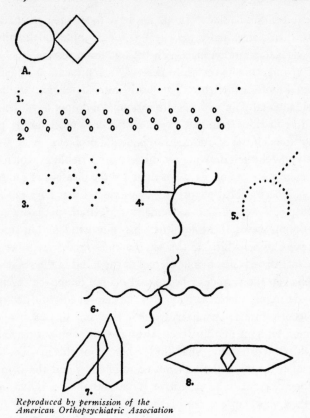

PLATE I

inclusiveness of structure, and natural geometrical figures. Kurt
Koffka has emphasized that the first law of gestalt is the relation of
the figure or structure to the background. He also emphasizes the
principle of inclusiveness and closure. These are the fundamental
principles of optically perceived organized form according to the
Berlin school of gestalt psychology.

Wertheimer and the gestalt school ordered their subjects to describe
their experiences. It was an important step forward when L. Bender
asked the individuals to copy these figures, because it is possible to

use the test on individuals who do not have the language capacity to describe their perceptual experience; as for example, small children, mental defectives, individuals with organic brain disease (including aphasia), and schizophrenics. In this way it represents an integrated perceptual motor experience. This leads immediately back to one of the fundamental points of this discussion. We do not have the right to separate motility from perception. L. Bender's procedure is, therefore, apt to lead deeper into the fundamental problem.

"We know the first drawings of children are scribblings which seem to represent pure motor play. It is done for the pleasure of motor expression. The scribbled picture is a by-product, it has no meaning. It is performed by large arm movement in dextrad, clockwise whirls or pendulum waves, if the child uses his right hand, and in sinistrad counter-clockwise whirls if the left hand is used." It is certainly correct that there is no obvious picture in the mind of the child when it scribbles in the way described. But I do not doubt that even this seemingly purely motor activity must be connected with perceptual elements of primitive character. Quite in the same way as there is no perception without motility, there is no motility without perception. It is difficult to determine what kind of perception this may be. There is a relation between these primitive scribblings and the primitive spatial perceptions. The primitive wave and the primitive vortex make their appearance in the perceptual area as in the motor sphere. J. Baldwin observed in a twenty-seven-month-old child that its productions in drawing consisted of loops in a clockwise direction with emphasis on the horizontal plane. In her studies, Bender reached the opinion that the visual motor gestalt patterns

arise from movement, probably vortical, and that internally organized gestalten evolve genetically by a progressive organization in connection with the integrated intellectual functions. It thus appears that the more primitive sensory motor patterns are dependent upon the principles of constant motion of a whirling or vortex type, with an associated radiating directional component and with a tendency to emphasize the horizontal plane. Fixed points are difficult and straight lines are not accomplished as the shortest distance between two fixed points, but as an expression of radiating tendencies. Crossed lines and angulated forms present great difficulties. The first evidence of expressed form was shown at the second year level as little units of whirls or loops which perseverated most freely in the horizontal plane in a dextrad direction. Some tendencies for gestalten were seen in the third year level as rectangular forms either near each other or inside each other. But some of the gestalt principles are functions of the more highly elaborated perceptual motor capacities and only appear at the higher intellectual levels. Above three years, we find the tendency to accentuate the horizontal base line, to control perseveration and to produce wavy lines instead of broken ones for the representation of straight ones, and there is some effort to cross lines. At the five year level there is some tendency to reduce the primitive loops to points and to make straighter lines and better recognized gestalten. At the seven year level there is a capacity for many vertical and geometrical gestalten on the principle of internal organization and crossing of forms. At the eight year level nearly all gestalten are possible, slanting forms are recognized but their relation to the whole figure presents difficulties. Pairing as determined by slight differences is not accomplished. The major difficulties at this level seem to be in relationships of parts to wholes. These things are satisfactorily accomplished above the ten year level. At all levels all of the original principles are in evidence and tendencies to revert to them are always present.

She writes elsewhere:

Visual motor gestalten may be tested by the copying or drawing of figures. They arise from motor behavior that first finds its expression in scribbling. The scribbling is modified by inhibition into loops or parts of loops that tend to take on significance as they correspond with the forms which are perceived by the optic field. I have previously pointed out that movement is the basis for the organization of the optic field. The two to three year old child can imitate motor activity to produce new forms more readily than it can copy new optically perceived forms. Thus dots, dashes and zigzags may be experienced first as motor behavior pattern and then either utilized more freely in response to optic stimuli that suggest them or are again forgotten, while the primitive loop is resorted to in order to express relationship in all gestalten. A simple enclosed loop on a background, loops in concentric relationship, or loops in horizontal dextrad direction are the first laws of gestalten. New principles may arise either from motor experience, dots, dashes, or zigzags in series or masses, or they may arise from enclosed forms built from parts of loops or, by inhibition, from partially closed or open loops. Crossed forms are difficult, and even more difficult are all slanting and oblique relationships. The niceties of actual sizes, distances, and perfection of motor control are added after the age of seven years, but most of the gestalt principles are established before that age. (See Plate II.)

In psychological terms we may say that the goal in children's drawings is to establish an equilibrium between the mental symbols as determined by the biological background of the perceptional motor pattern at the different stages of the maturation of the organism as a whole and the reality of the world as it is perceived. The traces that are used must correspond not alone to the stimuli that produce them but also to the organization characteristics of the sensory field.

We may conclude that there are gestalt principles which extend at first over the whole field. Under the guidance of actual experience, more definite gestalten are created. The further elaboration of the gestalt takes place by a maturation process that is continually influenced by experiences. In the sidewalk drawings of children these tendencies also appear. There is a continuous interrelation between the motility which leads to the general pattern and beyond it to more specific and elaborate forms in connection with previous experiences. New experiences are continually modifying the primitive perceptual patterns and the primitive motility. But there is another important fact that one can read from Bender's figures. The child does not change the primitive pattern when once it has been created, in the early stages of development, as, for instance, in the pictures drawn by a child of three years. It seems that the gestalt once created behaves in a more or less tyrannical way, neglecting many parts of the immediate perception.

There are some other important principles which can be derived from these figures. The gestalt principles are very often enormously simplified and at the same time exaggerated. On the other hand, gestalten which are typical for the adult may be more or less completely disrupted. When a number of points are copied, the subject reproduces the number of points rather freely. It is as if the important thing were not the exact number but "numerous points." In the adult the direction is insignificant; in the primitive stages, the difference between the original and the copy concerning the number of points can

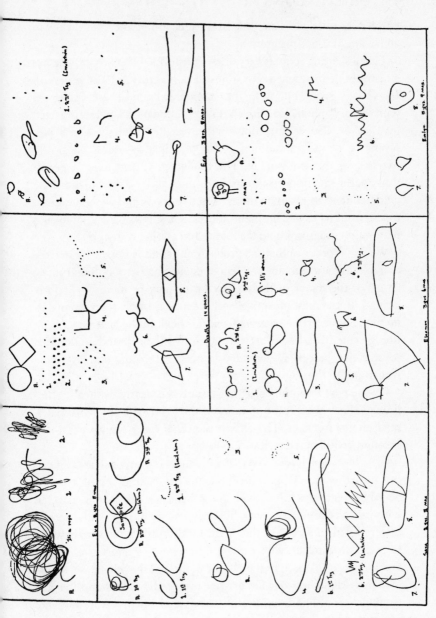

PLATE II

be very considerable. Reversals from right to left and from below to above are also not uncommon.

That a slanting series is very often transformed to a vertical one has already been mentioned. Rotations of 90 degrees are also observed. It is of very great importance that in organic brain diseases associated with sensory aphasia, one finds a disintegration of the more integrated internal detailed organization of the gestalten. But there is a perseveration of the outstanding gestalt principle by use of the primitive loop as the unit symbol. The fundamental principles of gestalt thus appear in a primitive form. In disintegrating cerebral lesions the gestalten tend to revert to more primitive levels and as the brain recovers from its injury they tend to follow the laws of developmental maturation in returning to the higher integrating responses.

We again perceive that the problem of gestalt is not only a perceptual one, but also a motor problem. Gestalten are sensory motor units, although the motor or the sensory factor may be more in the foreground. In the most primitive level the field is in the foreground and no single construction emerges from this field. In the next step, primitive gestalten contrast experience against this field, and a continual constructive process is necessary to adapt the configuration to the reality and to the object.

On the next level the object has been more clearly defined by continuous touch with reality (reality testing) and with the more elaborated motor function. The differentiation of figure and background becomes comparatively clear.

C. L. Morgan has observed that a cow may tenderly lick an artificial calf stuffed with hay but quietly eats the hay coming out of its body. Social hymenoptera kill individuals of their own nest that are covered with the juice of other species, but accept individuals of other species smeared with the juice of their own species. The Bantas male wood frogs try to copulate with everything moving; for instance, with a floating piece of wood. In the rat, the motion of the female is a sexual stimulus. Motionless females are not molested. Stone found that the combination of blindness, loss of the sense of smell, loss of the sense of taste, and the removal of facial tactile vibrissae in no way affect the sexual response of the male rat. Superficial and deep sensibility are fundamental in stimulating mating behavior. Females moving quickly when approached were most effective in stimulating sexual activity.

Monkeys cling to furry objects, to their living young, but also to dead bodies, chickens, and rats. They have no appreciation of death and they keep the carcass of the young until it is mummified (S. Zuckermann). The problem of which aspects of a stimulus are important for the perceptual object arises in this way. One might say that the reaction is determined by the smell or merely by the furriness. One would then arrive at a theory of action as determined by more or less insignificant details, and we would have the conception of action as a reaction to single aspects of experiences which are apart from total experiences. It is doubtful, however, whether such a conclusion is justified. In the ordinary world of the animal there could be a continual coincidence between the smell and other perceptions, and by our experimental condition we disrupt this inner connection. We must also take into consideration the fact that when a series of stimuli have very often occurred together, or have been related in some other way, every one of the stimuli may substitute for any of the others. This is, after all, the meaning of the so-called conditioned reflexes. If, to the sound of a tuning fork, food is several times offered, the sound alone will eventually provoke the salivary reaction. It would certainly be preposterous to assume that the sound is a real stimulus for food; it is merely the outstanding signal for the expected satisfaction in the perceptual world. It is also of importance that, at first, a sound of any pitch will be effective, whereas later, only a sound of the specific pitch used has influence in provoking salivation. I. P. Pavlov speaks of generalization and differentiation, terms which are not appropriate, as I shall later discuss. The fact remains that animals do not have any particular tendency to discriminate, because they are not forced to do so by their environment.

Many of the instances cited here are from S. Zuckermann's excellent book; he cites the attitude of monkeys towards furry objects to prove there is no true maternal instinct, since the mother is as much interested in the dead as in the living young, in a rat, or in a chicken. This form of argumentation is not correct. The furriness is in some way a signal for the whole world of maternal love, adhesion, and clinging. Even under the conditions of the experiment, the world is not a senseless accumulation of data, and our reactions are not generally determined by single stimuli although such an attitude may occasionally occur. The single stimulus is always connected with other parts of reality and forms units with them which, under the influence of action and repetition, become permanent.[2]

[2] Important material on this problem can be found in the papers by E. Brunswik. He has recently formulated some of these basic principles in a paper with Edward C. Tolman. Charlotte Buehler, O. Rubinow, and L. Frankl have followed the development of feeding responses in infants. The very youngest responded to the actual touch of the nipple only. Gradually sucking movements appeared with the laying on of the bib; and later, with the approach of any sort of pointed object, until finally, at about eight months, the infants responded to the presence of a nipple plus a white fluid and to that only.

CHAPTER X

PSYCHOANALYSIS AND THE CONDITIONED REFLEXES

I WRITE [1] about analysis and conditioned reflexes with hesitation, because of the excellent studies on the problem by A. R. Luria, N. E. Ischlondsky, and T. M. French. If I overcame my internal inhibition, I was especially guided by the idea that all these authors mentioned were overwhelmed by the classical experimentation of I. P. Pavlov and his school and by the immense amount of material collected in their books and papers. They took, therefore, the physiology and, I say it only with trepidation, the psychology of Pavlov for granted. Their task, therefore, necessarily has remained unsolved. Psychoanalysis with its close touch on the problems of real life can never be completely adapted to the artificial psychophysiology of Pavlov, which is based upon the conception of a mosaic in the organism and in the psyche. If there is any truth in the gestalt psychology and in the teaching of personality as a whole, Pavlov's theory must be wrong. We must, therefore, try to come to a decision and should not try to express two different psychologies at once without seeing the inner contradictions. Other investigators have not made up their minds. Sometimes they try to explain psychoanalytic situations in the terms of conditioned reflexes and sometimes conditioned reflexes in the terms of psychoanalysis. T. M. French, for instance, uses Pavlov's investigations not merely as illustrations but as proof for psychoanalysis. N. E. Ischlondsky seems to be of the opinion that psychological processes are only understood fully when considered in the light of Pavlov's experiments. I am attempting to arrive at a psychological understanding of conditioned reflexes. If such should be pos-

[1] Reprinted from the *Psychoanalytic Review*, January, 1937.

sible, and psychoanalytic psychology is valid, we would come to a psychoanalytic understanding of the experimental work of Pavlov. The other way would be justifiable only if we accept Pavlov's physiology and psychology as definitely established.

When food is placed in a hungry dog's mouth, a stimulus of the food in the mouth provokes a secretion of saliva of certain typical qualities. Saliva of another quality is secreted when diluted hydrochloric acid is put into the mouth of the dog. These are unconditioned reflexes. The response of the salivary glands to external influences is, however, not limited to the above-mentioned ordinary reflexes. We all know that the salivary glands begin to secrete when other receptive surfaces, including the eye and the ear, are stimulated. The sight or smell of the food is sufficient to provoke the salivary secretion. Such a stimulus is called a conditioned stimulus. It becomes ineffective on repetition when not followed by the unconditioned stimulus. Any visual stimulus, any desired sound, any odor or a stimulation of any part of the skin, either by mechanical means or by the application of heat or cold, stimulate the salivary glands if the stimuli are applied simultaneously with the action of the salivary glands. In contrast to conditioned reflexes arising from the feeding and the circumstances connected with it (natural conditioned reflexes), reflexes of this kind are called artificial conditioned reflexes. These latter are almost exclusively used in experimentation.

Conditioned reflexes can of course be formed not only with salivary secretion, but also with defense reactions of the voluntary muscles. This method has been extensively used by V. Bechterew and his school and by J. Beritoff.

One would be inclined to formulate the belief that the unconditioned reflexes are concerned with fundamental instincts such as feeding and defense. Conditioned reflexes can be formed in connection with such basic instincts. This formulation, however, is incomplete. Conditioned reflexes can also be formed concerning functions, the vital importance of which is not quite so obvious. Conditioning of the pupillary light reflex is possible, according to H. Cason. Of course, we suppose that there is a biological meaning in the light reflex of the pupils. The contraction of the pupil to light can hardly be called a basic biological phenomenon.

All the instances quoted could be called reflexes or they could also be termed organic reactions with little or no participation of the consciousness. Conditioning is not restricted to such reactions. It is easy to demonstrate it in actions of voluntary type also, as in the experiments of Heinrich Kluever with monkeys which, while confined in a cage, hauled in baited strings. The pulling-in technique can also be used in work with animals below the primates, even as low as rats. In experimentation with human beings one may use voluntary reactions instead of defense reactions.

A. Lenz touched the palm of the subject three times and afterward ordered him to turn his hand. The subject then turned the hand from a supinated to a pronated position. After several combinations, the subject turned the hand after the touches without waiting for the order. In the final analysis, the mechanism of so-called conditioned reflexes resolves itself into the mechanism which is usually called association and which can be better formulated in the following way: A total situation of a typical character has the tendency to reinstate itself when only parts of the objective situation are present. The total situation reinstates itself also in the sphere of involuntary innervation, and Pavlov's chief merits lie in the methodical use of this discovery.[2]

Pavlov insists on talking about reflexes, but what he calls a reflex is far from being a simple mechanical thing. It is a complicated total reaction, an attitude in which the personality of the animal, as Pavlov himself has stated, plays an important part. All these reactions may also be easily found in human beings. It is, of course, a matter of taste to state that animal and human activity consists merely of reflexes. The term reflex then loses every distinction and is merely used to indicate that one is not interested in the subjective side of the animal's reactions but is interested merely in the objective expression. There

[2] Hollingworth uses the term redintegration. As applied to the conditioned reflex, this term represents the fact that all elements, at or near the time that a response is evoked, themselves tend independently and indiscriminately to acquire the capacity to evoke substantially the same response. For our present purpose the indiscriminateness of the tendency is particularly to be noted (Clark L. Hull).

very often is a tendency to forget that such a subjective side exists at all. One may also concede that a study of objective reactions can be methodically simpler in many problems. For many other problems, a study of the subjective side is indispensable.

In the Viennese Society for Psychiatry, F. Mattauschek demonstrated the following case (I do not know whether a report of this case has appeared): "The patient had a severe epileptic attack in the course of a quarrel with his sweetheart. They separated. Some time later he met her by chance and had his second epileptic attack. Several months later he saw a lady in a restaurant whom he at first erroneously took to be this sweetheart, and had his third epileptic attack."

One of my own patients (a physician) has had a disagreeable experience with a certificate he gave a patient. Since then he has anxiety feelings whenever he has to deal with an official.

Another case is that of a girl who was struck by a car coming from the rear. She was not severely hurt but reacted with great anxiety. Several months later, when she crossed a street and saw cars coming towards her she had the feeling that a car was behind her and knocked her down.

In all these instances one sees the tendency to redintegration. A part of the previous situation or a similarity to it provokes the total previous situation, as in the first case mentioned with its severe organic consequences. In the second case quoted it is possible to attain deeper understanding of the situation, for the official represented father and older brother for him. V. Bechterew and N. E. Ischlondsky have shown similar mechanisms in the genesis of perversions. We do not deal, therefore, with two series which are in any way different, but we deal with identical phenomena viewed with a different technique. I do not doubt that for many purposes Pavlov's techniques may allow a more exact formulation. In many other cases a psychological approach will lead to a greater understanding.

The case histories quoted show the phenomenon which Pavlov calls irradiation.

If the original mechanical irritation of a certain skin area has been made, very clearly, the stimulus to the salivary glands then the mechanical stimulation of other skin areas also begins to call out the salivary reflex. Afterwards thermal skin stimulations show this effect and finally the irritation of other body surfaces. If you form a conditioned reflex to the ticking of a metronome and then try other sounds, you will find that other sounds also produce the salivary flow. If you make a conditioned stimulus from the tone of 1,000 vibrations and afterward try other tones of various vibrations, all of them have an effect. If you repeatedly combine the mechanical stimulation of the skin with pricking, this pricking calls out a secretion of saliva every time. Now when you subject other parts of the skin to the same pricking, they all cause the salivary secretion. This is because the stimulation has spread over the hemispheres.

There is a form of experiment in which we do not connect the activity of the salivary gland with stimulus but with its remain or trace: i. e., we give the stimulus and then allow an interval to elapse after its termination before putting acid into the mouth of the dog, or before feeding it. In the "trace reflexes" the excitation spreads still further. If you have formed a conditioned reflex to the metronome and then repeat this reflex many times, other sounds gradually lose their effect and at last only the metronome calls out the excitation. If you repeat the stimulation with the metronome long enough, it finally happens that only the metronome with the number of strokes you have constantly used will be effective. A dog may react to a stimulation of 100 ticks per minute but not to one of 96. If you form a conditioned reflex to a tone of certain strength, then only this tone and in a given strength is effective.[3]

In these cases of high concentration of excitation, besides repetition of a given stimulus, it is also important to repeat the other neighboring and related stimuli but without feeding. Pavlov speaks, in this connection, of concentration. The underlying idea is that the irritation irradiates and afterwards concentrates itself.

J. Beritoff has justly emphasized that the physiology of the brain does not know irradiations of the type Pavlov describes. Brain irradiation spreads quickly but also disappears quickly. The conditioned "irradiation" may persist a very long time. We cannot determine by physiological methods which way it will go. It seems, therefore, that Pavlov's connotation of irradiation has been created for a special purpose and it also seems very questionable whether this irradiation is not merely a physiological expression for facts which are psycho-

[3] Pavlov, *Lectures* (New York, 1928), pp. 102, 158.

logical and very well known. In the case of the physician who wrote the certificate, the official is the representative of any threatening power; the irradiation spreads to all threatening persons. The automobile which knocked the girl down extends to all automobiles. Of course, we may call this irradiation, but I doubt whether it is really a description of physiological spreading of impulses over the cerebral hemispheres. The whole procedure seems much more to indicate the idea that situations are at first perceived in a general way, and only with the progress of our relation to the situation do we learn to see the specificity of it. It is a matter of course that we are greatly helped when we have renewed touch with a situation and learn that only specific situations will lead to a specific consequence (Pavlov's "concentration"). Psychologically, we could speak about "generalization," but this term would imply that at first a single stimulus is perceived and is afterwards generalized. The truth probably is that at first the general aspect of the situation is seen and only later on, its specific aspects. Pavlov uses the term differential inhibition for the corrective tendency. It is another expression for the fact that we learn by trial and error and by continual touch with the world. One sees that I use a terminology emphasizing the relation to the world. Pavlov tries to catch the brain processes connected with it. This is certainly not an impossible undertaking, but it is questionable whether the psychological description which Pavlov gives in physiological terms is an expression of physiological processes going on in the brain.

I have pointed out on other occasions that the type of thinking which takes the single experience as a general law is an important part of unconscious thinking: God, father, power, are really one from the point of view of primitive thinking. Recent studies in children have shown me that taking the first experience as a general law is an important trait in the thinking of a child. When thinking develops from the unconscious into the conscious, it comes in touch with the different parts of reality until finally concentration takes place, or, in other words, the methods of conscious thinking are used.

K. Buehler has pointed out that in thinking we at first perceive general relations and we see the general sphere in which the solution of a specific problem lies. I have shown that thinking starts with such knowledge of a general type. I have given the name of "the sphere" to this thinking in general directions. In the process of thinking, this general direction becomes more and more specific with the help of continual touch with single experiences. Symbolic thinking with its broad and vague hints is substituted by logical thinking, which deals with the concrete facts of reality. The connotation of "the sphere" coincides in many respects with the psychoanalytical concept of the unconscious but emphasizes the psychological experiences which go on during thinking. I believe that unconscious thinking, in the sense of an absence of the quality of awareness, does not exist, but I believe that Freud has given a correct description of the psychic processes going on in the sphere when speaking about the mechanisms of the unconscious (System Ucs).[4]

Pavlov reports in *Conditioned Reflexes* an experiment by Dr. Kasherininova in which the presence of an extra stimulus did produce a strong inhibitory effect on the conditioned one. At the same time the extra stimulus acquired some of the excitatory functions of the conditioned one, so that when used alone it created a conditioned stimulus of second order. Experiments of this kind make it very probable that inhibition in the sense of Pavlov may inhibit the primary signal and not inhibit signals related to the primary signal.

It was interesting to trace the state of excitability in the neighboring and distant points during the action of the inhibiting stimulus. This has been done for another kind of internal inhibition in the experiments of N. A. Podkopayev. If the positive conditioned stimulus without being accompanied by the unconditioned stimulus is repeated several times in succession at intervals of some minutes, it quickly loses its stimulating effect. The conditioned reflex sinks, as we express it, to zero. This occurs in consequence of the development of an inhibition process at the stimulated point. As we have seen in the process of differential inhibition after the cessation of the stimulus, this process, too, spreads—it irradiates. If, through the development of extinguishing inhibition, the stimulating effect from a certain place on the skin has fallen to zero, and this zero effect is maintained by continuous stimulation (of course, without the unconditioned stimulus), Podkopayev has seen that the stimulation of other

4 See Chapter XVIII.

points of the skin is manifested in a very particular manner. The stimulation of all other points of the skin, neighboring as well as distant, acts positively, but with certain peculiarities. The latent period is clearly shortened (1 to 3 seconds instead of 4 to 5), but the general effect is less in comparison with the normal. The most simple explanation of this fact is that the sharp decrease of the latent period is a sign of an increase of the irritability of the stimulated points: but as both the inhibitory and the positive impulses fall simultaneously on the effector center, the resultant action is their algebraic sum.[5]

These experiments are important since they are an experimental analogy to what one may term "symbolism." The original stimulus loses its importance whereas the stimulus of a nearby place (related or similar stimulus) now gains a place similar to the original stimulus. Similar instances can be repeatedly found in Pavlov's work. The psychoanalyst will also view with interest Pavlov's "ultra-paradoxical phase" during which only the previously elaborated inhibitory agents have a positive effect. One immediately sees that it depends on the total situation whether the tendency to an action or secretion comes out in its original way or is distorted or even transposed or converted into its opposite.

One of the most important connotations in the Pavlovian system is that of inhibition. Pavlov differentiates between external inhibition and internal inhibition. In the external inhibition damaging influences weaken the conditioned reflex to make it disappear. Every change in the surroundings of the animal provokes an orientation reflex. Ischlondsky says it is as if the demand of the surroundings pushes the current action of the organism and the elaborated conditioned reflex into the background. I want only to comment that we know this demand situation very well in psychology. It is very questionable whether the term inhibition is correct. It is better to say that the individual is directed towards that part of a situation which is most vital and every change in the surroundings is more vital than the situation to which we are already accustomed.

The internal inhibition plays a much more important part. I may here refer to the five types of internal inhibition of a conditioned re-

[5] Pavlov, *Lectures*, p. 322.

flex: extinction; delay; trace inhibition; conditioned inhibition; inhibition by differentiation.

Extinction of a conditioned reflex occurs when the stimulus is given several times in succession and is not followed by the unconditioned stimulus. It is easy to show that the conditioned reflex is still present. Any additional stimulus may provoke it. We are not interested in the various techniques by which an extinguished conditioned reflex can be provoked again. A. R. Luria and T. M. French have justly emphasized the point that here we deal with a close analogy to the psychoanalytic statement that experiences which are no longer in the foreground are still present. A comparison between the various inhibitions and repressions offers itself, but it will be necessary to discuss this problem in a broader sense. The inhibition by differentiation is closely related to the simple extinction. When a reflex is first being developed, similar signals will also provoke a reaction. For instance, when a sound with a frequency of 800 cycles is systematically repeated accompanied by the unconditioned stimulus, and the sounds of other frequencies are used without reinforcement by the unconditioned stimulus, the generalized reflex becomes specific. It is then possible to differentiate a sound of 812 cycles from one of 800 cycles.

It is easy to understand that these so-called inhibitions occur because individuals live in a real world. When a signal is not followed by an unconditioned stimulus, the reaction of the organism becomes senseless. We continually adapt our actions and somatic reactions to happenings in the outer world. Conditioning means that we are put into a reality where certain expectations are justified. If these expectations are systematically disappointed we have to change our attitude. We act in accordance with reality testing, and we continue those reactions which are successful (lead to satisfaction) and discontinue those which are not satisfactory. Analytically we would, of course, have to ascribe these functions to the ego system. We could call this, from the point of view of logic, induction. A stimulus has led to a satisfactory situation so often that the organism has to be prepared for it. If the stimulus repeatedly leads to dissatisfaction, there is the probability that it will again lead to dissatisfaction. Or, in other words, our actions and organic reactions reckon with the probabilities of the outward world. There is no question that these mechanisms in the ego system have many points in common with the unconscious reaction and they lead to a warning not to make too great a separation between the ego and the id.[6]

If the unconditioned stimulus is added to the conditioned stimulus after the latter has operated for a certain length of time, for instance from one to three minutes, the conditioned stimulus has its effect at the moment when the unconditioned stimulus had previously acted. Sometimes these reactions have a tendency to creep forward in time and the reaction antedates the presentation of the unconditioned stimulus. The so-called trace reflexes are very similar. The unconditioned stimulus is added when the conditioned stimulus has already disappeared. There are also, as C. L. Hull has especially pointed out, anticipatory tendencies. Pavlov speaks of an inhibition. The weakness of the connotation of inhibition comes out here in a particularly clear way. After all, we must meet here the same basic principle we have pointed to previously. The animal reacts to a total situation as an indication that the total situation is present again. In a previous experimental study I have shown by introspection that expectation and preparation play an important part in the interval during which a conditioned trace reflex is formed. The interval of five seconds used in my subjects was filled by specific psychic structures of expectations and motor attitudes. It is easily understandable that the so-called anticipatory reactions occur so often. In working with a motor defense reaction, I found that the withdrawal of the hand from the electric stimulus is prepared long before the stimulus is expected.

I do not doubt that if we could condition a human being to food, in the period of delay an anticipation of the taste and satisfaction would take place before the real secretion of the saliva starts. In other words, the conception of excitation and inhibition as isolated forces conflicting with each other is untenable, and we have to substitute for it the conception of wholes or gestalten of specific struc-

[6] When a new field of experimentation is opened, as in the case of conditioned reflexes, we are entitled to a synthesis between the new and older experiences.

tures which are in close relation to the biologic needs of the individual. I object to the basic conception of Pavlov that there is "an enormous mosaic in the cerebrum consisting of excited points and inhibited or temporarily sleeping points."

If we take some indifferent agent, having no marked effect on the animal, and add this to a well elaborated conditioned stimulus, not accompanying this combination of pure agents by the unconditioned stimulus (food), the indifferent agent will gradually become an inhibitor of a conditioned stimulus, i. e., the combination of a conditioned stimulus with an indifferent agent is always null although the conditioned stimulus used alone is as active as before. This phenomenon we call conditioned inhibition.[7]

The conditioned stimulus and the indifferent agent together certainly are not merely a sum or subtraction but a completely different configuration. Pavlov's experiments on conditioned inhibition are experimental proofs for fundamental statements of the gestalt theory. The outward world is certainly not merely a sum of different single stimuli.

In a dog, the conditioned reflex of a sequence of four ascending sounds, a, b, c, d, is created. When the sounds are now given in the order d, c, b, a, no result occurs. Of the 24 permutations possible with these four sounds, the dog reacted positively to eleven. All the combinations which were chiefly ascending had a positive effect, whereas all the combinations which were chiefly descending had a negative effect. We have here an outspoken gestalt principle (Ischlondsky). There is no question that the method of the conditioned reflexes offers us an excellent possibility to study the efficiency of the gestalt principle and the single stimulus in the perception of animals. This formulation is far from a formulation which speaks of a mosaic of single excited and inhibited points.

We are now prepared for the discussion of what the different types of inhibition mean from a psychoanalytic point of view. French has already attempted to compare inhibition and repression. In psychoanalysis, the term repression means very different things. When we are directed towards a particular goal in thinking, many other things

[7] Pavlov, *Lectures*, p. 208.

have to be kept out of consciousness. The very formulation I have given concerning the development of thinking from "the sphere" into the full light of consciousness implies that a continual choice takes place and only those parts of the previous experience are chosen which lead in some way to the fulfillment of the needs in the reality. I already have mentioned that differential inhibition and the inhibition by extinction are close analogies to the process described here. Psychoanalysis usually does not use the term repression in this sense. It uses the term repressions chiefly when an active fight under the direction of the ego is directed against an experience which was fully in the consciousness. External inhibition corresponds much more closely to this connotation of repression. A new experience, biologically more important, leads to the neglect of another experience which has been, and otherwise would stay, in the foreground of the consciousness. The experiments of Pavlov offer other analogies to repression in this sense; as, for instance, when painful stimuli are chosen as conditioned stimuli and the defense reaction is repressed in the interest of the food reflex. Every attempt to say that external or internal inhibition corresponds to repression is from the beginning erroneous, since Pavlov's connotations and the connotations of psychoanalysis come from different fields of experience. It is absolutely justified to ask, in regard to every case of excitation or inhibition, what it may mean from the psychoanalytic point of view.

Beritoff has emphasized that Pavlov's connotation of inhibition does not correspond to the use of the term in physiology. The inhibition of the physiologists develops quickly and disappears quickly. Pavlov's inhibition, lasting for a long time, independent of the immediate presence of the inhibitory stimulus, sounds again more and more like a psychological connotation stated in the language of physiology. It is, of course, everybody's right to use terms in a different way. It is important, however, to know that Pavlov deals with behavior problems, habit and training, which are expressed in language taken from the physiological field. This free use of terms begins with the use of the term reflex and is also present in the use of such terms as irradiation and inhibition. By the use of such terms an artificial gap between psychology and physiology is created. I do not doubt that the terms reflex, irradiation, and inhibition in the physiological sense and in the Pavlovian sense have something in common. However, they belong to different biological levels and, therefore, do not have the same significance. The same remarks may also be made about another term which has an important part in Pavlov's system. Pavlov is of the opinion that an excitation provokes an inhibition around the focus and he has related it to the "successive induction" of Sir Charles S. Sherrington. Sherrington thought of antagonistic processes in identical points of the central nervous system. Beritoff doubts whether Sherrington's opinion is justified.

It is important to note that painful stimuli can act as a signal for a conditioned food reflex only when these stimuli are very weak in the beginning. Later on, one may gradually increase them and they do not lose their signal character. At the present time there is no possibility of explaining this in merely physiological terms, but we understand such a procedure and its results perfectly well from a psychological point of view. Concerning this experiment, Pavlov writes:

With the strongest current, as well as with burning and mechanical destruction of the skin, there could be provoked only the food reaction (the corresponding motor reaction and the salivary secretion) and there was no trace of any interference by the defensive reaction; there were no changes in breathing or heart beat, characteristic of this last reaction. It is clear that this result was attained by the transference of the external excitation to the food center and that simultaneously with this an inhibition of the center for defensive reaction must occur. This special conditioned reflex persisted for some months and probably might have remained stable under the given conditions had we not changed them so that the electric irritation was systematically transferred at every excitation to another new point on the skin. And when the number of these points became considerable, then in one of our dogs the condition suddenly changed. Everywhere, beginning with the first location of the skin stimulus and even with the weakest current there was manifested only the strongest defensive reaction, and not a single trace of the food reaction.[8]

[8] *Ibid.*, p. 341.

This is a clear instance of the breaking through of something which has been repressed when its urge became so strong that it disturbed the ego adaptation.

Not all cases are alike. When Pavlov differentiated a circle from an ellipse of the same size, rather delicate differentiations could be obtained. When the ellipse was nearly circular, the two diameters being 9x8, a new delicate differentiation appeared which always remained imperfect, lasted two or three weeks, and afterwards not only disappeared gradually but caused the loss of all earlier differentiations. The dog which formerly sat quietly on his bench was now constantly struggling and howling. Or, in other words, when the adaptations to reality become too difficult they are given up completely and the individual goes back to a primitive type of behavior, and the rather undifferentiated primitive action. One even may discuss such an attitude from the point of view of energy and say that when it is no longer used in adaptation to the outward world by the ego system, more or less primitive action breaks through. Pavlov continues:

Thus with the collision of the excitatory and the inhibitory processes, there appears either a predominance of the stimulating process, disturbing the inhibition (it is possible to say a lingering increase of the tonus of the excitation), or in other cases a predominance of the inhibitory process, with its preliminary phases, disturbing the excitatory process, i. e., an increase in the tonus of the inhibition.[9]

The conditioned reflexes disappeared also during the great inundation in Leningrad. When the experimenter was sitting in the room, the conditioned reflexes reappeared. When a stream of water trickled into the room, the dog returned to his former pathological state. When a part of the clothing of the experimenter was introduced into the chamber, it had the same effect. Seemingly the scent alone was sufficient. Also in this instance, under the influence of fear, differentiations and adaptations to reality were given up. Their reappearance in the presence of the experimenter is an experimental analogy to the transference situation. Since the flood could be substituted by the trickling of water, and the experimenter by the mere scent of his

[9] *Ibid.*, p. 344.

clothing, we have clear-cut instances of symbolic thinking before us. It is worth while mentioning that when conflicts arise, eczemas are also observed on the legs of the animals. If one goes in the opposite direction and tries, as L. S. Kubie has done, to interpret the analytic technique from the point of view of conditioned reflexes, one immediately comes into great difficulties. Transference can hardly be discussed in terms of inhibitions of any type. It is certainly arbitrary to state, as Kubie does, that the passivity of the analyst acts merely by the absence of external inhibition.

Neuroses in dogs, as described by Pavlov, certainly have a primitive structure. They can be cured by rest, bromides, and calcium, and if there is anything by which a neurosis in humans cannot be cured, it is by rest, bromides, and calcium.

Finally, Pavlov distinguishes between three types of dogs: The excitatory type, which forms conditioned reflexes easily and in which differentiation is difficult; the inhibitory type, in which are readily formed inhibitions that abolish conditioned reflexes; and the central type, which does not deviate in either direction. This personality factor in dogs makes many of their reactions unpredictable. Pavlov meets here the same difficulty we meet in every psychological field.

The learning curves of H. Ebbinghaus and the work of P. Ranschburg have led to results in experiments with humans similar to those of Pavlov's experiments with animals, and the degree of predictability is at least as great in these experiments as in those of Pavlov. In this particular field of psychology, which seems to be better mechanized than the others, the mechanical laws of association are not sufficient for the interpretation of results, as W. Poppelreuter has especially pointed out. In this field we find structures, gestalten, which are not sums but are definite totals of configurations.

Pavlov speaks about reflexes of freedom, and reflexes of slavery. These are, again, attitudes of the total personality of dogs. To call them reflexes again means a neglect of the fact that there are different levels of organization. If one calls all activities of all levels reflexes, the term reflex loses all specific meaning.

Of course, Pavlov asks from the dog only one simple response—

the drops of saliva. "The food reflex" consists of many more things. They are total reactions of the voluntary motor system. The dog tries to get hold of the food, its attitude changes. One needs merely to observe a dog devouring food, in order to see that one deals with an affair which concerns the total organism. In experiments, large parts of the food reflex are suppressed, since they do not fit the situation into which the dog is forced. When we count drops we measure only one side of the total procedure—a very incomplete measure for the total situation.

We should also give psychological consideration to Pavlov's theory of sleep. The dog is confined to the empty surroundings of the empty laboratory and the delay in what has been promised by the procedure of conditioning takes away the last interest in the outward world. What can the dog do but fall asleep? Ischlondsky justly remarks that repeated monotonous stimuli also provoke sleep. We are here on a ground with which we are familiar. It is better to talk about the psychological side than to talk about the spreading of an inhibition the connotation of which is not by any means proven.

The objective results which Pavlov has observed in the beginning of sleep are certainly remarkable.

It was noticed in many instances that in certain phases of drowsiness in dogs, there occurred a distortion of the facts of conditioned stimuli. The positive stimuli lost their effect but the negative became positive (experiments of A. A. Shishlo). In the light of this knowledge we shall understand the frequent fact that in the drowsy state of the animal an apparently normal salivary secretion sets in which is absent in the waking state. . . . The explanation consists in this, that in the beginning of the elaboration of the conditioned reflexes . . . many accessory stimuli . . . became conditionally connected with the food center, but later all these accessory stimuli are inhibited. . . . In drowsiness these inhibited agents recover, as we are inclined to think, temporarily their original activity.[10]

In drowsiness the conditioned salivary reflex may disappear and the motor reflex may remain normal. In later stages, the conditioned salivary reflex may return but the motor reflex may be absent, and

[10] *Ibid.*, p. 345.

the dog may even turn away from the food and resist its introduction by force. Seemingly, the organism does not maintain total reactions when it has been frustrated too often and the sleep diminishes the interest in the outside world.

Pavlov very often speaks of weak and strong stimuli. The result alone determines which stimuli are weak and which are strong. We deal with interesting observations, but it is impossible to determine the underlying physiological mechanism and we must be content with the psychological facts.

One may ask whether Pavlov's experiments after the extirpation of the parts of the cortex do not offer sufficient proof that we deal with well-defined physiological mechanisms. Pavlov extirpated the occipital lobe in a dog. Conditioned reflexes to light intensities could be elaborated, but not to lighted objects. It is not possible to differentiate symmetrical points on the skin by the method of conditioned reflex. If the corpus callosum is transected, a conditioned reflex can only be obtained by mechanical irritation of the same side, but not by mechanical irritation of the opposite side.

In the experiments of K. Bykof and A. Speransky (reported by Ischlondsky), when the posterior part of the cortex was extirpated, the animal was able to differentiate a single tone. The dog reacted in the same way when sounds were given in ascending and descending order. I do not doubt this experimental result, but it does not fit into the theories of Pavlov that the operated dog could not differentiate complicated combinations of sounds. Something more than irradiation occurs.

Of course, nobody has the right to doubt that psychological processes are dependent on cortical processes. What I doubt are the formulations concerning excitation, inhibition, and irradiation. The interesting experiments concerning the corpus callosum can be explained in the following way from a psychological point of view. Of course, the knowledge of one's own body has to be built up. In this process of building up, the impressions of both sides of the body have to be continually coördinated. There is no question that the process of coördination will be disturbed by transection of the corpus callosum.

I do not, however, believe that we deal merely with symmetrical connections of excited points.

Good psychology must necessarily lead to the same results as physiology. To pit one against the other is artificial. If there is a contradiction between psychology and physiology, one has to ask where the mistake lies. In psychology and physiology we observe data, and ask for their constant connections and sequence. When we describe psychic experiences we use words, but we use these words in connection with definite data indicated by them. Words are no less objective than drops of saliva. Either we have to give up the conception of the personality as a whole, and of wholes and configurations in general, or we have to give up Pavlov's idea of the mosaic of excitation and inhibition. We cannot keep both at the same time. The data of Pavlov's experimentations are valuable and interesting. His physiology is pseudophysiology, popular mosaic psychology expressed in physiological terms. Modern physiology has shown that in postural reflexes and motor attitudes, the totality of motor attitudinal impulses is of importance (R. Magnus, K. Goldstein, H. Hoff, and P. Schilder). We have no right to assume that the neurophysiology of the cortex is different or simpler. I am for a psychology and neurology of the total personality, and against a psychophysiology which considers the cortical activity as a mosaic of excitation and inhibition.

Out of a feeling of insecurity, psychologists and also psychoanalysts are too happy to find experimental proof in animal experimentation. If they observe correctly, they should not need proof from any other field. They will accept with gratitude every experience in a new field which will enrich the scope of psychophysiology. They should not feel that their observation needs corroboration to be certain. Animal experimentation can, of course, be sure of its results and not need any corroboration from the psychological side. When animal experimentation invades the field of higher nervous activity and behavior of animals, it should not be forgotten that its results cannot be valid when contradicting acknowledged results of psychological research. Psychological insight does not impair the results of objective investigations, but helps to a deeper understanding of them.

As stated before, it is possible to use almost any stimulus as a conditioning stimulus. It is only necessary that conditioned and unconditioned stimuli act simultaneously, or the one shortly after the other. One may draw the conclusion that the important fact is the senseless coincidence, or in the language of association psychology, the objective association by contiguity between the conditioned and unconditioned stimulus. Conditioned and unconditioned stimuli indeed do not form a whole but are primarily a sum. And still, it would be wrong to draw the conclusion that we are reacting in the world to senseless situations which consist of the chance sum of single elements. Such a conclusion would be erroneous. If there is no inner connection between our conditioned and unconditioned stimulus, the unconditioned stimulus in nature would not follow the conditioned one and the conditioned reflex soon would be extinguished. In nature, a conditioned reflex can only occur when conditioned and unconditioned stimuli have an inner connection with each other and form a definite configuration. If in the experiment we create a conditioned reflex, we create a definite configuration which is more than the sum. This configuration is created by welding together the conditioned and unconditioned stimulus. One might even formulate that the conditioned stimulus is not a part of the configuration but only one side of the configuration. If this formulation would be true, we would have before us the experimental creation of configurations. The human intention of the experimenter is seemingly sufficient to weld two unrelated stimuli into a unit.

The study of the conditioned reflex mechanism shows with absolute clearness, therefore, that impressions which have occurred together for a long time or repeatedly form a unit, not only in perception but also in regard to the motor answer. In other words, single experiences do not exist. The single experience is immediately examined by the organism to determine whether it is related to other experiences. A unit is formed and the unit immediately is disintegrated if it does not stand the test of action and experience. A conditioned reflex disappears the moment the conditioned stimulus is persistently not followed by the unconditioned one. Or, in other words, in order to maintain unified experiences we need continuous reassurance by unconditioned stimuli. If this does not take place, the unit is immediately dissolved and the stimuli have only their immediate influence.

Clark L. Hull mentions the following interesting experiments: A conditioned reflex can be produced using pupillary reactions. One says the word "contract" to an individual who is at the same time exposed to an increase in light, until the pupils finally contract when only the word "contract" has been spoken. One can continue the experiment by ordering the subject to say the word "contract," and the pupils will again contract; and finally it will not even be necessary for the subject to say the word, when he merely thinks it the pupils will contract. Hull comes to the conclusion that such an experiment may perhaps give insight into the genesis of actions out of reflexes which are in general out of the realm of conscious influence. It is questionable whether the experiment justifies this assumption. The pupillary reflex is indeed generally outside the voluntary reach of an individual. So is salivation. However, pupillary reflex and salivation are merely a part of attitudes which express themselves in the motility. Every attitude also finds a reflection in the vegetative sphere. That does not say, however, that the attitude originates in the vegetative sphere. Conditioning shows particularly clearly that the attitude is one of the total organism. The word spoken to oneself is an action as well as the word which has been spoken aloud. The experiment also shows clearly that an attitude built up concerning a word which has been heard can be transferred to an attitude based on a word one speaks or imagines oneself. One sees here clearly the interrelation between perception, thought, and action.

CHAPTER XI

STIMULI AND SENSATIONS

EQUIVALENT STIMULI

IN ORDER to quote verbatim from reports on the experiments of H. Kluever, I am forced to use in the following paragraph the word "stimulus." This does not indicate, however, that I approve of the general theory which lies back of the term. Perception is psychologically not a stimulation of the sense organ; the response is not a response to a stimulus but to a change in the situation. We therefore mean by stimulus a supposedly simple change in the situation, which is answered by a change in attitude or action.

We know from the experiments of W. Koehler, K. S. Lashley, D. Katz and Kluever that animals very often do not react to the isolated stimulus (absolute reaction), but to a relation between two stimuli. Kluever, in studying the behavior mechanism in monkeys, used the pulling-in technique in experimental work with Old World and New World monkeys, and especially studied reactions to weight relata, auditory relata, and to sudden changes:

The method of equivalent stimuli was systematically employed. In all instances the point of departure was a differential response to a certain set of stimuli. In "critical" trials the stimuli used during training were varied along various lines to see whether the changes introduced would or would not affect the consistency of the differential response. In such a way groups of "equivalent" and "non-equivalent" stimuli were determined.

The conclusions of Kluever are so important that I repeat them verbatim.

1. A differential response to weight relata is not upset by certain changes in the "absolute" and "relative" weight of the boxes; changes in the material and in the optical appearance of the gliding surface; changes in the pulling-in device; changes in the optical appearance of the boxes;

changes in the distance of the boxes from the cage; change in the number of boxes; changes in the "affective" value of the stimuli.

2. A differential response to auditory relata is not upset by very pronounced changes in the attributes of the sound stimuli employed during training; by certain changes in the optical appearance of the boxes; and by the introduction of the additional sound stimuli.

3. A differential response to visual relata, for instance to stimuli differing in size, is not disturbed by certain changes in "absolute" and "relative" size; in color and brightness of the stimuli and of the ground on which the stimuli are presented; in the form of the figures; in the distance from the cage; in the device for pulling in the boxes. A differential response to visual relata differing with respect to the absence or presence of "intermittence" is not upset by certain changes in brightness, color, size, form or configuration of the stimuli; changes in the duration of the "light" and "dark" periods in the intermittent light; changes in figure-ground relationships.

4. A differential response to sucessively presented relata in the visual field is not upset by certain changes in size; form; "absolute" and "relative" brightness; color; and temporal properties of the stimuli.

Among other findings, Kluever mentions the fact that not every change in the environment changes the behavior of the animal. He refuses to talk simply in terms of generalization and abstractions of elements. He also emphasizes that the independence of the relations from the relata has certain limits, and that also the relata must be given due weight. He prefers various experimentally determined forms of independence and emphasizes that there are involved not only phenomenal properties such as color, size, greater distance, sudden change, but also restlessness and aggressiveness. He points to the general idea that properties which make heterogeneous situations identifiable not only have relation to the problem of neural integration but also to the problem of interest, drives, and needs.

One may ask how this discussion leads to the question of the construction of the object and in what way these data are related to the data of the senses we have discussed above. We previously spoke about intersensory analogies. In regard to Charles Hartshorne, his material and his conclusions are uncertain, although his basic statement that every sense datum appeals to something which is beyond the single sense is doubtless correct. This is due not only to the fact that the brightness quality is common to all senses, but also to the fact that all senses finally lead to objects which appeal to all senses. A sound, for instance, comes from an object which is potentially reached by all other senses. Especially in primitive perception this is much more than a mere possibility, since immediately there is a tonic and phasic response to the sense datum which enriches the sense datum connecting it with the other senses.

One may even go a step further and say that the sense datum does not exist without its motor response and the motor response is common to all senses. This motor response immediately decides whether we deal with constant connections which lead to the unconditioned reflex and the unconditioned sense datum, or whether there will be a disappointment by the absence of the unconditioned response. The intersensory connection is, therefore, to a great extent dependent on actual motility, or still better, on action, and only this perpetual trial and error process determines the final unit of action, with the satisfaction to which it may lead. This final unit of action is the object.

The term "satisfaction by the object" needs a clearer definition. We are accustomed to measure satisfaction by the intestinal reaction, which is either ejection or injection. We think especially about food and sexual cravings which lead to more or less obvious vegetative phenomena. It should be emphasized that these intestinal phenomena are related to all sensory impressions. In particular smell and taste are closely related to phenomena in the vegetative sphere. It is probably wrong to suppose that satisfaction is merely connected with the last step of ingestion of the object into the mouth. It is probable that ejection processes always counteract introjection processes, and that the creation of the object is not merely the creative satisfaction of devouring, but that independent pleasure is had by constructing the object outside of the limits of one's own body. A large part of *The Image and Appearance of the Human Body* is devoted to the attempt to show that we need objects outside of ourselves, such as the bodies of others and every other object outside of ourselves. In order to be satisfied we need objects which we can touch, which are independent from ourselves and which continually offer us resistance. It would be wrong to suppose that the creation of the object is undertaken merely to ingest it into ourselves. We need the outward world which we are continually perceiving. It is in our organization to have before us a perpetual outside world. Only touch and pain are immediately brought into contact with our bodies, whereas all the other senses point irrevocably to an outer world which we do not care to have in a chaotic state. The chaotic state of the outer world means not so much the absence of organization but an organization which offers insurmountable difficulties for organized action, such as continuous movement, the vortex, the wave, and the intimate relation of the one part of the field to the other part of the field. This primitive perception provokes primitive motor answers, which finally lead to crystallization of configurations of a more definite character. Whereas the primitive perception is in large part streamlike, continually moving and "intransitive," coexistent attempts at construction lead to clear-cut configurations of the primitive type. There are always attempts to bring this moving world to a standstill and to make of it a world which can be grasped in a simpler way. I have, therefore, emphasized that gestalten of a rather rigid character are coexistent with and follow the stage of the vortex. It is the first crystallization and this first one is comparatively rigid. The motility and especially the vestibular apparatus are of outstanding importance in the genesis of this first configuration. With the configuration, the seemingly objectless stream and movement become crystallized, but such a configuration is only one point in development and cannot last. In the play of children and in their spontaneous sidewalk drawings (L. Bender) one very often sees that the seemingly objectless movement is the starting point of the configuration. The scribblings of children are sooner or later related to objects of the outer world, become adapted to them, and so more and more mark the beginning of pictorial drawing. When one studies drawings of a human figure (Florence L. Goodenough) one sees how the primitive configuration crystallizations are at first used as approximations to the human figure and finally are integrated into the complete figure. A continuous process of construction is going on, in which the primitive gestalt is a transition point. In general, primitive objects have the following characteristics:

1. The primitive object is more or less embedded in the field. It is less distinct from it.

2. When the object is first perceived, it is taken out of the field prematurely, without considering all the possibilities of actions in the outside world.

3. The object created prematurely has enormous persistence which hinders further development.

4. By the process of satisfaction and dissatisfaction the premature formulation can be dissolved.

5. All these processes take place under the continual guidance of motility and the trial and error method.

6. Motion in the primitive perceptual world is a factor which corresponds closely to the motility which is an inherent factor in primitive perception.

7. The terms instinct, emotion, feelings are meaningless outside the primitive sensory motor unit which one may call instinctive and emotional.

8. Feelings should not, therefore, be considered as independent entities. An instinct should not be separated from motility (compare Heinz Werner).

FEELING

The problem of whether psychic elements exist is indeed a fundamental problem of psychology. It is at least as wrong to say there are only sensations and their qualities as to say that feelings are independent entities. Emotions of joy, of fear, and of grief exist; and although they contain definite sensory elements, they are clearly separated from the experiences of a bright color or a house, or a chair in a room. The indefiniteness of the primitive world as we have described it is certainly qualitatively different in the emotions from the fully developed world. Motor reactions are of a still different kind. There is more threat, more danger in a world of indefinite objects.

Such concepts as brightness or dullness are thoroughly insufficient to describe or to explain the emotional qualities of these experiences. It is true that feelings are localized in the body. Anxiety has relation to the heart. Restlessness or peace may be localized in the genitals. One may feel happy around the heart or in the stomach. The observations of C. Stumpf on "Gefühls-empfindungen" are certainly correct. Nevertheless, all these observations do not change the fact that emotions are experiences which are different from mere perceptions. It is true that there is an emotional element in every perception and a sensory element in every emotion. However, the total configuration is different and the accent of emotion lies on another side of the experiences. It also is not justified to reject perfunctorily the idea of Otto Kuelpe and his school of imageless thought. I do not doubt that thoughts are always connected with some more or less incomplete processes of imaginations and pictures. Still, the final outcome is not the same in the thinking process and in a process of imagination. It is very simple to say that there are elements in sensation. Such a statement neglects a fundamental of my own standpoint, namely, the inner motility of the sensation and the motility of the total organism. There can be no doubt that the total reaction of the organism changes when we progress from the primitive perception to the developed object. What from a descriptive point of view appears as a difference in elements is indeed a difference in total reactions.

E. G. Boring has said:

The convincing identification of feeling with sensation came about, not from the arguments of Bourdon, von Frey and Stumpf, but from the introspective experiments of J. P. Nafe. These results, regarded at first with some skepticism, have been confirmed in other researches. With sensation equated to consciousness the concept of sensation lost much of its significance. For the differentiation of conscious terms it was natural for psychologists to look to the attributes of sensations, as the different sensory characteristics were called. Sensations have always been distinguished by their qualities. Every sensation can be said to have an attribute of quality, which designated it as red or yellow or bitter or cold or C sharp. Fechner first accomplished the measurement of sensations by measuring their intensity. It was natural, therefore, for Wundt to assign the two attributes of quality and intensity to sensation. Wundt deals with space and time in the mental world as providing forms of sensory organization, but Kuelpe saw that extension and duration must be added to the list of attributes if spatial and temporal forms are found in consciousness. One can observe a visual extent as readily as a visual quality. Titchener, facing the problem of the description of attention, which hitherto had appeared in systematic psychology in sinister dynamic guise, now concluded that sensations have an attribute of clearness, that a sensation in passing from the margin to the focus of attention is really changing its degree of clearness. Everyone admitted the first four attributes and Titchener held to five. Later (1924) he named them quality, intensity, extensity, protensity and attensity. By these correlative technical terms he gave the attributes professional status in psychology, except for the fact that they were, in his opinion, no longer attributes.

Psychologists arrived at their conception of sensation by a very complicated process of isolation. Perceptions are experiences, like that of seeing a forest, without a particular inner participation in which the structure of the world is our chief interest. In emotions we are aware of a great participation of the self and the body, when directed towards a situation which we perceive. The two cases are different from the point of view of the motor and the vegetative participation (which is a part of the experienced situation). We mean sensation when we consider a perceptual experience more in relation to what is happening in our body than to events in the outside situation, and when we emphasize the relation between the perception in the outward world and the experience in our body. We may, of course, fill volumes by defining the multiplicity of ways in which philosophers have used these terms. The definitions given here are more useful, in my opinion, and underlie most of the psychological and philosophical discussions.

This definition immediately ends the artificial separation of sensation, perception, and emotion. We always deal with actual situations in which the organism lives. Every situation comprises perception, sensation, feeling, emotion, and motility. It is our task to give a correct description of the attitudes, actions, and reactions of the organism in a given situation. It is not to be wondered at that, if one starts psychological analysis with an artificial unit (as sensation), this unit can be found even when primitive perception occurs and when primitive attitudes and a world with more motion and less stability are in the foreground. Objects are less rigid, and motor and vegetative functions are less isolated and less specific. There is no denying that we deal with a difference in the total aspect of behavior, which we usually call a difference in feelings. The building up of an object is, as the previous discussion was intended to show, far from building up sums of sensations different in intensity, quality, brightness, and the like. One errs in starting the analysis of sensations with a discussion of the different attributes of sensation instead of starting with the search for the primitive object, and from there building up the complicated object. There are no simple elements out of which the object is created. There are no elements of sensation, feeling, imagination, and thinking. There are processes going on which bring the various aspects of the total situation into the foreground and these processes are always based on motility in its various forms.

CHAPTER XII

SPACE

SPACE AND PERCEPTION

PSYCHOLOGISTS and philosophers have often postulated perception and sensation without spatial characteristics. They then had to develop complicated theories to give spatial characteristics to perceptions and sensations. An abstract space has often been put in the center of the discussion. I offer the thesis that perceptions and sensations are in space and that spatial characteristics are necessarily inherent in every perception and sensation, even in the most primitive. The world of colors and seen movements is before us. Even with closed eyes, black is perceived in a spatial relation. It is true this space is necessarily a primitive one, since no particular actions are possible in it. Whatever we may see is seen in space. This at the same time means that there are distinct relations between experiences and our actions. This optic space is never fully independent, since an isolated perception or imagination does not exist. It is always related to the self and the body. I have previously discussed the fact that the body image is an image in space. There are no human experiences without the experience of one's own body, and perceptions are outside of one's own body. One's own body always has an extension in space. Psychology has never previously taken cognizance of this fact. E. G. Boring writes: "In the present century the most important development in the psychology of space has been the development and acceptance of the concept of extensity as an immediate phenomenal datum."

He did not make the fundamental distinction between the space of the body and the space outside. I have already considered the space of the body in *The Image and Appearance of the Human Body*. Certain sensations, as that of pain, occur only within the body space. But even in these sensations there are elements which extend beyond

the borderline of the body into the outside world. Tactual experiences
arise within the body as such, but also extend beyond it. H. Hartmann
and I have shown that when we touch an object we perceive a space
between the object and our body. Every tactile perception has distinct spatial qualities relating to the body and to the outside world.
There is only one rather interesting exception to this rule. When we
touch an object and gradually diminish the pressure exerted on it,
the object and the space between the object and skin disappear but
the sensation on the skin remains. There is, at the same time, a distinct sensation that the skin is bulging as if reaching for an object.
According to a personal communication from E. Lindemann, this
phenomenon is increased in hashish intoxication and in mescal intoxication.

It is erroneous, therefore, for K. Goldstein and A. Gelb to assert
that there are no primary spatial qualities or primary space perceptions in the tactile sphere. According to W. Bromberg and myself
there is a distinct spatial quality in olfactory and gustatory experiences. Even when the smell (which is experienced as a substance) is
spread in the air and in the nose, it is distinctly outside of the body
and separated from the "sensation" in the mucous membrane. The
tasted object remains distinctly separated from the tongue. There is
no need to stress the spatial qualities of hearing, which we have discussed in a previous chapter. We have emphasized sufficiently that
primitive perception shows motion in the majority of the sense-
modalities and this inner motion is another spatial quality. We have
stressed the point that this inner motion is eliminated during the
process of building up an object. When a moving object is grasped
it becomes firm and acquires definite spatial qualities and characteristics. Kinesthetic sensations are important for the final elaboration
of space. However, one should not overrate the importance of kinesthetic sensations, because optic and tactile perceptions provoke motor
reaction. Groping and grasping bring new qualities into experience,
which is finally formed with the help of kinesthetic sensations. Primitive space perceptions of the various senses also originate in connec-

tion with the various openings of the body and of the face. In this respect the eye is considered an opening.

These diverse spaces of the various senses have comparatively little inner contact. Only by the action of the vestibular apparatus and by active motility is the final confluence of a unified space created. It is probable that a vague concept of a general space is present in the primitive spaces of the senses. Acoustic and optic spaces are indeed difficult to separate, and the olfactory space is also closely related to them. The space of taste and the space of touch have more separate qualities.

Optic experiences of course play an important part in the elaboration of the tactile sphere. If our general idea is correct, the primitive sensation is more synesthetic than the developed one. But when the object is finally created, it again is an object for all the senses and we deal with synesthesia of a higher order. In the development of space, the tendency towards unification becomes stronger. Tonic and phasic motility play the leading part in the final elaboration of space. They guarantee the final combination of the spaces of different units.

It is clear, on the basis of these experiences, that we cannot follow the Kantian conception that space is something which is added to the experience of the senses. Space is a creation and a development. Unified space is a late product of development and is in no way given before experience. It also is in no way the form with which experience is melted.

In the differentiated organism, action is primarily bound to the immediate nearness, the space of the mouth, the space of the fist and fingers and later on as far as the arm reaches. The motor function is basic for every space perception. When the space extends itself into the distance, the active movement of the total body plays the important role although occasionally the passive transport of the body and the sensations provoked by it may coöperate. Certainly all senses participate in these primitive experiences of space. To perceive means, in a sense, to have a body from which the objects are separated in space.[1]

---

[1] P. Schilder, *Gedanken zur Naturphilosophie*, p. 44. See also C. Buehler, *Die geistige Entwicklung des Kindes*.

Only on the basis of this physiological consideration are we able to understand the facts of pathology which show how much our perception of space is dependent on our emotional life. Tone, motility, and instincts are repeatedly seen to be closely related to the emotional life. Our further task is to show the influence of tone and motility upon spatial relations and to follow this by a discussion of the emotional life upon spatial relations. It is pointless to consider any psychic phenomenon as an isolated experience of the senses. The problems of the total personality necessarily must express themselves in the sensory experiences.

The experiment of persistence of tone may be performed by ordering a subject to stretch his hands forward so that one arm is parallel to the other, and then to raise one arm at an angle of about 45 degrees above the horizontal. After 25 seconds the subject is ordered to close his eyes and lower the upper or mobile arm into the same position as the resting or horizontal arm. The mobile arm always remains several centimeters higher than the resting arm. Conversely, the order may be to lower the mobile arm and to bring it back to horizontal; in this case, the mobile arm always remains several centimeters lower than the resting arm. The subject does not know that he has made a mistake; he thinks that both arms are at the same level (*The Image and Appearance of the Human Body,* page 75); in spite of the fact that the one arm is higher, the individual's space perception is altered. When an individual in whom persistent tone is present takes a rod with both hands, the rod appears horizontal even when it is actually inclined. "Whatever changes take place in the perception of the position of one's own body will also influence the perception of the outward world" (Hoff and Schilder).

Tonic influences from the cerebellum and from the centers for postural and righting reflexes in the medulla oblongata, brain stem, and parietal occipital lobes are of the utmost importance for the perception of the position of one's own body and, therefore, they must also influence the perception of space. Even the perception of a straight line is dependent upon the vestibular apparatus. Every vestibular irritation changes our perception of space. In the old experiment of J. Breuer and E. Mach, otolith irritation changes vertical orientation. This change is absent when the otolith apparatus is destroyed.

In pathological cases in which the tone of one side is changed, one not only finds unconscious movements and changes in the position of the body but also a change in the perception of space. There is a difference in the perception of the main directions in space. In a case of A. Gelb's, the patient leaned towards the left side, especially when he had his eyes closed. A line inclined from 8 to 12 degrees to the left at its upper end was experienced as vertical; the objective vertical appeared to be inclined to the right side. The experienced horizontal direction was perpendicular to the subjective vertical of the patient, and in comparison with the objective horizontal direction was too low on the left side. The patient saw his whole surroundings inclined towards the right side. There are several other cases of this type in the literature, which were collected by Erich Feuchtwanger, who also reported five new cases. In his first case, in which there was a lesion of the right frontal lobe with traumatic epilepsy, the patient had attacks in which he felt his body slowly inclining itself toward the right side. The ground, houses, and people appeared inclined to the left side. He then felt himself standing upright. In three of Erich Feuchtwanger's other cases, the patients deviated, either in grasping or in walking, too much to one side. In most of his cases the peripheral part of the vestibular apparatus was unimpaired. Feuchtwanger also points out that difficulties in space orientation occur on the basis of tonic changes. Patients either do not find their way in a room which they perceive correctly from an optic point of view (compare P. Marie and R. Béhague) or they use the wrong route.

The great significance of the tonic body space is demonstrated by these disturbances. This outward space is experienced as differentiated from the body Ego, and the body Ego moves in it. . . . The connotations of "the direct way," "to be directed to" and of the detour prove the great significance of the body tone and its spatial factors for the psychic structure of the coördinated outward space and the position of the objects in it.

Feuchtwanger believed that disturbances in tonic stabilization in space are possible without disturbances of the vestibular apparatus. He acknowledged that the peripheral vestibular apparatus may take part in disturbances of this kind, but emphasized the importance of the cerebellar and frontal systems, and concluded that the cerebellar-frontal-lobe system with its connections (temporal lobe and pons) should be considered in connection with the maintenance of the tonic part in the body space system. His final formulations are similar to those of Gelb. The discussion of the vestibular apparatus has indicated that disturbance of this kind may be connected with one half of the body and may occur on monocular fixation.

Many of Feuchtwanger's patients experienced their difficulties in short attacks, and careful examination was therefore not possible. K. Goldstein and A. Gelb remark that the amount of transposition and distortion to which an object in space is subjected depends to a great extent on the quality and structure of the object. Gelb writes that optic contents which are easily distorted and transposed are those which impress us as changeable by their very nature; they are not firmly connected with their surroundings. It is of importance that one should not consider phenomena of this type as rare exceptions, as curios. These factors are fundamental for the way in which we experience space. In the chapters on optic perceptions I described phenomena belonging to this group. E. R. Jaensch has made many similar observations. The continually varying tone of the body has a definite and lasting influence on the perception of the basic directions in space, on the localization of objects in space, and the spatial relation of the parts of the object itself. Space is built up on the basis of tonic attitudes and one can see that, through final action, the individual gets more and more new impressions, and that on the basis of these the final elaboration of space takes place. The eye muscles certainly play an important part in the elaboration of space. In many respects they are the most restless part of the body and are continually in action. J. Wilder is correct when he stresses the importance of oculomotor disturbances in some of the cases of pathological changes in the perception of space and its directions.

Erwin Straus reproaches the psychologists because they have emphasized only the gnostic element of experiences, that is, they stress
the perceptual quality but not the pathic element—the way in which
we are affected by colors and sounds. He quotes Heinz Werner who
believes there are four steps of sound experience: the level of the
clear-cut objective tone; the level of the tone in space; the tone in
the body, which itself becomes in some way the sounding vessel; and
experiences which merely take place in the body. Straus states that the
pathic element is not, as Werner believes, present only in specific experiences, but is an important part in every experience, and in every
perception and sensation. He thinks that there is a specific motility
connected with the movement of the trunk in which the pathic element of experience expresses itself in a more open way. He thinks
that while dancing, the individual lives in a different space in which
the relation to action is different. He calls such a movement "pre-
sentische Bewegung" ("presentic movement"—a movement which is
satisfied with its own existence).

When walking we move through the space from one place to another and
when dancing we move in space. . . . The movements of the dance fill
the space completely from all sides. The dance is correlated to the symbolic qualities of space. The subject-object tension is abolished when we
are dancing. Dancing does not change the outward situation. The action
is an historic process. Presentic movement which is not directed consists
only of swelling and its decrease, of an increase and its ebbing. It does
not produce any change; it is not an historic process. Therefore we rightly
call it presentic in spite of its duration in objective time. The disappearance of subject-object tension which reaches its completion in ecstasies is
not the aim of the dance but is at the basis of the dance from the very
beginning.[2]

Can there be any movement without an aim in the outward world?
Children usually do not dance. For primitive people dances are certainly more than mere enjoyment and have a very definite purpose
in regard to cult and magic. Animals do not dance, and what looks
like dancing in animals is more or less a part of mating behavior and
has very definite aims. Experiences are always pathic, since they are

---

[2] Erwin Straus, *Die Formen des Räumlichen.*

impossible without the image of the body and we experience as human beings with a body. It is true that the accent of the various experiences can be on the body image or on the *outer* world, and in bodily directed experience the qualities of the space of the body may become most important. The body is always in an outside space. In many respects the body itself always remains outside of the ego-environment boundary. Therefore, I do not think that Straus's attitude is justified, for it neglects the constructive side of the experience of our body. I have previously stated (*The Image and Appearance of the Human Body*) that in the dance and by vestibular irritation we try to get rid of the configuration of the body which we have created. This is only one step in a new construction of the body image. It is a very pertinent observation by Straus that the center of the ego seems to wander from the head toward the trunk during dancing. This is indeed a sign that the ontogenetically late differentiation of the body image given by the head and the distance receptors of the head is temporarily given up. There are no experiences that can be separated from very definite aims, actions, and emotional problems and that are not based upon our total personality. The connotation of a "presentic movement" is, therefore, erroneous.

C. Hartshorne says:

In these and innumerable other ways one may verify the statement that space is simply the form of social externality (otherness) as such. The spatial depth of perception is its social independence. . . . A perceived color is a feeling felt objectively, as socially other than one's own feelings.[3]

This statement neglects the question of the more primitive spatial qualities we have previously discussed. However, it does illuminate an important aspect.

We have discussed the question of the creation of the object so far. An object is not only something for me, but is also an object for others. Indeed, the object is a social creation. I have pointed to this view in my discussion of the creation of the body image. Experiences are socialized since they are based upon actions. This world is a world in which we act, and we act in space. An action which is merely in

[3] *The Philosophy and Psychology of Sensation*, p. 199.

connection with oneself is senseless and does not exist. C. Hartshorne is correct in his basic statement that sensations are socialized. This is also true of the "pathic sensations." All experiences take place in space. I do not think that space is merely the social aspect of experiences. There is a deep inner unity of a social kind in every phase of experience and the spatial quality of experience is merely one side of the total experience. Activity is basic in all parts of perception and is also basic for space perception. Activity is also directed toward the outside world, toward objects and toward other human beings. Activity is therefore the primary factor in the creation of the object but is in its essence a social factor. Activity is of course not only a motor factor but includes the factor of drives and instincts.

Not only tonic influences change the perception of space but perceptual changes also have such an influence. I have quoted the case of K. Goldstein and A. Gelb in which optic agnosia provoked a severe disturbance in space perception. In occipital lobe lesions, disturbances in orientation are not uncommon. A specific form of geometric optic disturbances has been studied especially by M. Reichardt, J. Rieger and Otto Poetzl. Otto Isakower and I have made similar observations. Less is known about spatial disturbances provoked by agnosias of other senses. In many cases a clear-cut optic orientation seems to substitute for other spatial data.

PSYCHOANALYSIS OF SPACE [4]

Philosophers and psychologists have not given sufficient attention to the fact that there is not only a space outside of the body but also a space which is filled by the body. The image of the body extends in space and implies space perception. Without an outward space, body space is strictly senseless. When we speak of narcissism we should not forget that an outward space and the space of the body are the necessary basis for the unfolding of narcissistic tendencies.

This primitive space is probably less unified than the developed space. The primitive space is centered around the openings of the body and so has several centers. Narcissistic space can be character-

[4] P. Schilder, *International Journal of Psychoanalysis*, XVI (June, 1935).

ized by space experiences in mescal intoxication. I reproduce here a
protocol of K. Beringer and W. Mayer-Gross:

The space of one's own is difficult to describe. It is not clear to me any
more, and I don't think it was during the experiment. Therefore, I can't
describe the perception of space proper but only the details. It was a space
of other, that is, bigger, dimensions. The color phenomena took place in
this space. When motion took place and something shot out of the depth,
it came out of this universe. In spite of that, it did not seem difficult to
reach it with my hand. When I tried it then, I realized that the hand lived
in the normal space.

The space was fundamentally not different from the normal space; it
had all dimensions. The starting-point, the relation to myself, was absent.
I could not have said which was below or above, right or left of me. The
law of gravity did not exist. There were no definite distances. When I
tried to localize a pinprick or a noise, I moved my hand in the air, wanted
to go through my head but realized this was not possible. Then I tried
to find the point behind my hand and became aware that my hand existed
in another space than myself. "I" was in another space like a point in a
universe for which the connotation below and above, right and left, horizontal and vertical, do not exist, because they all mean the same. I felt like
such a point surrounded by an infinite space in which diverse distances
must be present but with no starting-point from which to measure the
distances. . . .

When I was lying with open eyes trying to orient myself in the room,
the different objects mixed with each other. Everything was equally near
or distant. . . . I had to "spell" the optic picture of the room in order to
perceive the differences in the distances of objects. For instance, Dr. X. is
sitting here. There is a table between; behind it (because of being half
covered by it) is Dr. Y. Therefore, Dr. Y. is farther away (the distance
of the table) than Dr. X. I saw, therefore, the room without depth but
with correct perspective, so that I could draw my conclusions, as if the
room were projected upon a screen.

W. Mayer-Gross concludes that the experience of space is fundamentally changed in mescal intoxication, and also calls attention to
similar experiences of schizophrenic patients. It seems that spatial
experiences of this kind are only possible when there is no definite
possibility of or tendency to action, and therefore motives for definite
localization and perception of distances are absent. We are accustomed to say that space and time form a union, but from a psycho-

logical point of view this is not absolutely true. In marihuana intoxication, optic phenomena and disturbances in space perception are occasionally observed. W. Bromberg's case reported that houses and objects were crooked. Generally, time disturbances are in the foreground and are seemingly the basis for many space perception disturbances. I reproduce the protocol of one of my students who had taken marihuana for experimental purposes.

The observations I have made on this subject were derived from two experiences with the drug. On each occasion I smoked half a marihuana cigarette, the first time in company of two male friends and the second time in company of two females. Besides producing a remarkable state of abstraction, an exaggeration of the ego, euphoria, vivid and colorful visions, an accentuation of sexual impulses and a feeling of unreality about one's own voice and the voices of others, marihuana produces bewildering effects on the perception of space and time.

During intoxication with cannabis, time seems to pass more slowly than it has ever passed before. You glance at your watch and the second hand creeps at an inexorable snail's pace. It is as if some force were arresting time in its path. You try the following experiment: You note the time and tell your companion (also intoxicated) that later you will ask him to tell you how much time has elapsed. A long time goes by. You ask your friend how much time has passed and he remarks, at least half an hour. The watch, however, reveals that only five minutes have passed.

Space, like time, undergoes a remarkable exaggeration under the influence of cannabis. The effect can best be explained by relating an incident that occurred during the first intoxication. My friends and I after having taken the drug (it was about 10 P. M.) took a walk to a golf course about twenty minutes distant from my house. By the time we got there the effects were well marked. We set out to walk from one hill to another some 120 yards away. Finally, after what seemed like a very long time, we arrived in the middle of this little valley. Now I experienced a bewildering sensation. No matter how many steps I took, the hill in front of me came no closer. The hill behind did not recede in the distance. It was as if one were doomed to walk forever in this valley, never approaching one's destination, never getting farther away from the place one had left behind.

The passing of time is eternally slow, and distance is enormously enhanced, yet one does not complain. For under the influence of cannabis one walks with ease and grace and without perceptible effort or fatigue.

Whether the effect on the perception of space is due to a distortion in time perception or vice versa it is impossible to say. It is certainly true that time passes slowly under marihuana, whether one is in motion or not. Actually, I believe that the perception of each in turn affects the other. We conducted a little experiment that is interesting in this connection. We marked off two lines at a distance of some ten yards apart. Each of us attempted to start at one line and with eyes closed walk to the second and stop as close to it as possible. Invariably we fell short by half a yard to a yard. How this is to be explained I am not sure. Either it is due to the effect of prolonging distance or of enhancing time. One has the feeling that one has walked farther than one actually has, and therefore stops short of the mark. Marihuana, rather than helping to solve the problem of space and time, renders it more mysterious than ever.

Additional questioning brought the following answers:

I had not the feeling that my speech was slow, but that I was walking very slowly. The distance of objects appeared great only when I was walking. During the second experiment I felt the sofa very hard, the back of the sofa, especially, felt like concrete. The concrete of the sofa, however, was distinctly separate from my back.

The fact that the dimensions of space seemed to be enlarged when the patient was walking make it at least probable that the change in time perception is primary to the change in this particular disturbance of space. This case is also a clear instance of the close relation of the time factor to the motility. It is interesting that closing the eyes changes the relation of the action to space. The subject emphasizes the time which has passed and, therefore, overrates the actual movement in space.

Time, space, and movement are, therefore, closely interwoven and when we speak of a primary disturbance in time perception we should not take the relation of primary and secondary too mechanically. Our subject also experienced "primary" changes in space perception. He reports the vision of an auditorium: "Light came through the glass ceiling and in spite of knowing that I was in a small room I had the feeling that I was in a tremendous space. . . . I saw a large face—it was very near; it was grinning and had bad teeth."

Space disturbances in schizophrenics are of a very similar type. In schizophrenic hallucinations of hearing, distance is very often taken in a symbolic way. The individual lives not in this real world but in a world of unity and identification. The same is true of schizophrenic hallucinations of touch, which have been studied by me with W. Bromberg. The schizophrenic lives in a world full of meaning; the world becomes the expression of his own libidinous situation. Symptoms akin to depersonalization, simply going one step further, are common. Subjects then lose their value and seem to be farther away. On the other hand, the borderline between the space of one's own body and the space of the outer world is continually changing. As in obsessional neurosis cases, actions in the outer world immediately influence the body.

In *The Image and Appearance of the Human Body*, I stated: "Magic action is an action which influences the body image irrespective of the actual distance of space."

Franz Fischer has pointed out the changes in the structure of space in schizophrenics. Normal space recedes in the distance and another space of indefinite qualities appears. These two impressions mix with each other. One of his patients says: "When it comes into my mind that I should be like a room myself, everything else is connected with it. It is difficult to describe; it is quite empty; it is terrible; maybe it would be better to die. The emptiness works on me; there must be something right in it. It has a false power over me."

When one reads the protocols of Franz Fischer's cases it is difficult to decide what the actual experiences of these patients were. It seems as if their expressions merely symbolized by spatial expressions the inner uncertainty concerning their actions. With his emotional inability to reach definite action in the world, the schizophrenic must also have difficulty in orienting himself in space. This orientation is a disorientation in the symbolic qualities of space, whereas the sensory experience of space is not fundamentally changed.

It is therefore correct when Eugene Minkowsky states that the immediate experience of experiencing oneself now and here is impaired. "Le schizophrène par contre, sait où il est, mais le moi-ici n'a plus sa tonalité habituelle." [5] In psychoanalytic terminology we should

[5] *La Schizophrenie* (Paris, 1927).

have to say that the space of the ego is preserved but that the space of the id has undergone changes. Or, in other words, we live in a double orientation in space. There is the space as a phylogenetic inheritance which is comparatively stabilized and which is the basis of our actions and orientations. It is the space of the perception-ego.[6] We live our personal lives in relation to love objects, to our personal conflicts, and this is the space which is less systematized, in which the relations change, in which the emotions pull objects nearer and push them farther away. When the emotional life regresses very far, the perception-ego space loses more and more of its importance. In this retrogressive space, identifications and projections continually change the space and its value. This is the id space which finds expression in schizophrenic experiences. It is the space of magic.

Schizophrenia is not merely a regression to the narcissistic level. On the way back from objects to narcissism the individual revives primitive levels of psychosexual development. He reaches for them, at first, when striving back to the fully developed objects. The following observation is interesting in this respect.

The thirty-two-year-old Ignatz complains:

There are three persons above and three below. Their below is above me. Some are men and some are women. I won't tell that either—they tell me what to do. They gave me the pain. (How?) The three above by their motion. I was on the left. I would put down the train on schedule if he was on the right. Naturally the stick would hit me on the back of my head, across here and across there. [The patient draws a diagram showing that the pain crosses posterior part of the head from the right to the left side.]

(What is the difference between a midget and a child?) The midget has higher heels, longer dresses and shoes. As far as skin is concerned, the flesh is much older, does not expand so much. A midget is sort of a lady.

[He feels the effects of Dillinger being shot, in his own abdomen, and he feels the pain of being embalmed right above the belly button.] . . . They speak from below and sometimes from above—from any direction. You can even feel a shot from below. The heat in the body generates and degenerates. Yes, they influence sex parts. The sex parts are cool—you

---

[6] Perception-ego (*Perzeptionsego*) is equivalent to the psychoanalytic "Ego." Where otherwise used, the author uses ego in the philosophical sense, similar to that of K. Koffka and W. Koehler.

might be in an ice box. (What do they do with your sex parts?) I don't know whether they do or not. They try to hit me—sometimes in sex parts. I felt severe pain in my left leg before the Roosevelt election. It generates from mind, speech, three above and below. Sometimes I feel it in my leg, my head, my anus, my phallus. I feel the effects of it. . . .

Probably I might have his left. Probably they do it when I am asleep. They might have sexual intercourse with me while I am asleep. (Are you a man or a woman?) Well, she was a man and he was a woman. She wasn't a bad-looking woman. I don't know who she was. (Are you a good-looking woman?) I never looked at myself from below—I don't know.

With this patient, "below" is a continuation of the openings of the body. Right and left have sexual significance. Space is sexualized. His interest in direction is sex interest. There is a magic contraction of space and there are identifications. If the regression does not go so far as this, the space disturbance centers around the organs of special erogenous value.

The twenty-eight-year-old Simon M. reports:

I am in a daze all the time. Worry, that's the most important thing. Sex is lately predominating me more than it ought. Walking down the street, I feel a desire for every woman that passes by. If I desire more than one woman at a time, it means that I don't desire any woman at all. When a man speaks, I feel at times as if the organ of the man was in my mouth. I don't feel it but I have the sensation of it. I put a pipe, cigarette, or straw in my mouth to try to prevent it, but it does not help. . . . I have a sub-conscious feeling when I see a woman that I am entering that woman. It is a mental state only. When a man talks and his organ flies into my mouth it makes me feel I am a woman. Why should this happen to me? I am not a homosexual. . . . I thought of suicide a thousand times. Once I had hallucinations; when two people talked, my head went in their direction as if the sound of voices drew me towards them. When I urinate I feel I am urinating into somebody else's mouth. People would talk about me. Once they said, "Your balls are on the table." When I sat down next to a girl in the subway her sex organs flew up to my mouth. (Did you enjoy it?) Not a good food substance. [The patient has the feeling that he has poison in his stomach, although he sometimes says that he thinks he is sick of a gland or a boil.]

The distortion in space in this case centers around the sex organs, and the case is simply an illustration of the principle previously dis-

cussed, that the dimensions of space are changed around the erogenous zones. The case is remarkable also in that the genitals of other
persons are drawn towards his mouth.

This case is one of schizophrenia, but obsessional trends are
in the foreground. At any rate, we can see that space of the body and
the space outside of the body have different relations to each other in
such cases.

In obsessional neurosis cases, the same problem comes into the
foreground. In one case where the obsessional neurosis followed pro-
static pain, the bladder and phallus of the patient were felt to be on
the street and crushed by passing cars. A dog took the penis away.
In another case, the patient felt that her head was flying away so
that she was in danger of stepping on it. Her body was dispersed in
space, her arms were flying around and she had to go into a hallway
in order to collect her limbs again. "I am completely in pieces—there
is no ground under the feet when you are not on earth." We do not
know why, in this case, the aggressiveness of the patient destroyed
the body space in such a far-reaching way. The tendency to self-
punishment was strong. Throughout her whole life she was fighting
against the desires of her body.[7] In the case first mentioned, projection was helped by the pain experienced in the genital region.

Another aspect is seen in the case of a thirty-two-year-old woman
with severe obsessions and aggressive impulses to kick and hit other
people. She felt that she kicked cars which passed her, so that her
foot caused automobile accidents. She had a particular fear of drugs.
She was afraid of spreading drugs and thus being responsible for the
death of many people. When she passed a drugstore she had the feeling that she had gone into the store to mix drugs there, and so may
have killed people without knowing it. The aggressiveness here transgresses the borderline of space.

If I let myself go I would swing my arms and legs, would run around and
talk continuously. I would be terrifically active. When I pass in a bus
and look into a gas hole I feel as if I would put my arms out, reach into

---

[7] This case is described in detail in *The Image and Appearance of the Human
Body.*

the hole and do something which would harm others. Look at the gas hole—I have the feeling that I have touched it. I sometimes think that I have gone into the bathroom and mixed poisons. When I feel bad I feel that I have lived a million years.

This is a patient who from her earliest childhood has had an enormous urge to action in the outward world. This enormous urge made her a very affectionate child, always craving for caresses, which urge was never completely satisfied. She felt particularly hemmed in by her mother, against whom she felt manifest hatred. In her early childhood, an episode with her brother played an important part. The brother had blood poisoning when she was about three years old. She reconstructed a memory that she had scratched and hurt her brother, of whom she was extremely jealous. She has queer experiences of an inner pain, reminders of anxiety which she felt for the first time at the age of five or six, when she had a longing for the world and wanted to take it in completely because it was so beautiful.

The patient does not differentiate between seeing and touching. What she sees immediately becomes an object of activities of an aggressive type. She continually feels that she has kicked somebody, thus causing death in a direct or indirect way. She is never sure how many people she may have killed in this way. She may have caused the spreading of some kind of poison, and even a little quantity of this poison may have been the cause of somebody's death. The connotation of quantity does not exist for her in this respect. Even the most minute particle of a chemical substance may cause the death of somebody. It is another peculiarity of the thought processes of this patient that the vaguest possibility becomes reality for her. She may have pushed somebody on the street, may have disturbed the driver of an ambulance, the driver may have touched an electric wire or a gas pipe, thus leading to a disturbance causing the death of a score of people.

Her aggressiveness makes the space between her and objects shrink. All objects come within the immediate reach of her activity. The uncoördinated love drive has become an uncoördinated aggressiveness in the whole field of perception. The aggressiveness, however, does not transgress the immediate spatial perception, and the optic horizon is the boundary of her aggressiveness.

In obsessional neurosis we may find a shrinkage of space. The sexually desired part is brought near to one's own body, but also the object of aggressiveness is brought from the optic space into the space of grasping. Besides this, we may find the reverse type in which the space of the body and the organ of the body is extended into outward optic space where they are subjected to aggression of the outer world.

The disruption of space therefore takes place under the influence of perverse erotic desires and under the influence of aggressiveness. The disruption generally is not a disruption of the total space but only of the space which is in immediate relation with the partial desire, or to aggressiveness. Our material is not sufficient to make a definite decision as to which specific infantile situation is responsible for the diverse disturbances in the space perception.

It is to be expected that the aggressiveness of the depression may lead to similar space phenomena. One depressed patient had the feeling that she was flying around and destroying objects in space. When doubt is in the foreground of the depressive case and when action in space becomes a matter of doubt, space itself takes on the same ambiguity. One of my patients said: "I don't know whether this room is one room or several rooms." Another one of my patients said: "I groped for the stars, tore them down, but every star was a world." Another patient said: "You can't go out of this house; there is no other world. Only the house exists."

Some of these utterances are taken from the patients reported in my study on atypical depressive pictures. I add some more remarks made by these patients:

Case I. "I do not know where I am. I feel that I am in the space between. That frightens me."

Case II. "I am not sure whether this room is one or more." While in Annapolis, she believed that the second row of the men drilling there was only the reflection of the first row. The same patient said:

"I wonder if I am older than two years and four months" (she has been in the hospital that long). "But what did I do before? I am not sure I am in D or whether I was married and had a child or not." She asked a nurse if the nurse were not two persons.

Case III. Complains that the doctors have disappeared in the same way as the girl from the theater box office disappeared from her seat.

Case IV. Sees things waving and moving. They get large and small. "Yesterday, people got so terribly large when they came though the door. . . . I can't keep track of time. Things are moving which should not move and objects disappear. The chair turns into a kind of animal."

One sees that the disturbances in space perception go very far, according to the enormous destructiveness of these patients. They may even lead to a sadistic annihilation of space.

L. Binswanger goes further in many respects. He feels that space experiences should be characterized by the way in which the space is filled, whether it is compact or diluted, whether the objects are nearer or farther away for use. He finds differences in the space experiences in manic patients as well as in depressed patients. In the manic cases, everything is nearer at hand; but, on the other hand, they live in a larger space. He is inclined to judge the space of depressives in a similar way. In another paper he speaks of "der gestimmte Raum," and means something similar to E. Straus' "pathic space experience." He follows the changes of space experience through all emotional and esthetic experiences. He is, of course, aware that one does not deal here with a mere change in space perception, but with the fundamental fact that human existence expresses itself in space, and that it is impossible to separate the "existential" problems of humanity from space perception in this sense. The discussion of an analysis of a neurotic case may be of further help.

Alma, sixteen years old, a well-developed girl of German descent, was the youngest of five living siblings. Two others had died, one with epilepsy and the other after an operation for cleft palate. She was an intelligent girl and successful in her high school studies. During her thirteenth year she had an attack in which she got dizzy and shook all over. In June, 1933, she had a second seizure, which was followed by several others. She was easily upset by noises, and cried a great deal. She stayed at home, never made friends, spent the day reading and helping around the house, and was often sad and depressed.

She came to the Bellevue Mental Hygiene Clinic for treatment August 31, 1933, and was treated there until September 22, when she was admitted to the ward. She was discharged October 21, but psychotherapy was continued. She did not only complain about the spells:

I can't bear to be around people. I get frightened when anybody comes close to me. Noises drive me crazy. They make me jumpy. I am afraid of falling things. At times my eyes feel funny and I can't move them. I get strange feelings; my eyes, legs, and body get heavy. The people in school laugh at me. I want to die but I make myself stop from suicide because it would worry my mother. At times I feel as if I would like to choke people. At times I sink into black depths. I feel that I want to have pain. I like the injections I got in the other hospital. I like to be stuck. I stick my bobby pin into my hands and arms. It is not sharp enough. I try to choke my neck and see how it feels. My thoughts get mixed up and confused.

The patient submitted readily to pinpricks and other painful stimuli, and stated that she enjoyed them. She had the same attitude during her stay in the hospital. She did not move at all, even when strong pain stimuli were applied, and did not even react to strong faradic currents. She never withdrew her hand and it was impossible to condition her to pain stimuli. In marked contrast, however, she reacted very strongly to sudden noises and became jumpy whenever an unexpected sound occurred. In the course of the treatment no further experiments were made in this direction. Pain never provoked any marked changes in the psychogalvanic reflex, whereas other stimuli and noise provoked approximately normal reactions.

During the first examination she often clasped her hands as if under a great tension and wanting to suppress some impulse. Very often she moved the upper part of her body rhythmically to and fro. At times when she was in the ward she especially showed this phenomenon but during the course of the treatment it subsided. In the ward she usually stood alone, leaning against the wall. Outbursts occurred from time to time, in which she got pale, started to shake, cried, and did not talk. Such outbursts lasted up to one hour. However, she did not lose consciousness. In the beginning it was difficult to make her eat. The alarming symptoms disappeared in the first part of her stay at the hospital, and after discharge from the hospital she continued her school work successfully. In the ward the patient always showed a helpful attitude.

The analysis showed the following: She was deeply attached to her mother. She did not want to leave her. The fear of being left by the mother went back to her earliest remembrance. She had slept with her mother since earliest childhood until recently, when at the height of her illness she did not feel any love towards her mother and was afraid of being touched by her.

She showed great affection for one of her sisters, who was eleven years older than she. For a long time she had been sick with rheumatic heart disease. This sister used to tell the patient fairy stories over and over again. One of her earliest remembrances is that of having "fairy parties" with her favorite sister. There were acorn cups, bread, sugar, and water. A still earlier remembrance is that of being held and sung to by someone and rocked to sleep in a rocking chair.

Her hatred against her father was outspoken. There were many family quarrels in which the father became rather violent. She never liked her parents because they shouted at each other. When she was six, her father beat her sister with a strap; she ran to the roof, screaming, while he followed. The patient was terribly frightened.

Her brothers and sisters also used to fight. Knives and forks were thrown. At six, she wanted to stab her father. When she was five, the father used to kill chickens on a chopping block. She saw or imagined a chicken wriggling after its head was chopped off. She was terribly frightened and ran away. She also used to hear violent quarrels of the family in the next apartment.

The father seemed to represent to her a picture of wild and dangerous aggressiveness of which she was afraid. He killed chickens, beat her sister, and made loud noises. She protested against his violent aggressiveness by aggressiveness of her own. There was a masochistic attitude with very early roots, which drove her to surrender. About her third year she had the following dream: Big mattresses were moving towards her on tiny straight pins, threatening to crush her. When she awoke, the door was closed; she called, but the door seemed to be "far away and deep down."

Around her seventh year she dreamed of a spinning wheel coming to chop her up. She was also afraid of a straight line moving slowly and continually in front of her eyes. At five, she was feeding chickens grass with a pair of scissors and "cut off a piece of her thumb." The blood spouted. She ran to her mother, crying, "I fed the chickens a piece of my finger." At seven she hurt her nose which bled profusely. A little while later she fell while skating and broke her wrist.

She always had animal pets. A white rabbit died, when she was four. Her dog was run over on a railway line. It was cut open and bloody, and was a horrible sight. At six, she saw a woman in a coffin in a dark room. The patient started to laugh. When she was six and a half, an older sister died. (The sister had epilepsy, but it is possible that her death was suicide.) The patient saw the coffin.

Her attitude toward pain seems to be closely connected with her early experiences. Pain gave her pleasure. It is the pleasure of masochistic surrender to the father. Everybody who came near her threatened her as her father did. Loud noises reminded her of the aggressive father. Her obsessional impulse to choke people expressed her repressed sadistic attitude. There was an early remembrance of her father putting his hands on her when she was sleeping between her father and mother, and she shuddered away from it.

Her insensibility to pain was partially the attempt to escape heterosexuality. She was completely ignorant in sex matters when she came to the clinic for treatment. The sex information she was given there increased her repulsion against sex. Death wishes and death fantasies were other methods of escape for her. When she imagined herself dead, she thought about immobility and a cataleptic state with preserved consciousness. With her sister she escaped into a fairy story world. She liked fairy tales, and it is characteristic that she mentioned "Sleeping Beauty" as a fairy tale which appealed to her more than others. She hated any kind of apparel, even shoes. At two or three years, she pulled her hat off. "I never liked hats." She hated it when other girls talked about dresses.

She overcompensated her sadistic attitude by an increased attitude of helpfulness. "I can't bear even to see flies killed." There was a strong desire to be loved, which has not been satisfied. She was afraid that others might not believe her, and might laugh at her. She thought that she was extremely ugly (which in reality was not true, although she did have acne which slightly disfigured her face). As a child she was too fat, and was laughed at while she was in school. Sometimes she felt that her head was bumpy and her nose disfigured. In one of her later dreams her attitude towards her own body came out very clearly. "People look at me loathingly and hate me for what I am thinking."

There was another group of phenomena which deserve interest. "Last night, before falling asleep, I saw a man tumbling and falling in front of my eyes." At another time before falling asleep, she saw a chair with shoes piled on it. "They were putting piles of bread right before my face. The door looked far away; farther away than it should have been." At another time, before falling asleep, she saw cups and saucers tumbling over her face. "I was in the linen room, where I was folding linen. The shelves and the linen felt piled too high. They kept rising higher. I could not see straight. I had funny feelings. The lines were out of proportion. They grew."

At another time she complained that she was sitting in class and the teacher looked far away. "I wondered what would happen if she should die. . . . I felt very big today, high up. . . . I always wanted to be tall. . . . My forehead feels low." Before falling asleep on another occasion, she saw an exceptionally tall man falling from a diving board. As he fell, his face grew larger and came nearer to her. Later in the course of the treatment she felt as if her legs and arms did not belong to her and were separated from her. On another occasion she felt too tall, as if she were towering above everybody.

In the beginning, she had the following dream: "I dreamt of water again. It was a flowing river. Somebody was in a motorboat. Somebody had a cold and had to take medicine. There was something about a pumpkin pie." Her associations were: She loved to watch the water. It was beautiful. From her early childhood she went to Coney Island with her mother and enjoyed it. She would like to travel to distant countries. She would like to travel alone. She likes to read sea stories and about submarines. She likes motorboats because they rush so much. She likes rapidly moving things, but is sometimes afraid of them. She felt funny the day before. "I felt I would go mad if I didn't do something. I wanted to smash the dishes. I felt so wild. I felt like going crazy again. A crazy person does odd things, may kill people or may have suicidal mania. I often wanted to be buried under water. There are queer shapes and creatures under water. I like penknives, daggers and swords. I like stories about knights." She often had colds. Her mother had said something about pumpkin pies the night before. The patient did not like to eat; but in her childhood she was very fond of sweets and she often had sudden cravings for sweets. She once dreamed that she was sent home because she ate cakes and meat at night in her sleep, but she denied this vigorously. Since her earliest childhood, her mother had to make her eat.

Her attitude toward speed was related to her sadistic attitudes. She wanted to do things quickly. She liked to walk quickly. She wrote very rapidly and her handwriting was difficult to read. She liked to rush. She often dreamed of walking fast, and of speeding trains. The fast movement also took her away from the present. In one dream she went up in a dirigible and in some way got out of this world. The slow-moving line in her childhood dream was extremely distasteful to her. In one dream she was in a fast-moving elevator that changed into a very fast train.

She often wanted to jump out of a window, and felt herself doing so. When she saw someone on a roof, she felt afraid that he might fall off. She also often dreamed of wide expanses. In one dream she wandered with her brother to a huge garden. "I dreamed of babies. They played on a vast expanse of sand. Somebody poured out toys which were disproportionately large." Once while she was reading, the print appeared very small, no matter how near her eyes she brought it. One day she felt queer, as if she herself and the house were on stilts and crooked and leaning to one side.

In another characteristic dream she was in school in the English class. She felt the beginning of a nervous attack. She was breathing fast and her heart palpitated. She waited in the corridor, leaning against the wall. Teachers and nurses passed her. The English teacher returned with a nurse, and had her taken home and put to bed. She knew that someone was outside looking through the keyhole and saying, "She will go to sleep soon." She felt rather dizzy and weak. They entered and did not find her asleep, so they grabbed her and pushed her down. The doctor said: "Do it quickly before the blood freezes in the brain." She struggled and lashed out with her legs, but her legs seemed to be quite loose and had a shorter span than usual. The doctor sprayed air or liquid into her face and she lost consciousness. The scene changed, she was on the street with someone who was leading her. She was much shorter and her head was hollowed out—just a bare, empty shell. The person leading her had his hand in the hollow of hers and was urging her along. "I don't know exactly whether it was I or another person, for I seemed to see the figure and yet be it." She felt happy, since she had no real head and could no longer think or worry. It seemed to her that an experiment was done on her in the room, and made her this way. Then they passed by a railing where a short, ugly deformed girl was standing with a few other people. She asked for milk. This seemed to be the second stage of the experiment. Soon there passed a fairly tall girl whose head was in the shape of an octagonal plate glass. She seemed to be quite pretty. She was carrying what seemed to be a long, narrow bundle. A sign of recognition passed between them, that this was the first stage, and the experiment was progressing satisfactorily. The girl seemed to be her favorite sister. They said about her: "Every day, when passing, she can see Bobby (her sister's little son)."

The patient also had changes in the perception of time. Often occurrences which had just taken place seemed to her to belong far back in the past. "I remember things—they are further back—it seems as if it had happened in a dream; even things which happened yesterday seem to be further back."

The important phenomenon of pleasure derived from painful stimuli is directly related to the scenes of violence between her parents, which she witnessed as a child. There were quarrels in which the father beat the mother. The patient wanted to be hurt by the hated father. She wanted to stab him. She felt the pleasure of painful stimuli for the first time when she was stuck by the needle when the physician took her Wassermann test.

She succumbed to the sadistic love object. This attitude was fully developed at the age of seven. At that time she dreamed that a spinning wheel came close to her in order to chop her up. This was an anxiety dream. There were other anxiety dreams. A mattress was coming on rolling pins to smother her. This nightmare again refers to her violent father.

Her hatred was not only provoked by the violence of her father. She slept with her mother and was deeply attached to her and to her older sister who was a substitute for the mother. At the height of her illness she was not able to maintain this homosexual relation. At that time every relation to others provoked deep inner resistance, and she was afraid of being near anybody, and was obsessed by the desire to strangle people who were near her. Defending herself against masochistic subjection, she became sadistic. Disappointed in homosexual and heterosexual relations, she regressed to a sadistic attitude for which she tried to compensate by a particular kindness and readiness to help. The father chopping off the heads of the chickens represented a castration threat. Her memory of cutting a part of a finger away with a pair of scissors points again to the castration fear and castration wishes. One may interpret her complaint that the chicken devoured a part of her finger as the fear that her penis may be bitten off and devoured. She also has very strong oral tendencies which she denied in the beginning of her illness. She tried to escape from these conflicts into the peace of death, which for her meant a cataleptic state. She would then have again been in a passive masochistic position, which she could enjoy without remorse.

Her moral problems are reflected in her attitudes toward space and time. When she awoke from her first anxiety dream, the door seemed to be "far away and deep down." After being crushed by her violent father, she reversed the situation. She was not below any more, but higher and farther away from the door through which a helping human could come in. At the height of her illness, other human beings were too close to her. Because of all these moral conflicts, space lost its stability. Things were falling from a cupboard. Laundry was piled too high and was in danger of falling over. Persons sometimes seemed to be too far away. Space widened to vast expansions. She and the house in which she lived appeared to her as if on stilts, crooked and leaning to one side. Her libidinous problems thus found an expression in the changing relations of space. Space relations are primarily determined by relations to other human beings. Space is for her an interhuman phenomenon; it reflects her relation to her mother and father; it expresses the various phases of her aggressiveness, and her struggle for a deeper relation to homosexual and heterosexual love objects. When she experiences the vastness of space as such, this is a secondary phenomenon.

It is difficult to separate problems of space from problems of time. The patient liked speed and motion. In her dreams there were fast-running trains and elevators. Momentum, which in physics increases the impact and the danger, expressed her aggressive and sadistic tendencies. Fighting against her aggressiveness and doubting every one of her actions, her life was not full of the present, and when the present had passed it seemed to recede; it was as if it had happened long ago. She tried, indeed, to go out of the everyday world into the timeless world of fairy stories in which beauty substitutes for aggressiveness.

Aggressiveness destroys and distorts the image of the body. Our patient experienced lengthening and shortening of her body, and distortions of her head. There exists an inner relation between outer space and the space of one's own body. When the dimensions of the outer space are changed, there is also a change in the dimensions of the body image.

The disruption and annihilation of space is similar in obsession neuroses and depression, except that neurotic disturbances are more easily shown to depend on attitudes toward specific love objects. Our patient says: "When I felt so horrible today, the girls in school were separated from each other." One of her dreams goes as follows: "Sister was at home. Two firemen came in, tall as the ceiling and thin, in order to help her. She looked out of the window; the railroad stretched far. There was a music band and the sound retreated. They were playing a military march." One day she felt very small and things were remote. She felt anxiety; she wanted to have a teddy-bear in bed so that she could touch something which was solid and real. In the auditorium at school, the girls looked small and the teacher far away. On a similar occasion she wondered what would happen if the teacher should die. "At six or seven, I was always afraid that Mother would leave me alone. I never wanted to leave her."

In a case [8] in which self-observation played the outstanding part, the patient often got the impression that the analyst was sitting far away on a wooden chair. To "chair" he associated throne and electric chair. He had a fever when he was six or seven, and at that time the doctor always seemed distant. The sadistic attitude toward the analyst father plays an important part. In contrast to the obsessional neurotic mentioned above, here the change in the dimensions of space chiefly concerned a human being in its totality. The sadism in this and the previous case are directed more toward the removal of a person as a total person than to a destruction of parts. Therefore, the space difference is merely a difference in the distance of the total person. The sadistic attitude expresses itself in the removal of a total personality or his death.

Both cases had depersonalization features. In depersonalization cases, objects are often seen as flat. With improvement, the vision becomes stereoscopic again. In other cases, objects seem to be at an enormous distance. In the *déjà vu* phenomenon, objects appear smaller

[8] See *The Image and Appearance of the Human Body*, p. 127.

and farther distant. For one of my patients, the room seemed alternately smaller and larger. In a case of mind blindness of Willbrandt, in which the clinical picture corresponded to depersonalization, objects appeared smaller than when she had seen them before. None of these patients has been analyzed, so we can merely surmise that uncertainty concerning human relations, which is the outstanding characteristic in our cases, is responsible for the loss of the third dimension, for the change in size, and for the greater distance of the objects.

In cases of hysteria, changes in the size of objects and the dimensions of space are outstanding. It is particularly important to study space perception in cases of anxiety. In typical anxiety neurosis cases, the space between the love object and the person is the only real space. If the love object is far away or out of sight, then space becomes immense. In a case of exophthalmic goiter, to the patient—who was extremely attached to his mother and who suffered from anxiety states—space sometimes seemed to be immense. Separation from the love object then leads to the fear of sudden death. Speculation concerning the distance from the mother or from the love object in some of my cases has led to speculation about the relativity of space. For these patients, space is the distance from the love object. In phobias connected with walking, patients occasionally dream that their feet do not touch the ground. This symbolizes the distance of their genitals from the mother. One of my anxiety neurosis patients had a dream that two dwarfs were fighting with each other outside the bedroom of his parents—this is a symbolization of the genitals of the parents during intercourse. They were in the air above the ground. In all these cases the spatial relations of the genitals are symbolized.

The following fragment of a dream analysis comes from a well-analyzed patient with depression and difficulties in adaptation. At the time of the dream she had reached the heterosexual level and the transference was strong. The dream was, therefore, somewhat hysteriform in structure. It shows that the libidinous structure also has a decided influence on the size of objects.

I seemed to be crossing a wide street towards a building with steps. As I got up to the top of the steps I was aware of being beside huge columns. There seemed to be more than one row of columns. There were very distinguished looking people, elegantly dressed, tall, the men with long, brown beards, who seemed foreign to me. I stared at them as we (I do not know with whom I was), having reached the center, turned to re-trace our steps. Back on the street again, it seemed dusk. We crossed to the center of the street through heavy traffic. The impression was very vivid of a danger coming not so much from the number as from the fear-ful speed of the automobiles. One with glaring lights approached and I ran to get across in front of it, though a moment before it had been quite far down the street. When I reached the sidewalk I was in front of two very unpretentious American houses, such as were built in the 90's, with wooden porches. My sister came out of the one my brother and sister-in-law lived in, though I felt she lived in the other, probably with me. She was carrying a box the size of a cigar box, only not so long. My sister-in-law had started in labor. It seemed she was in bed in the box and my brother was in there too, as in a room. When I looked in the direction opposite that from which I had been watching the automobiles come, I saw a dirt road which led over a steep hill, like the side of a mountain that had not been cleared of its primitive vegetation. A walk of boards (at right angles to the direction of the walk) crossed the road and went down to the left through a heavily wooded gorge, toward the hospital, I felt. I held the box against my left side, elbow out, swung forward on my toes to start to run, and felt I could make it easily. As I felt the free movements of running, it came through my mind that if they knew it was I, not my sister, they would let me know if my sister-in-law began to bleed. I could stop and complete the delivery—I thought of it as "take care of things"—as I am a doctor.

The associations lead from the huge columns to the Parthenon, and from there to the sexual genital problems of the dreamer. The automobiles with the fearful speed point to the danger which the dreamer would run by sexual satisfaction. The small box symbolizes hermaphroditic tendencies of the dreamer, to which the columns also point. At the same time she replaces her mother. I do not intend to go into details of the sexual meanings of this dream, but only to indicate that the outer dimensions are symbolizations of the sex organs and sex problems of the dreamer, and are in immediate connection with the acute transference situation. In this dream the problems of speed are closely interwoven with problems of space. The dreamer says: "I had been awake an appreciable time before I realized there was anything incongruous about the size of the box and its contents."

I have come to the general conclusion that the size and weight of objects, the distance and dimensions of space, speed, impact and motion, become more or less the immediate expression of the total libidinous situation.

Space perception is a function which depends on the libidinous structure of the individual. Id functions modify it continually. They are dependent on the biological situation. E. R. Jaensch has proved that the function which he calls attention modifies the perception of depth. The oculomotor apparatus has special influence here. This apparatus is also in the service of the ego. It is paradoxical that hysteriform mechanisms have a deeper influence on the organic apparatus than more aggressive mechanisms. Conversion mechanisms belong to hysteria, although narcissistic regression also opens the way to organic changes, but these latter mechanisms chiefly influence the autonomic system. One also sees intestinal symptoms in obsessional neurosis. The influence of the hysteriform mechanism on the body is more universal and in the majority of cases goes further. In the case discussed in detail, conversion mechanisms played a great part. They influenced the vestibular apparatus in its peripheral and central parts and also the great apparatus which serves to maintain posture and attitudes. Both are of paramount importance as physiological bases for space perception.

Psychological factors are at work in building up the perception of space. There is at first an undifferentiated relation between an incompletely developed body image and the outside space. Clearer differentiations take place around the openings of the body. There is a zone of indifference between body and outside world which makes possible distortions of body space and outside space by projection and appersonization. These distortions are corrected by a continuous process of testing by action (reality testing). Aggressiveness may draw objects closer to the body. Generally, space develops around erogenous zones in close connection with the drives of the individual. This space is not unified and has separate parts. Under the influence of genitality the separate space units are unified. When space distortions take place on the genital level they mean either genitals or persons as units. The final appreciation of space is dependent on our appreciation of personalities. Space is, therefore, decidedly a social phenomenon. It is worthwhile to compare the space disturbances discussed so far with the space disturbance observed in organic lesions of the brain. E. Minkowsky has emphasized that the subjective core of experiences of general paresis and Korsakoff cases is not changed. To put it in a paradoxical way, the psyche remains intact in organic brain disease. It merely distorts actual orientation in space. The gnostic apparatus and the apparatus of thinking are in the periphery of the personality. In other words, in paresis and Korsakoff cases we deal with disturbances in the ego system. I have come to a similar formulation in my *Introduction to a Psychoanalytic Psychiatry*. In space disturbances the same principles come into appearance which we find in psychic life generally. Space is not an independent entity as Kant states, but is in functional relation to instincts, drives, emotions, and actions, with their tonic and phasic components.

CHAPTER XIII

PSYCHOLOGY AND PSYCHOPATHOLOGY OF TIME [1]

THE WORLD in which we live is never at rest. There is always motion. In the world of primitive experience, this motion is all-pervading. The primitive experience is, in the different senses, always an experience of moving objects. In a process of gradual construction we come to the experience of comparatively stabilized objects. But these objects have been here before, and we suppose they will remain. The object at rest exists in time. The changing of objects is based upon an experience of time. Some of the changes in the outer world have a periodic character. There is the change of day and night, the change in seasons, and the changes in the celestial bodies. We form definite expectations concerning these changes. In inanimate nature there is always movement, but there are also characteristic changes in animals and human beings and in the plants in our surroundings. Plants change with the season; animals and human beings grow and die. There are also continuous changes taking place in ourselves. We awaken, become tired, and fall asleep again. We are hungry, and become satisfied. A continuous change is going on in the experience of our body and its needs.

Time is inside as well as outside of ourselves. Time is perception. It is a part of the outside world, but it is also a sensation immediately experienced in ourselves. We organize and crystallize the perception of time into the concept of a continuous flow, which we measure by clocks, and we try to apply the same measures to the time experience in ourselves, to what we may call the time sensation. There is no

[1] Reprinted from *Journal of Nervous and Mental Diseases*, LXXXIII (1936), 531–46.

reason why we, like Kant, should call time the form of inner experience. Time is an inherent part of the world of perception, outside and inside our bodies. To be sure, it is difficult to differentiate it from other experiences; but the same is true of space, and analysis of the continuum of experience of the world is difficult with regard to any experience of the senses and any object.

Perceptions and experiences of other varieties are in no way stabilized entities. It is true that our anatomy, the form and function of the organism, basically determines our experiences. However, the organism is living, it is in motion, it is in function, it is striving. It is a psychical organism with emotions and drives which determine the final structure of our perceptual world. Time perception will be dependent on the same factors. We may start with the following simple instance.

A colleague, twenty-seven years old, gives the following report:

Once during an examination week, which had followed quite a trying period of my life, I had lost much sleep. I remember riding home on a trolley car. I had a peculiar feeling that time and all things about me were standing still, that the seat on which I was sitting was higher than in actuality, that the sidewalk was farther away. This sensation remained, though I knew I was moving. It faded out before I reached my destination.

Such phenomena are not so rare in fatigue states. In the so-called *déjà vu,* the world seems far away. Time does not seem to move, and whatever happens seems to be a repetition of what has happened long ago. *Déjà vu* and depersonalization are very often combined with each other, as Bernhard-Leroy has shown. It is known that these phenomena occur especially when fatigue is present.

Physiological and psychological factors seem to have an equal importance in the phenomena described. In the instance just quoted it seems as if the individual were refusing to go on in a world in which there are so many difficulties. The world is removed, farther distant in space, and time does not progress. The *déjà vu* in epileptic dreamy states corresponds to the unconscious desire and fantasy of returning to the mother's womb. The timeless existence is the existence in which one is removed from all problems. Psychological attitudes express themselves in the way in which we experience time.

Depersonalization cases offer material rich in data on disturbances in the experience of time; I have collected this material. A patient of D'Allonnes complains that she has lost the immediate experience of time. She can orient herself in time but merely by mnemonics. Objective disturbances in time perception are absent. A patient of Krishaber feels very far distant from his previous life. A case of Pierre M. Janet complains that the word "time" has lost its meaning. Patients of P. Loewy and Heveroch, and one of mine, experience the present as if it were the remote past. Another of my patients says that the immediate past immediately becomes the far distant past.

Although we are far from a complete understanding of the psychogenic factors in depersonalization, we know at least that narcissistic, voyeuristic and sadistic elements are of importance. C. P. Oberndorf emphasizes the eroticization of thinking and the conflict arising between feminine and masculine ways of thinking. These psychogenic factors certainly influence the time experience and time sensation. If life has become empty, if we no longer live more fully in our experiences, the experience of time changes, too. "Present" means that we are able to enjoy ourselves and to progress into the future. A deeper understanding of these problems is attained by the study of cases of obsessional neurosis. W. Bromberg and I have observed an obsessional neurotic tortured by fear of death, which for him meant continuous torture and annihilation. In his sadistic world there was eternal destruction and mutilation without time limits. When sadistic attitudes came to full expression, as in the obsessional life of this patient, they demand eternity. An eternity of torture may eliminate death to a certain degree. It is a partial expiation for the murder of others. The psychogenic determinants in this patient, who was analyzed for a long time, were comparatively clear. Homosexual sadistic attitudes toward the father were most important. The conception of hell, with its eternity of hell-fire, probably has very similar psychological roots.

The relation to time in obsessional neuroses may also be disturbed in a different way. One of our patients complained:

I had the feeling that time was flying. I was here one minute and gone the next. I feel like I am talking to you one minute and talking to someone else the next. I have the feeling that time is flying away. I figure how short time is. We die soon. The pictures in front of me never stay; they are always moving. I cannot concentrate on my work. I feel depressed. The thought of time flying depresses me. I know we die in forty or fifty years but the idea depresses me.

This individual feels that he cannot fulfill his aggressive tendencies towards life. Life is going away and the content of his obsession is the fear of death before he has satisfied his aggressiveness. A similar case has been described by Gebsattel, in which a woman was forced to think continually that time passes. She complained of her inability to get a full grasp of life. Her obsession came especially when she saw someone moving. Clinically, the case was classified as depression.

E. Straus has analyzed depressive patients' complaint that time no longer moves. Nothing actually happens any longer. Straus gives a more formalistic interpretation; but I feel that the depressive is inhibited because he is afraid of his own aggressive impulses and does not want to act, since acting means murder. Straus speaks of the halting of inner time by the depression; this makes progress into the future impossible. He thinks that the structure of time experience allows deduction of the other symptoms of depression. He takes the time disturbance as the expression of an organic process and neglects the psychogenic determinants.

When the destructive attitudes of a depressive break through, the individual complains that he has destroyed the world from the beginning and will continue to destroy into eternity. Time and eternity become equivalent. They are filled with unending destruction. The patient may then say that time does not pass at all. He complains that he cannot die. One of my patients said: "I am Adam, the first human being, who cannot die. My whole nature has changed."

Time-perception disturbances are marked in some of the cases of depression which I have recently published. For instance, another patient complained: "I have been here for years. My mother has to live for two thousand years in torment and torture." Another patient said: "I have ruined the world; I started when I was little and didn't know." This indicates that some of these patients show a disturbance in the time sensation (time no longer passes) and that this disturbance also may appear in the delusional and hallucinatory content. One of the patients complained of voices that told her, "Your mother will be tortured for millions of years."

Franz Fischer describes disturbances in time experience in acute schizophrenics. One of his patients complained that everything was continually changing. He felt more at ease when he saw moving things; but after he regained his understanding of time by its relation to moving things he again lost this understanding. Another patient felt an emptiness of time. It seems as if the schizophrenic, in his regression, lost the inner relation to the time experience. Time experience becomes senseless when libido is withdrawn from the more complicated structure of the world.

One of Fischer's patients, a psychopath with sadomasochistic symptoms, says: "When I feel well, time passes so quickly that I often cannot go with it, but when it goes well I don't like it. Others call me irritable. Sometimes it goes too slowly. Then I am sad and depressed. Nothing wants to go to an end and I can't start anything and I have only the wish that it would stop." One of his schizophrenic patients says: "My head is a clock, an apparatus. I make the time, the new time as it should be." Another patient complained that time suddenly stood still. Still another patient said that she was like a piece of ice— silent, as if frozen; she must remain quiet, whereas outside in the field little fires were burning; many things moved around that she must look at. Another patient said: "I can't orient myself in the world—I am not clear any more. Previously, I was a human being with body and soul and now I am not such a being. I don't know anything any more. . . . The body is light and I am afraid it will soon fly away. I continue to live in eternity. There is no hour, no noon, no night. . . . Time does not move. I am wavering between past and future." Another patient said: "Is there any future? Previously, I had a future, but now it shrinks more and more. The past is so obtrusive, it throws itself over me and draws me back." And another complained of feeling that he would like to die and that nothing moved any more. He felt that there would be no more time and that he himself was timeless.

One cannot help suspecting that many of these protocols have a more or less artificial character. They are not merely descriptions of experiences; they also express in a symbolic way the feelings of the patients that their libido has withdrawn from the changing experiences of the outside and inside world. These time disturbances are farther away from the immediate experience than the time disturbances observed in depressive cases and in depersonalization cases. Still, it is an important fact that the patients use a time symbolism. We measure ourselves by the experiences we have had, and from time to time everybody experiences the feeling that he has withdrawn from the world and that the flow of time is then changed. Everybody has some symbolism of time. Language itself contains much of a similar symbolism. We say the future is before us, but "before" also means something spatial—a direction in which we have to go actively. To leave something behind signifies a time relation as well as a space relation. Human beings are always in action, and in acting we go into the future and, furthermore, act in the space before us. Time concepts themselves lead very easily to symbolization. The past is the time where action is no longer either possible or necessary. We like history and fairy stories when we are afraid of doing something in the present and future.

E. Minkowsky sees fundamental symptoms in the relation of the schizophrenic to time experience. He writes: "Our knowledge and our memory group themselves around the fundamental 'I-here-now' (*moi-içi-maintenant*), and allow us to say according to circumstances, I am now in Paris, in England, or in my office. In general paralysis, the information, the memories, or in one word, the static factors are absent. The patient is disoriented in space, in the common sense of the word. The fundamental relation of the *moi-içi* is intact and inactive. The schizophrenic, on the contrary, says where he is but the *moi-içi* no longer has the usual tone and is disturbed." Minkowsky and L. Binswanger compare the schizophrenic disturbance in time perception with the time perception in manic-depressives. From the psychogenic point of view we must ask why time changes and what time means for the schizophrenic. Time experiences are always connected with experiences in the outer world, although more plastic than many other perceptions inside and outside our bodies.

From analytic experience, J. Harnik shows, in agreement with Ernest Jones, that obsessional neurotic patients and anal characters may be as parsimonious with time as with feces, and that there are close relations between ideas of time and anal eroticism. He believes that children first appreciate time in connection with defecation. He also emphasizes the importance of hunger in the experience of time. The interest in the use of time would be merely a sublimation of such tendencies. He comes to the rather far-reaching conclusion that time in the unconscious is the introjected devoured father who has become fecal matter. We shall not accept this conclusion, but it is true that the relation to objective time may be changed by all kinds of drives and these changes also will influence the subjective experience of time in which we are at the present time chiefly interested. (See I. Hollos.)

Time experiences cannot be isolated from our aims in life nor from our relations to the future. We live in the present and are directed toward the future. We have aims and goals which must be understood. S. Spielrein has shown that the child lives chiefly in the present and immediate future, and David Wechsler and I have confirmed this observation. In mental defectives, interest in the future remains limited, as has been observed by ourselves and others (F. Rossel). Hans Keller shows that we involve the future when we expect something—when we are conscious of our ability to do something, so that our present experience is completely imbued with the future.

When one studies the ideas of children concerning life and death and their attitudes to general problems of human life, and afterwards compares these with similar ideas in adults, one is astonished to see that the uneducated adult, whose answer is not merely verbal, has thoughts neither more profuse nor more clear than those of the child. The ideas of the adult about the future—except the immediate future—are also vague and indistinct. All his other concepts of the future are unanalyzed and highly symbolic. One's choice of profession, one's plans for marriage, one's wish to have children, one's idea of activity in later life, are in most cases far from being the result of logical thinking and planning. They merely summarize in a symbolic way, the present libidinous state of an individual. The experience of the future lies in the more or less present striving of the individual. Again, we see that we experience time as an expression of our strivings and that every change in the libidinous situation changes the time experience.

It may seem that we have neglected the organic factor mentioned in the beginning. According to the findings of psychologists, there is a certain agreement as to intervals which are considered absolutely short and those which are considered long. The material can be found in a monograph by V. Benussi and in textbooks of experimental psychology. According to E. R. Jaensch and A. Kretz, even here the type of personality plays an important part and the factors of attention, attitude, and rhythm are also of importance.

Jaensch and Kretz try to coördinate the findings concerning time perception with the general psychology of types as developed by Jaensch. They are of the opinion that the concept of "durée" in the sense of Bergson is to be found in the S (synesthesia) types of Jaensch. In Proust's novel, also, time is merely an undifferentiated coming back of experiences which remain inner experiences closely knitted with each other. Differing from this time perception is the time perception of the I (integrated) type in which time in the sense of "temps" predominates as a sequence in connection with outward objects. I have professed skepticism toward the typology of Jaensch and typologies in general. It is true that time experiences have many aspects and the individual uses sometimes one and sometimes another aspect of time experiences. "Temps" and "durée" belong to the time experiences of everyone. We observe the sequences in the outer world and experience the flow of our inner life. They are correlated to each other. With varying attitudes of the individual, different sides of the time experience come into the foreground.

Psychologists have clearly shown that the objective order of two stimuli is not always the order in which the stimuli are perceived. Expectation here plays a great part. One sees that, even in the perception and experience of small units of time, personality factors cannot be completely excluded.

We return to organic factors which change time experience. Bromberg has collected the literature of the disturbance after mescal and hashish intoxication. During the intoxication, time appears remarkably lengthened. Looking back, the period seems extraordinarily compressed. "Thus, Case 2 stated that after the period of intoxication was over he realized that what seemed like several days, during it, was but a few hours." According to Joel and V. E. Frankl, this change in time sense seems to be independent of spatial or movement perception. In a way, they consider the time-sense disruption to have an absolute existence. As Fernberger expressed it, "Time is extremely slowed and space is extremely extended." One of W. Bromberg's cases gave the following report about the time experience: "I thought I was just barely moving. My knees were very heavy. When I walked it was as if somebody were holding me back. When I walked I did not gain. I felt as if I walked very slowly."

In one of my own cases as reported above, the subject said:

You glance at your watch and the second-hand creeps at an unobservable snail's pace. Five minutes appear like half an hour. Now I experienced bewildering sensations. No matter how many steps I took, the hill in front of me came no closer. I was doomed to walk forever in this valley, never approaching my destination, never getting farther away from the place I had left behind. One walks with ease and grace and without perceptible effort or fatigue.

Both reports emphasize that the time disturbance is especially pronounced when the individual is walking. The motor factor must play a part in the time-perception disturbance. One must also not forget that most of the cases at the same time had optic experiences of quick motion. The contrast with the perceived experience and the difficulties in movement play a very important part in the time-perception disturbance. W. Bromberg has seen cataleptic postures in his cases. In certain phases of the intoxication, movements seem to be quicker.

H. Hartmann observed that a patient with cocaine intoxication reported everything was moving faster. The impression of movement in the outer world and in relation to the motility of the body is doubtless an important factor by which we appreciate the length of time which has passed. In mescal intoxication also, time does not seem to pass. One's own movements are felt as very slow. W. Mayer-Gross quotes a schizophrenic case of Kurt Beringer, in which changes in perception were in the foreground. In this case, personal action did not seem to progress.

There is no reason to suppose that time-perception disturbances in the conditions described are "primary." They are in close relation to perceptual disturbances, including the perception of motion and the changes in motor impulses.

The idea of a chemical clock within ourselves which teaches us the time elapsed has recently been defended by several authors. H. Hoagland describes the dependence of the time perception on the temperature of the body. The latter is partially dependent on the amount of motility. W. Grabensburger investigated the time perception of ants and termites. When the insects were trained to get their food at a given time, quinine delayed their reactions, whereas thyroxin hastened them. Stertzinger found the same results in experiments with human beings. Quinine retards the metabolic processes and thyroxin speeds them up. The authors seem to draw the conclusion that time perception is basically the perception of the speed of the metabolic processes. If this were true, time would be a "sensation" like red, green, and would have no deeper connection with the other experiences of human beings. Of course, all these authors are conscious of the fact that other experiences may modify time perception. Othmar Stertzinger discusses the problem at length. I do not think, however, that time is a "primary datum" in this sense. I believe in the close connection of time experiences with other perceptions coming from inside or outside the body. It is worth noting that W. A. Gardner did not find any definite correlations between the state of the thyroid and the appreciation of time. He comes to the following conclusions:

The majority of all individuals tested experienced a "subjective minute" greatly shortened with reference to clock time. (Active test.) This shortening was more marked in the presence of a non-toxic thyroid adenoma than in the non-thyroid control group. Removal of the adenoma was associated with slight additional shortening. Frank cases of hyperthyroidism exhibited a "subjective minute" longer than all other groups. Removal of such overactive thyroids was associated with a striking reduction in the "subjective minute." Cases of subthyroidism did not show a defect opposite to that of cases of hyperthyroidism. The evidence at hand does not support the hypothesis that time consciousness is a direct correlative of the body rhythm of pulse and metabolism as mediated by variations in thyroid states.

Even if the contention of H. Hoagland, W. Grabensburger and Stertzinger were true, one might still ask on which actual data of experience time perception is based. Since experience clearly shows the time factor in every sensation, it is not sufficient to relate the time factor to general metabolism, but it must also be brought into connection with the metabolic processes connected with every experience. This formulation makes it clear that time experience cannot be separated from other experiences and that it is unsound to relate time experience merely to general metabolic factors.

We know little about the physiological basis of these disturbances. When in vestibular dreams all objects seem sometimes to increase in size, one also sees that everything moves very slowly. A neurotic patient with marked psychogenic depression experienced the same phenomena. In alcoholic psychoses one may make similar observations. For instance, one patient said there were elephants moving very slowly. Another said:

I seemed to be on a beach where a river was flowing by, and a large body of men passed as though they were going fishing. They walked slowly. Boats on the river were going very slowly. I thought they were so lovely that it would be nice if they would not go by too fast, so that I could get a good look at them. The draperies on the windows in the hospital were very beautiful. Every color stayed perfectly still as though the windows were closed. (How did time pass?) It seemed very long to me. I fell asleep at nine o'clock and when I woke up I thought it was about six in the morning but the nurse said it was two o'clock.

The symptomatology of the case makes vestibular influences probable. The vestibular apparatus not only changes our perception of motion but it also exerts a strong influence upon our tonic impulses. J.
Stein observed a patient with central vestibular disturbance (similar
to cases described by Von Weizsaecker) by whom measures of all
kinds were overrated on one side. This was true for optic impressions as well as for tactile impressions. At the same time, time intervals were underrated. Examination of the chronaxy of this patient
showed that to produce irritability a longer exposure of the stimulus
on its affected side was needed. This observation indicates that the
immediate perceptual factors are changed and that the change is one
not only of space but also of time. Also, this patient saw "quiet" objects in movement. Movement seems, again, the primary symptom; in
other words, the time factor is closely connected with a space factor,
and the perception as such is changed. A. Flach and C. Palisa observed
a patient with oculogyric crisis who experienced slowing down of
his own movements and those of others. K. Goldstein and F. Reichmann have observed in cerrebellar cases overrating of distances on the
skin and of time intervals. We may question whether we do not deal
with basically identical phenomena in these cases. L. Bender has observed a delirious episode in which the experiences of movement as
well as those of time seemed to be enormously increased. Histopatho-
logically, the case showed a picture of arteriolitis with considerable
narrowing of the lumen of the blood vessels in some layers of the
cortex, and with changes in the cerebellum especially in the region
of the Purkinje cells. One might suppose that slowing of the blood
stream had something to do with the disturbance in time perception,
and this may be a cerebellar function, although in this case, it still remains a question, as to whether perceptions as such were not changed.
We do not deal here with primary disturbances in the sense of time.
When there are disturbances in time perception there are also disturbances in the perceptions which have become more primitive in
function, undergoing a distinct change in the innate motion of the
perceptual sphere. We now understand better why, in the observation

first mentioned, not only time perception but also space perception is changed.

O. Poetzl, E. Redlich, K. Goldstein and others have observed in optic agnosia that movement is not perceived. Instead, the object appears in different places or in several editions. Similar observations have been made in mescal intoxication, by Beringer and Mayer-Gross. One may call disturbances of this kind disturbances in the perception of movement and also disturbances in perception of time. This shows again, the close relation between the perception of motion and time. Alfred Gross is probably correct when he interprets the dream of a patient who sees several small boys on a decline as the gliding of the male sex organ, and analysts are correct in believing that in dreams multiplicity in space may substitute for movement. Poetzl and Hoff observed in a case of left-sided hemianopsia probably due to occipital lobe lesion, that persons in the environment seemed to move faster, following which their movements were slowed down. The occipital lobe has a relation to primitive time experiences. This relation is different from that of the temporal lobe to time experiences. In the so-called uncinate fits, occurring in lesions of that part of the temporal lobe related to the perception of smell, the individual very often experiences *déjà vu* with its well-known characteristics. It is interesting to note that these fits are connected with experiences of smell. This organic lesion drives the individual back to a past and mechanizes the present.

I have thus far discussed disturbances in time perception which were experienced as such. In some diffuse diseases of the central nervous system one finds disturbances which probably have a similar basis. In an alcoholic encephalopathy case, the patient said that the time spent in the hospital seemed longer than it was. Six weeks appeared to him as six months. The days also seemed longer. Very often at two o'clock he said that it was five. A. Struempell reports cases of typhoid, in which the patients overrated the time which had passed. One patient, for instance, said that she had already been seventeen years in the hospital. L. Bouman and A. A. Gruenbaum observed a patient who, after an influenzal psychosis, experienced a shortening of time. A conversation of twenty minutes seemed to him five minutes, and one of sixty minutes seemed fifteen minutes. Six days appeared as three days. The patient stated that the days were now not so long as they had been before. The patient also reported from time to time that objects were disappearing. I think we deal in this case with a changed experience of time perception. But there is probably another element which has not so much to do with immediate perception as with the problem of the perception of longer time intervals and psychic elaboration. In order to come to an understanding of this problem we must discuss the problem of the perception of longer time intervals.

Objects of immediate experience either stand still or move. There is a continual flow of the experiences of one's own body. Immediate time experience is connected with these perceptions. Immediate time experience is not a mathematical point, but a flow with extension in time. The immediate past is the sensual impression. The immediate future, in connection with libidinous strivings, tonic attitudes, and motor impulses, is a perceptual datum.

The problem of the appreciation of longer time intervals has been approached by studying time appreciation during sleep. E. G. Boring reports an experiment by E. N. Brush in which certain observers who lived in a quiet community were awakened at different times between midnight and five o'clock during the long winter nights. They were asked to estimate the time and to report the conscious basis of the estimate. The average error turned out to be about fifty minutes. The subjects found in their own bodies a state of affairs that served as a pretty good frame of reference for the time.

K. Frobenius found that many subjects were able to awaken at a specified hour. In another series of experiments the subjects were asked to awaken after a given number of hours. In almost two-fifths of the experiments the subjects succeeded in awakening at the time set. Frobenius is inclined to believe that this is due not merely to stimuli coming from the organs of the body but to an undefined higher function of a time sense. There is no proof for such an assumption. During sleep, many more psychic processes occur than we are usually aware of.

H. Ehrenwald could show that hypnotized subjects exactly estimated short time intervals during sleep, and estimated more correctly than waking subjects the duration of sleep. Hypnotized persons also estimate the duration of the time of sleep during the night more correctly than those asleep under normal conditions. It seems, therefore, that there are sufficient data present to make possible the estimation of time passed. These data are not always utilized in the definite forming of the perception of time.

When we hypnotize subjects and ask them for a more correct estimation of time, we do not address ourselves to a mysterious higher function of time, but request the individual to utilize his perceptual data more carefully. The constructive efforts of the individual are paramount in the final elaboration of appreciation of the time passed.

It is interesting to study these problems in cases of amnestic gaps on a psychogenic basis. Three cases were examined. One patient with an amnestic gap of about a month felt that about one month had passed between his last memory and his first memory after coming to himself. In another case in which the amnestic gap extended over eight months, the patient felt that the last remembrance and the first remembrance were separated from each other by merely one night's sleep. In the third case, in which the amnestic gap was only about two days, the time elapsed seemed to be considerably longer. We know that it is possible in all such cases to restore the correct sequence and time relation of all events which occurred during the forgotten period. Time perception may, therefore, be repressed like any other perception, and the perception of longer and shorter time may be dealt with like any other perception. The experiments using sleep show that, for this type of perception, sensations coming from the body are roughly sufficient; and that restriction in the sensory perception during sleep does not impair the correct appreciation of time.

When an experience coming from the body or from the outside world has disappeared, the memory of it remains. This memory has at first full sensory qualities and is present without any active effort to provoke it, but soon becomes progressively weaker. Its importance for the actions of the individual diminishes. It passes out of the present situation. It is revived only when the present situation forms a unit with the past situation. The past situation is revived in the service of the present situation. The entire past of an individual is, in this respect, potentially present. When we are in an actual experience, a continual scanning of past memories occurs in order to discover which pieces of the past fit into the present situation, which can be integrated into it, and which cannot. The degree of fading of the memory and the amount of active integrative effort to bring forward the memory give us preliminary hints of the localization of the event in time. It is impossible to treat these problems in a merely formal way. Evoking the past means not only the evocation of one event but also the restoration of the sequence of events in their relation to the total experience. It is not only the position of one event which matters but also the connection between this event and other events. The past thus emerges by an active process of continuous testing of the past in connection with the present situation, its emotions and its drives. It is true that this order of the sequence of events is not identical with the appreciation of the passing of time in shorter intervals.

Ehrenwald has shown that Korsakoff cases with severe memory disturbances, in the usual sense, have exact appreciation of past time when hypnotized. I have already stated that present time perception is a utilization of specific experiences and that the past, which is farther away, presents a completely different problem. It is easy to understand that the complicated structure required in building up the past and concepts of the past cannot be fully developed in children. In adult mental defectives one sees similar difficulties. In Korsakoff cases one sees clearly that memory as such is not impaired. Experimental psychology has shown that the Korsakoff patient shows retention in learning experiments. The confabulation of the Korsakoff patient brings forward material which he cannot remember actively. The order of experiences cannot be reëstablished, but the experiences as such are present. One of my patients had completely forgotten that she had borne a child. She continually confabulated, however, that children were lying in her bed. The experiments of Betlheim and Hartmann, who told indecent stories to Korsakoff cases, are of special importance. A patient to whom a story of sexual intercourse had been told, afterwards spoke of a "staircase on which women descended." In other words, memories may appear in a condensed and transposed symbolic form. Analysis has shown that the majority of past memories at first come back in such a symbolic way. In the practical procedure of psychoanalysis we observe this daily. It is also interesting to see that in the recovery of past time the individual tries at first to get some general outlines, fixed points of orientation, to which other details are added by a prolonged process of construction and reconstruction. In analysis one sees, for instance, that changing from one apartment to another, the death of a beloved person, the appearance of a new companion, the beginning of school or of kindergarten, offer possibilities for a preliminary diagram of experiences. Indeed, recovering the past is a constructive process. (The title of Proust's novel is *A la recherche du temps perdu*.) This process is dependent upon emotional factors and on the actual biological situation.

Actual time experience now becomes continually interwoven with this constructive process. It is symbolically extended into the past. The order of past memories is a different problem. Specific parts of the brain are indispensable for its function. Ehrenwald has published a case of parietal occipital lesion in which this function was impaired. General considerations, which I cannot discuss here in detail, make it very probable that the parietal lobe and adjacent parts of the temporal lobe (in connection with the vestibular apparatus) are important stations for perception of the sequence of experiences in time. Gamper has related the memory disturbances of a Korsakoff case to a lesion of the mammillary bodies. Although it is probable that the lesion of the vegetative centers that one finds in alcoholic Korsakoff cases is not without influence on the Korsakoff syndrome, and especially on the drives which lead to confabulations, I do not think that this is the only factor in play. I am inclined to believe that cortical lesions are indispensable in the pathology of Korsakoff's psychosis (L. Bender and P. Schilder). Karl Kleist relates amnestic symptoms concerning time to the diencephalon, and also stresses the relation to the vegetative functions. He states that in the Korsakoff syndrome, no relation to the ego is present, but his psychological analysis is insufficient and he does not bring any new proof to the problem of localization. In my opinion, problems of localization can be solved only on the basis of a previous careful psychological analysis. It is wrong not to see the fundamental difference between this problem and the general problems of the perception of time as an immediate experience.

I have already discussed the experience of the future. The intentions for immediate actions and for immediate needs contain an element of future. Plans and fantasies stretch the immediate future into the distant future. Even the experience of the next day is beyond all imagination. The future is seen in perspective and is foreshortened. In its details reality surpasses all possible imaginations and fantasies.

Symbolic transformations, condensations, and transpositions are important expectations in the future. It is impossible to imagine approximately what it will be like to get married, to be in love, to have a child, to be betrayed by somebody whom one loves, to be rich, or to be poor. All these expectations are merely symbolic expressions of the present libidinous situation. This principle of the foreshortening of the future and the symbolic character of expectation has never been fully understood, and has led psychologists and philosophers to wrong conceptions of the time problem. With this foreshortening, a new process sets in, which we may call the process of verbalization of the future. Words without definite contents, merely the product of the emotions of others and oneself, and loaded heavily with prejudices and unanalyzed feeling, become the signposts for actions. The better educated a person is, the more is his conception of the future a product of vaguely understood words which are the carriers of unanalyzed emotional complexes. They become a hiding place for unanalyzed symbolic expectations.

I would not have discussed these time problems if insight into them were not a necessary condition for a deeper understanding of psychotherapy. The aim of psychotherapy is to understand the drives and aims of the personality. Unless we understand the symbolic character of the expectations of life and the plans of life, we shall be inefficient in handling our patients.

The final problem remains that of the physicist's approach to the time problem. He makes possible a careful expectation of future but only concerning the uncomplicated mechanical side of life. It is a construction in order to handle problems in the sense of reality. It uses in a constructive process the subjective experiences of human individuals, blends them with insight into the nature of objects, and in this way comes finally to an objective time which sums up the experiences of the passing and remaining of objects in the outer world. Time then appears unlimited, going in a straight line from the past into the future. The physicist's conception of time is in no way different from any other of his conceptions which are based upon the necessity of action. The construction of the physicist is therefore dependent upon the needs of effective handling of mechanical problems, and his conceptions vary accordingly. He may even introduce the conception of a relativity of time, a conception which is philosophically senseless as long as the velocity of light is taken as a constant. Velocity contains in itself the primitive factor of time perception.

We insist upon the biological approach to the time problem. Philosophers, deceived by the word "time," have taken the phenomenon of time as an entity and have used this word in order to satisfy their own emotional needs. When Heidegger, one of the leading philosophers of Germany, asserts that the experience of inevitable death is the basis for the true experience of time, he is incorrect. I have shown in various investigations with Bromberg and Wechsler that the word "death" like the word "time" is used for many varied experiences. There is no unified time experience and no unified experience of death. The idea of death of a given individual merely expresses his expectations and drives toward life. The same holds true of our attitude toward time. We have instances of how language has deceived philosophers and psychologists, and we have the task of going back to the actual biological experiences of human beings. The analysis of the time problem, like that of the problem of death, becomes a fundamental point for psychologists and also an important part of psychotherapy. We get more enlightenment from primitives than from philosophers. The primitive tribes of Oganda, according to H. Werner, call 6 A. M. the time of milking, 3 P. M. the time for watering the cattle, and 5 P. M. the time for the cattle to come home. If we can bring the neurotic to a similarly clear understanding of his theoretical concepts, we have made an important step forward.

By analyzing the psychology of time we gain an insight into the way the mind works. There are the perceptual data, the sensations in ourselves, the world outside, the objects and the data coming from our bodies. There is also the living individual with his drives and urges, who by a process of continual construction and reconstruction gives final shape to objects and to their relations in time. These constructive energies in ourselves bring final order into our experiences and so create the final perception of the flow of time. The psychology and the psychopathology of time help us to a deeper insight into the constructive energies of the psyche.[2]

[2] Further material can be found in the article by Raoul Mourgue ("Une Decouverte scientifique: la durée bergsonienne"), which discusses the problem from the point of view of Bergson.

CHAPTER XIV

ACTION

HUMAN action has aims and goals. The aim is the aim of the personality and the body expresses the needs of the personality. One might raise the question whether there is something else besides the body, and whether the assumption of a personality, which is not the body, is not more or less useless. I speak here about the body in the sense of an immediate experience, in the sense of the body image. We also experience an outer world and a direction towards this outer world.

There are definite tendencies and attitudes without which a body is but a lifeless mass. From the point of view of social psychology we not only experience our own body but we also experience other human beings as personalities with definite drives and directions which are expressed in their bodies. I have previously shown that the individual in every action must start with an orientation toward his own body and the bodies of others. Every action is based upon the body image. Action means a dynamic change in the body image, which is in a state of equilibrium before an action takes place. It leaves this equilibrium, during action, and reaches it again with completion of the action.

Objects are in a definite order in space. Space is, psychologically, not homogeneous. A. A. Gruenbaum has especially emphasized this fact. We do not act toward isolated points in space. There is a well-regulated system of geometrical coördinates of space in which the vertical and horizontal planes play an outstanding part. Furthermore, there is a network of object relations and orders of manifold type. An object always has a definite relation to the body image. An object is the crossing point of many worlds. It is in the world of physics and in the world of practical and moral values.

The end of an action not only means a new equilibrium in the body image, but also a new orientation in space and morals. Physiological impulses of tonic, rhythmic, and phasic character, which are in such close relation to the impression of the senses and the formation of the object, determine space in its properties and the dynamic relation of the body image to space. The body image continually creates a new space equilibrium around itself.

The investigations of E. Feuchtwanger are particularly important in this respect. In discussing space, it has been mentioned that there is a primitive tonic system of space and that the phasic system is built upon this tonic system. Tonic and phasic systems build up the object, space, and also the basis of action. The tonic component, however, is already action. It means an adaptation to the outside world; tone leads either towards the object or away from it, when the object becomes too threatening. In this respect it is of particular importance that the investigations of R. Magnus and A. de Kleijn, F. H. Quix and others have shown that the orientation to gravity is important in tonic attitudes. The plane of action is emphasized in investigations of Bender and myself, which show that experimentation with different planes of action and gravitation are important functions in the primitive play of children.

Tone is not merely dependent upon space but is space creating and correlates the fundamental directions of space. Tone is both an attitude and an action. The fascinating task of following this problem through the range of animal psychology and the tonic reactions of animals cannot be dealt with in detail here. Newer investigations have shown decisively that the tonic reactions of lower animals are not merely tropisms or mechanical consequences of physical chemical influences but are primitive actions. Actions might also be expressed in physico-chemical terms except for the complexity of physico-chemical functions.

Space, action, and body image are determined not merely by tonic innervation but also by phasic action. I have mentioned that the term "reflex" has been abused. The patellar reflex seems to be so simple that it looks almost mechanical, and the older physiology took reflex as the unit by the complication of which final action is created. If there is any relation between reflexes of the type of the patellar reflex and action, then the reflex is a product of schematization, simplification, and degeneration of action. One can see this particularly clearly in a reflex such as the scratch reflex. The scratch reflex is not a reflex but an action with an aim, namely, to restore the body image from a distortion which has taken place; the same may be said of reflexes involved in walking. Walking changes the situation of the body image in space and carries the individual away from something or brings him closer to something. The individual retains his relation to gravity in its final outcome, but must experience rather decisive gravitational changes before coming to a new equilibrium. This constructive process is guided by continuous impressions from the soles, joints, and muscles. It is basically the expression of central tendencies.

Reflexes and tone are split-off parts of actions. The split may sometimes generate a more primitive unit of action but we have no right to assume that the higher type of action is merely a summation of so-called primitive units. Sherrington considered the reflex as a biological unit, and did not ask to what it led and what its aim was. In the further pursuit of his study, a mechanical point of view became more and more apparent. The problem became one of flexor and extensor muscles and their tone rather than that of the actions to which flexion and extension lead and of which they are a part.

The stretch reflex seems to be much more mechanical than the scratch reflex. It is very questionable whether one should consider the scratch reflex as a rhythmical series of movements, or whether it is not better understood as the removal of a disturbance to the body image. If we search for primitive units of action we certainly shall not try to find them in a meaningless tonic contraction. Sir Charles Sherrington's work contains the important nucleus of further biological studies. Decerebrate rigidity can be understood very well in relation to standing and orientation to gravity. C. Richter and L. H. Bartemeier have found that the sloth's decerebrate rigidity is a flexor rigidity. This clearly shows that the central nervous system serves functions. A function cannot be understood from the point of view of anatomy alone, but only from the point of view of environment and situation in relation to anatomy.

The standing of the dog corresponds to the hanging from the tree of the sloth, and the decerebrate rigidity merely exaggerates the basic orientation to gravity. Further elucidation can be gained from the investigations of Magnus and de Kleijn. The postural and righting reflexes are dependent on the position of the head in space (otolith reflexes) and on the body's surface pressure and whether the animal is in usual correct position or not. The animal tries to get into a position of comparative stability. The biological implications of these findings have been extensively studied by K. Goldstein, who has shown that the problem of tone is also the problem of being directed towards or getting away from something. He has further introduced the concept of the "comfortable position" and the tendency to return to this "comfortable position." He has pointed to the importance of the different planes in which motility takes place. One should stress the importance of gravitation and the comparative static phases in the body image. Without the concept of the body image, no deeper understanding of action can be gained. Tone has something to do with the outer world and the adaptation to qualities in which physics is interested. The "tonic" individual considers the world chiefly from the point of view of physics, inertia, mass, gravitation, and also from the point of view of preparedness of the organism. In order to do something, one must at first adapt to the general situation of mass attraction. It is true, for instance, that for ctenophora floating in the water the orientation to gravitation and the physical qualities of water are almost all that is needed. Where finer qualities of the objects are involved, tonic adaptation becomes insufficient. Tonic adaptation is chiefly of importance when we deal with rather stabilized conditions.

We must turn, therefore, to more decidedly phasic actions. Grasping and sucking offer themselves as the first activities to be considered. Both have been the object of extensive studies by psychologists and physicians.

We begin with a consideration of sucking. Sucking has two phases.

When an object is brought close to a child's mouth, the child turns its head and eyes, and the body follows with open mouth. Sometimes the head is withdrawn as if the child expected that something would drop into its mouth. When the object is finally brought to the mouth the lips close around the object and sucking begins. We again deal with a rhythmic activity. It seems that the touch of the lips initiates the sucking movement. During the sucking process, the child clenches its fists and increases its grasp. Two types of lesions permit this activity to reappear. One is a lesion of the prefrontal area and the other a lesion of the brain stem, especially seen in alcoholic encephalopathy. That sucking is not only cortically initiated in human beings is proven by a case of E. Gamper, in which sucking was present although the hemispheres were lacking and only the brain stem was preserved (without optic thalamus). One is inclined to believe that grasping and groping are subsidiary to sucking. This is not correct, since as we know, the child does not grasp the food which it needs and in E. Troemner's case of anencephaly grasping alone was preserved.

It is true that in later development the child puts objects into his mouth immediately after receiving them. Apparently in development, grasping and sucking are independent of each other for some time. It is true that when a child is sucking, the sucking invariably provokes grasping. Functions which are independent in early development may be united in later stages of development. One might say that the unification which is in the plan of the organism has not yet been performed. This means that parts may take an independent course in development, or the development may unite two independent units in their later course. (See G. E. Coghill.) Development probably takes place piecemeal and in this respect is comparable to eidetic imagery as described by Kluever and by myself.

Further information can be gained from study of the grasp reflex. In studying tonic perseveration in grasping and groping, F. M. R. Walsh and E. G. Robertson found that grasping and groping appeared only in lesions of the prefrontal area. They consider the tonic perseveration which can be elicited by stretching the fingers to be a true grasp reflex. It cannot be elicited by tactile and visual stimuli. This grasp is strong, cannot be voluntarily released and increases as the muscles are stretched. They consider this grasping to be a true reflex, and differentiate this reflex component from an associated volitional component for which visual and tactile stimuli are important. The grasp reflex disappears in coma. They differentiate psychic from physiological grasping. Grasping, in contrast to the grasp reflex, is merely psychic, according to their opinion. This, however, can easily be refuted. My own investigations with I. Bieber have shown that increase in grasping by repetition of the stimulation very often provokes groping in the same hand and is often transferred to the other hand as grasping and groping. The unbreakable grip of one hand may be transposed to the other hand. The grasp of the contralateral hand may be released by conscious effort of the patient. During grasping there is strong tonic innervation in the arm, even if it were not present before. The tonic innervation is not grasp, for grasping and groping have directness and the tonic innervation is merely subordinate to this aim. Grasping and groping in the newborn monkey or human being is a fundamental action and cannot be understood merely as a tonic phenomenon. Clinging pronate to the body of the mother is thereby achieved, especially during the act of sucking.

Tonic innervation, in the sense of Robertson and Walsh, is a part function of grasping and there is no justification for separating psychic grasping from the "neurological" grasp. In alcoholic encephalopathy, grasp may also become unbreakable. Usually the patient can open his hand even when its muscles are stretched. The muscular changes in these patients resemble the changes observed in tonic innervation. In both groups grasping, groping, and sucking are usually present at the same time. Very often the sucking reflex, although otherwise not present, can be elicited by an increase in the grasp reflex. Sucking itself increases grasping, as mentioned above.

The difference in tone after cortical destruction and after subcortical lesion is merely a greater variability of the tonic increase in the subcortical lesion. Grasping and groping is a unified function, which becomes tonic because tone is the sense and meaning of the function. As shown by J. B. Watson in humans and by C. Richter in monkeys, the grasp reflex occurs when the individual tries to hold himself against gravity. We observed three post-encephalitic paralysis agitans cases in which grasping was particularly obvious when the patients were in danger of falling backwards from retropulsion. This factor is mentioned also by A. M. Rabiner. In alcoholic encephalopathic patients, we have found that the patient almost invariably has a tendency to fall backwards. Grasping should not be considered as subservient to oral activities only. An individual with a frontal lobe lesion acts as if grasp were fulfilling its function in maintaining posture, although no objective need be present. One might call this motor preparedness due to dysfunction in equilibrium, or (if one wants to be paradoxical) a motor hallucination concerning the maintenance of equilibrium.

One of our most important functions is to maintain our orientation to gravitational forces. At first, grasp helps in clinging to the mother's body (Hermann). Later on, grasp develops other relations. The maintenance of erect posture is secured by tonic influences in the first level and by grasping in the second level. The great importance of these functions can also be seen in patients with cerebellar disorders, who frantically try to maintain their equilibrium. Since the postural reflexes are not only preserved but decidedly increased, one sees that equilibrium is very often maintained against odds. Children with cerebellar agenesis show very important psychological trends in addition to these motor disturbances. They cling to adults from whom they get support (L. Bender). The grasp reflex is only one line of defense in maintaining one's position against gravity; the other one is an attempt to get support by clinging. The mother is not only protection in general and an agency for food for the child, but she protects the child against the ever present enemy of gravitation. Dependence also means the wish to have help in standing upright.

When grasping and groping appear to be futile, then pointing, which is functionally the same in that one finger reaches for the distant object, takes their place. Another development leads from grasping to hand shaking, which is an attenuated form of grasping, gives mutual support, and hinders aggressiveness. The other person cannot hit you with his hand when shaking hands. One sees how many activities develop as a natural consequence of such primitive activity. Sucking also has inner developments. The opening and closing of the mouth, single phases of the sucking act, are used in functions different from the act of oral incorporation.

Indeed if one considers grasping and sucking as the beginnings of human action, it seems that primitive human action expresses the urge to come into apposition to objects. The destruction of the object does not seem to be the primary aim. An important part of the psychology of grasping is dependent upon the preservation of the love object. Closer approach to an object is likely to interfere with the structure of the object and to be destructive to the object, especially when the individual tries to put it into his mouth and devour it. It is wrong, however, to see only the physiological function of devouring. The relative functional independence of grasping from sucking, in spite of their interdependence, is of great psychological importance.

Quite in the same way as imagination and perception not only build up objects but also destroy them, there also are destructive tendencies in motility. Experimentation with objects, and especially studies of their consistency, may sooner or later lead to their destruction. Action gives a sense of power over other objects, animate and inanimate. Action in itself thus becomes a moral problem, which is outside the field of our discussion. I consider grasping, groping, and sucking to be the nucleus of the function of the ego and the ego instincts. No trace of a death instinct in the psychoanalytic sense is to be found, and it is wrong to overemphasize the idea of destruction. Destruction is an important phase, but destruction is not the final aim and goal of human action.

It is not our task to follow the development of action. Reflex, instinctive action, expressive movement, and voluntary actions are merely phases of the general process of adaptation. Darwin has shown succinctly that expressive movement may be considered as a derivate of voluntary action.

We have thus far neglected reactions of defense in our analysis of primitive functions and actions. There is at first a closing up (encapsulation) of the body so far as possible; closing the eyes, as in crying and secreting; closing the lips, and even protruding the lips, as in pouting; pushing the tongue forward; and finally, movements of closing the pharynx. The arm may be drawn protectively before the face and body. When defensive measures are not sufficient, pushing away occurs, in which abduction and extension movements play an important part. Grasping is chiefly a flexor and adductor function. It is important to consider the organism and its motility from the point of view of abduction and adduction, flexion and extension. One tears objects apart by abduction, and puts them together by adduction. Kurt Goldstein has developed similar ideas. Adduction and abduction are also very important for the construction of the object. Motility is not merely directed towards the object, but it is concerned in the creation of the object. The resistance of objects to push and pull makes them objects. Push, pull, and momentum of objects are object qualities closely related to the motility of an individual. Human action progresses by creating more complicated objects, which give opportunity for further development of action.

CHAPTER XV

SUMMARY

THIS is an attempt to summarize what we know of perception and action from the point of view of a psychology of the constructive energies of the psyche.[1] In *The Image and Appearance of the Human Body* I have tried to show that we build up the knowledge of our body by a process of continual construction. Vague and general experiences are only formed through continual touch with the outer world. The schema of the body, the knowledge we have concerning our whole body, is not something which comes to us as a gift in its complete form. In the continual process of construction, action, trial, and error play outstanding parts, and by this process a picture of one's own body is gained as well as pictures of the bodies of others. Based upon these studies I have come to the conclusion that every sensory impression has its own motility. It leads immediately to action of either tonic or phasic character, which in turn enriches the impression. The separation between sensory impressions and motor expression and motility is more or less artificial. The concepts of sensibility and motility merely designate the sensory motor process in different aspects. The object which is one's own body and the objects which are the bodies of others are the result of a psychic sensory motor construction and an expression of the constructive energies of the psyche.

The result of such a construction is in this particular case an object with a characteristic configuration. The gestalt here finds its original and most apt application.

On the basis of this insight an attempt has been made to investigate whether other objects are merely analyzable data of experience, or

[1] Reprinted in part from my article "Language and the Constructive Energies of the Psyche," *Scientia* (May, 1936).

whether they are not also the result of a creative psychic construction. The truth is that no "sensations" are merely experiences of an individual. Every sensation points at a happening in the outer world. The term sensation is used only when we emphasize the phenomenally subjective side of an experience, and the term perception is used when the experiences are considered as phenomenally objective. Primitive experience is, therefore, not only sensation but perception. Primitive experience is an experience of movement which is indefinite yet fills the whole field of experience. This is particularly clear in the optic field.

The unified object which serves as a goal for the action is not an immediate experience. Primitive optic experience consists of colors, motion, spirals, and vortices, only incompletely differentiated from the background. It is connected with a mass reaction of undifferentiated motor impulses. When these impulses lead to a closer contact with the object by tonic and phasic impulses, differentiation of the perception takes place. This makes more detailed action possible by revealing optic, tactile, and other new qualities of the object, and thus giving it a more distinct articulation and providing clearer spatial relations.

The experience of an object is, therefore, the result of a constructive psychic process in which not only motility and action are of importance but also vegetative phenomena. I have tried to show that the experience of time and space is built up in a similar way. I summarize the main points in the psychology of the constructive energies of the psyche as follows: (1) the close connection between sensibility and motility; (2) the character of motion in many of the primitive sensory experiences; (3) the motor response to the motion in perception; (4) the mass character of the primitive motor reaction; (5) the inner unity of the motor reaction with emotion, drives, and instincts; (6) the gradual shaping of experiences under the influence of actions and trial and error; (7) configuration as the result of this continual interplay between action and impression and the development of the configuration; (8) the tendency to break up the construction in order to gain a newer access to the objective world; (9) the objective world as the guide to the psychic constructions (reality-testing); (10) the direction of this whole process by the vital drives of the individual, which express themselves in the desires and instincts as well as in the sensory motor field; (11) the unity of the fundamental forces in the construction of the body image, the objects of the outer world, and the problems of personality and morality; (12) the body image as well as the object are built up by continuous interchange with other human beings; they are therefore socialized. Socialization is thus the fundamental form of human experience.

PART II

HIGHER MENTAL FUNCTIONS

CHAPTER XVI

LANGUAGE: PSYCHOLOGY AND PSYCHOPATHOLOGY

PSYCHOLOGY OF LANGUAGE

IT SEEMS worth while to consider language from the viewpoint of constructive psychology.[1] A new-born child is rarely completely quiet. When awake it is always making some noise, either crying or screaming. Soon the child starts babbling, which is apparently a more or less playful action. Even deaf children start to babble but do not continue. Imitation of what the child hears from others comes comparatively late. The child "understands" language before he can use it. An awareness of emotion as expressed in words and an appreciation of the melody of speech precedes the understanding of the content of words. The connection between words and objects is formed gradually, as the name of the object and the object itself are brought simultaneously to the attention of the child. This is the mechanism of the so-called conditioned reflex,[2] and the child reacts in many respects to the presence of the words as if the object as such were present too: the word has become a sign of the object. The object is not merely a sensory and intellectual impression but a summons to a set of actions. These actions may be voluntary movements of striated muscles but they may also consist of involuntary innervation of smooth muscles and gland, as in Pavlov's experiments. When a conditioned reflex is formed, there occurs not only the secretion of saliva but also a change in the total motor reaction of the dog.

---

[1] Reprinted in part from my article, "Language and the Constructive Energies of the Psyche," *Scientia* (May, 1936).

[2] In Chapter X, I have shown that Pavlov's term is not appropriate. Conditioned reflexes are not reflexes in the common sense. I use Pavlov's terminology merely in order to facilitate understanding.

When the food stimulus has been connected with a light signal, the light becomes a stimulus for food. When the signal comes, the organism prepares itself for food. This same relation exists between the word and the object which it means. The word has the function of a signal for an attitude of the organism which may express itself either in an action or in a change in the innervation of visceral organs in the broadest sense. The solution to the problem of the meaning of a sentence, which has been so puzzling to investigators, will be found in the preparedness of the organism to the object promised by the signal. This preparedness is not merely a physiological state but is perceived by the individual.

Logicians always have declined further analysis of the signal function of words by saying that the variety of sensations, representations, feelings, and their changing character indicated an occurrence in psychological experience which was completely different from meaning in the logical sense. Attempts to relate meaning with functions of the psyche which are better understood from an empirical point of view have been decried as psychologistic. If we take as the unit, action based upon experience and upon the attitude towards objects, objections of this kind are not possible, and the highly artificial distinction between impression and expression must be given up. The irregular sequence of disconnected shreds of representations and images and the irregular fluctuations of feeling and feeling tones have significance only by being a part of a total situation, which culminates either in an action or in preparedness for action. Actions are indeed definite, even more definite than the preparedness to action; this, in our opinion, constitutes meaning.

This discussion of the signal function of the word of course takes for granted that language exists and is merely transmitted by the adult to the child. J. B. Watson and Bertrand Russell have emphasized that words act as signals in the process of conditioning. Russell is of the opinion that the structure of sentences must be considered differently. He thinks it cannot be explained in a behavioristic way. He believes that the correct use of relational words—that is, of sentences—involves what may be correctly termed perception of form (this involves a definite reaction to a stimulus which is a form). The first words of children usually have the significance of sentences. The child expresses pleasure by the word which names the object. The word "sugar" says: "Look how nice it is; I would like to have it." Now sugar and spinach are not simple data of experience which wander into the child's head; both objects have been built up by a series of constructive processes, not only in the child's mind but also in the child's actions. We speak of an object merely when some kind of stability in action has been reached. A word which designates an object of relative stability becomes a reliable basis for action and a definite entity or concept. If you forget that objects are products of a construction in which trial and error play such an important part, and forget about the motor part in every perception, you will misunderstand the sign function of language and the meaning of meaning. (See C. K. Ogden and I. A. Richards.)

One may ask how the word has acquired such signal functions for man and why man has decided to take words and not movements of the fingers or of the toes as signals for objects. To get an answer to this age-old question it is necessary to go to observations on children, who have not as yet acquired the signal function of words through education. This is the period of spontaneous crying and babbling. The crying of the child is an expression of biological needs. It very often ceases when the biological needs are satisfied. Siegfried Bernfeld justly calls it an instinctive action with a definite aim. The crying stops when the child starts sucking. From the beginning the oral apparatus is the center of important biological functions. Taking food is connected with noises. There is the smacking of lips. When sucking is replaced by chewing and biting, other specific noises occur. To make these remarks more graphic, consider a dog devouring its food. Anton Delbrueck relates the "Ma" sound, which plays such an important part in the early utterances of children, to the sucking movement of the child. G. E. Wundt emphasizes the fact that organs of the mouth which serve eating are named by sounds produced by the same function. It is possible to hypothesize that speech is the expression of an oral tendency to get hold of objects, and also expresses the wish to devour the object. Darwin emphasized the importance of speech and singing in the sexual amenities of animals. The mouth and the vocal organs serve manifold biological needs, and this, their primary function, enables them to produce signals for objects.

In babbling the child experiments with sounds. According to E. A. Esper, who contributed an excellent paper on language, the stimuli which lead to babbling are chiefly internal. So-called stimuli are probably never merely internal or external. We react to the world according to the internal state in which we are. There is no purely internal state because we are always directed toward the world. Internal and external are correlated with each other. Once he realizes that his efforts can produce sounds, the child tries to reproduce the sounds he hears. In experiments on acoustic imaginations, Sam Parker and I found subjects who could imagine the sound of a tuning fork only if they imagined themselves hitting the tuning fork.

The child babbles because a diffuse motor activity is as characteristic for motility as continuous sensation (as in idioretinal light) is characteristic for the perceptual side of psychic life. Not only the vocal organs but also the motility of the total body of the suckling are continuously in action. The organism is in a continuous flux-motion, from a sensory as well as from a motor point of view. These primitive sensory and motor activities are in many respects rhythmical in character. They probably represent a primitive tendency to adaptation. The babbling corresponds to the vortices and currents in the visual field. It is a field of action. Rhythmical function also goes on in the electrical field, as is shown by the Berger rhythm obtained from the cortical region, especially from the occipital region of the cortex. It is characteristically modified by the incoming sound, as E. G. Weaver and C. Bray especially have shown.

Continuous activity is necessary for the child to gain understanding of sounds. He has to reconstruct them. There is not a mere coincidence of motility and the sound of babbling. Modern psychology is not inclined to put emphasis on imitation. F. H. Allport tends to reduce imitation to conditioning. Still, imitation undoubtedly does exist in language, as the investigations of C. Stern and W. Stern have shown,

It is a genuine tendency. When one observes behavior and utterances of children one continually finds instances of imitation. Children often answer a question, which has previously been directed to another child, with words almost identical with those the other child used. Analysis of the meaning of imitation is necessary. In the case quoted, it merely may be simpler to repeat. The repetition may express admiration for an intelligent answer of the other child, or may even be based on a wish of being completely like the other child.

In Pavlov's experiments, conditioning means preparedness and does not mean a mechanical sequence of events. When a child babbles continually, after he has heard himself babbling, he may do so only because the sound has given him full control of his muscles and he wants this whole situation back. Motility of the entire body brings the organism into continuous touch with reality, and so creates new sensory impressions. There is no fundamental difference between the vocal organs and the mouth and the other organs of motility.

Our relations to objects are twofold. We try to get hold of the object. Motility serves this purpose. We grasp with hands and mouth and we are directed towards the object or away from it. The second mechanism is that of identification. We may identify ourselves with the object, may become like the object. We act in the same way as the object acts. It is a matter of course that we must have some inner relation to the object in order to desire identification. The identification mechanism cannot be prior to and more primitive than the object mechanism, as Freud himself and many other analysts are inclined to believe. Although the object relation is a necessary prerequisite to identification, identification is an independent biological attitude, indicating the social character of living beings and their experiences. (This problem is very fully elucidated in *The Image and Appearance of the Human Body*.) Whatever the relation between imitation and identification may be, they belong close together. In psychoanalytic terminology, identification is a specific psychological mechanism explaining conscious imitations as well as actions which we may class as "unconscious" imitations.

Direct imitation of sounds which do not have the character of speech (onomatopoeia) does not play a very important part in the development of language. Whenever it occurs, the explanation is simple. Sound emitted by an object may easily become a signal for the object. Sounds produced by the mouth during eating are natural signals for the presence of food. Noises emitted by the sexually excited person show the particular state of mind present in an individual. Noises concomitant to vital functions are signals to others indicating the biological state of the individual. All noises emitted by the mouth have an immediate social character and social consequences, which in the course of events may be sought by the individual, who then will feel inclined to give the signal again. Signals, by their very nature, have a social function. It is possible that signals may acquire their final meaning only by the effect they have on the social group. According to the investigations of Frisch, the homecoming bee starts dancing, touching, and pushing other bees, which thus receive its contact and smell. The other bees then leave the beehive for the feeding ground. One may call this dance a signal. Probably the dance has a decided individual function for the bee; it acquires the signal function since it expresses itself in motion which makes itself felt. This is a signal, irrespective of whether the bee wants to signalize or not. It has a social function and leads to social actions. It is hard to believe that this social function is merely an accessory.

Noises provoked by eating are a signal to others, whether or not one wishes them to be so. Generally speaking, signals have a social significance. Pavlov's dogs relied on some unknown force (if the experimenter were not in the room) to supply the food after the light signal, which was a promise. We speak of signals and promises in such terms as "lightning promising thunder." We cannot provoke the lightning ourselves. Of greater importance are signals produced by ourselves or by other living beings to express a definite announcement that something else will come. Lightning is a sign that thunder will come. When regular sequences occur, the beginning of the sequence signalizes its continuance. Words are self-produced signals. Signal systems are at first always comparatively crude and have to be worked out in a process of gradual adaptation by trial and error. But signs and signals are never as reliable as the object itself. The development of the modern rules of contract bridge is an amusing instance of this kind. To look directly into the hands of the other players would certainly be a simpler and more reliable procedure than to indicate the strength of a hand of cards by one's bidding.

The drops of saliva in Pavlov's experiments indicate that the dog expects food, or in objective terminology, that he is prepared for it. The light or sound which provokes the conditioned reflex is a signal of the food to come. The dog cannot produce these signals himself. By the drops of saliva the dog expresses its appetite; the meaning of the drops is that the dog wants food. The meaning of the light or sound signal is that food is promised. The saliva indicates that the promise is understood, that the meaning of the signal is clear. Nature itself would seem to be continually promising something, since there are regular sequences. The first part of the sequence promises that the other part will follow. In Pavlov's and Bechterew's experiments the signals are chosen arbitrarily by the experimenter. In language, the adult chooses the word for the child. That language signs have been chosen as a by-product of the vital function of devouring is merely an historical derivation. It is remarkable that Pavlov's progress in experimentation is closely connected with the substitution of "artificial" signals—such as bell, metronome, light, skin irritation—for the natural ones of sight and smell of the food.

If sound or light acquire a signal function it is at first inexact and only later becomes precisely differentiated. In the words of Pavlov, differential inhibition "must occur when from any definite agent a conditioned stimulus is elaborated, then all similar and related stimuli also have somewhat the same effect. But when the chosen stimulus is repeated many times these extraneous stimuli gradually become ineffective." Pavlov further writes [3]:

We have made a conditioned stimulus from the mechanical irritation of a certain place on the skin. At first after this conditioned reflex is established other points of the skin also show the same effect when they are

---

[3] *Lectures,* p. 298.

stimulated, and the closer they lie to the first point, the stronger their effect. This spontaneous generalization of the stimulus has a special biological significance, and is the expression of the irradiation of the excitation in the mass of the cortex. By repeating the stimulation of our chosen point in the skin and accompanying it with feeding, and not accompanying the stimulation of other points by feeding, these latter become inactive; now they are differentiated, negative, conditioned stimuli. This kind of inhibition we call differential inhibition.

Differential inhibition fulfills a still more complicated task; it forms the foundation of the differentiation, delimitation or separation of the compound stimuli which have been previously extended in the cortex of the cerebrum by means of the coupling activity.

Similar results may be obtained with sounds of different frequency. In the process of differential inhibition, very specific and fine differentiations take place. Differential inhibition is a process of trial and error which leads to a better understanding of the quality of an object, which in this case is the signal character of the excitation of the skin and of the sound. The differentiation takes place under the guidance of experience. Experience is not mechanical repetition but construction and reconstruction, under the guidance of biological needs or by the guidance of goals and aims of the individual. We may say that the stimulation of the skin and the sound are at first general concepts and later become specific connotations, in a process of differentiation.

The term "general concept" is perhaps not quite correct. The dog merely has no interest or reason in differentiation: it is simpler for him to expect food after every sound. Children use concepts and words primarily in the same way. One child said: "People die of pneumonia." He had heard from adults that in one specific case this had happened and, until he acquired new relevant experiences, he had no reason to think otherwise. Probably every general concept gets its final "meaning" only by continuous contact with reality.

The child believes the single case to fit everything. David Wechsler and I call this "the principle of undue generalization." One may say that thinking starts with general concepts, although this is incorrect if we take the term "general concept" in the formal logical sense. The general concept of the child is a single experience, taken without analysis as representative of many other experiences. In the experiments of Pavlov, a differential inhibition takes place. This differential inhibition may occur when the sound is repeated often enough, but the differentiation takes place more correctly and more quickly when the unconditioned stimulus follows only the one specific sound, whereas the other stimuli are not followed by the unconditioned stimulus. We obtain a specific insight into the nature of a signal only by trial and error, or by the way of fulfilled and disappointed expectations.

Of course, dogs do not talk, but we may expect that, if we form a so-called trace reaction, the dog may think in the meantime, "Now after awhile I shall get food," and it is probable that the image of food will come into its mind. The behaviorist will say that we have no proof of this; but, if one experiments on human beings, one can easily prove that an electric shock, given an individual five seconds after a signal, is psychologically anticipated. It may even be reproduced with hallucinatory vividness. It may be that we deal with the most simple case of a memory image and, furthermore, with an hallucination. In such a case the memory image is a part of the inner preparedness for the unconditioned stimulus and belongs to the total reaction. The past situation returns in the service of the present. The memory image and the representation are a part of the conditioned reflex, in Pavlov's sense. If the word is really a signal for the object, the picture of the object and the memory of the object must be closely related to the word. We should not forget that the object or its memory image also provokes a set of reactions or actions. In Pavlov's dog the conditioned reflex is not only the secretion of saliva but also motor reactions, which lead to the grasping of the food. Only because of the artificiality of Pavlov's experimental set-up is this side not fully apparent.

The meaning of the word comprises, therefore, the object (its representation or memory image) and the motor reactions and physiological reactions connected with it. The object is the foundation for the concept and the word is the sign for the concept. To have an intention or direction toward an object in thinking is related to a reaction of the total organism. The meaning of a word may become founded in organic reactions rather than in the memory image. We then deal with thinking which is to a great extent independent of imagination. The object is supposed to have some kind of stability. A word that designates an object forms a concept purporting to be a definite entity, which is unchangeable, and which therefore offers a reliable basis for actions. One may, of course, say that the word "horse" may mean a specific horse, or it also may mean all horses. In the latter case we deal with a general concept although it is easy to prove that in everyday life these general concepts are far from being general. They merely claim to be a possible basis for action in an unlimited number of cases. If one tries to use general concepts as a practical basis for action, one soon finds out that they are approximately as reliable as the sound which conditions drops of saliva, before differentiation has taken place.

What we call a mere word, or what we call a sentence, is always more or less arbitrary. When I say, for instance, the word "horse" and nothing else, I imply that I do not intend to be explicit and do not want to commit myself. The concept, in the sense of logicians, is a mere abstraction which does not exist. When I pronounce a single letter of the alphabet I merely want to emphasize that we deal simply with a sound without any definite relation to another object. Or, in other words, whatever we say, be it a letter, a syllable, a word, or a sentence, yields sound patterns which we use as signals for the total situation that should be the basis for our actions. Sentences offer problems of their own, although language becomes flexible only through them. It is difficult to divide a word into parts. If it were possible, the word would not be a mere word but a sentence. Characteristically in a sentence, an object or a fact is considered as having different aspects or parts standing in different relations to each other. One might say that the different grammatical forms of the word and the different prefixes and suffixes were subdivisions of the word. However, the different grammatical forms have meaning only in a sentence and not in relation to a single word. The prefixed or suffixed word is merely a word which can be divided into part-sounds but not into part-meanings. In our attitude towards objects we do not want objects that are completely stabilized. We tolerate a motionless, changeless object only for a very short time, and continue by dividing it into parts and considering its different aspects.

The history of the indivisible atom is interesting from this point of view. What are the qualities of the atom? Does it move? Does it stand still? What is its form? Even the indivisible had to be divided and subdivided till there finally remained a mysterious energy quantum, which has either no definite velocity or no definite place. The atom has become divisible, has lost its constancy and stability and is now much more inconstant than an object of the senses. The development of physics is dependent upon basic psychologic principles of psychic experience, as I have pointed out in my book on the philosophy of nature (*Gedanken zur Naturphilosophie*). The development of the theory of the atom shows that psychologically we cannot tolerate constant and static entities. The stabilized object is a psychological borderline concept. We see sides of the object, parts of the object, and also like to see the object in pieces. We put the pieces together and try to make a new unit out of them, which we again destroy.

If language consisted only of words, it would not have sufficient flexibility and could not picture the breaking of the objects into parts and pieces. Grammar leads to a rather complete breakup of words and so reflects the breakup of the situation and objects which, as emphasized above, play such an important part in perception. On the basis of the same qualities, the constructive process becomes possible. Since grammar chiefly reflects the breaking up of the object or the construction of the object, the relation of the whole to the parts and pieces becomes the most important content of sentence and grammar. The expression of attributive relations is, therefore, one of the most important functions of the sentence. Grammar develops language into a scientific system for breaking up and composing total situations.

What is expressed in a sentence? Bertrand Russell correctly says that sentences signalize relations. But so do words; and every object is a relation. The relations indicated in sentences are probably more complicated, or perhaps more specific. Erdmann is of the opinion that sentence and judgment merely express an attributive relation. A noun designates an object, and the verb, adjective, and copula express an attributive relation. If this statement is true, the similarity between judgments and concepts becomes still greater. In the simplest case we would deal merely with an object and some of its qualities. Russell has justly added that the attributive relation is only one of many other relations, although according to our opinion it is particularly important from the point of view of the constitution of an object. There is the relation of above and below, front and behind, small and large, slow and fast; or, in other words, the richness of total experiences. The sign function of languages is far developed in many of these cases. It is true one can always say that every discussion finally leads back to an object and its qualities or, in the words of the logicians, to the problem of attribution. There are innumerable theories of judgment. Franz Brentano stated that in a judgment we say "yes" or "no" to a proposition. The inner act of saying "yes" or "no" would thus be the real essence of judgment and the real function of sentences. Previous discussions do not leave any doubt that psychic life is active and constructive. We always intend to do something, and we build up. We have emotions and we are continually acting. It is probable that different types of action are necessary for different psychic acts. When we construct an object and when we construct relations between objects, the psychic activities involved must be different. We are much more conscious of our activities when the construction is complicated. In judgment this may appear like a definite agreement or disagreement, but it should be understood only from the general point of view of construction of object relations, which are necessarily connected with a higher degree of organization. Therefore, I do not think that Brentano's statement is of very general significance, but the theory may help us to reach better insight into the emotional background of judgments. The primary function of judgment is either to lead us toward or away from the object.

In previous years I used as basis for a discussion E. Gamper's formulation reproduced in C. K. Ogden and I. A. Richards, *The Meaning of Meaning,* from which I quote the following:

In every complete statement (*Aussage*) we can distinguish: A) The Sounds (*Aussage-laute*), i. e., the verbal form of the statement, or better the phonesis (*Lautung*); B) The Import (*Aussage-inhalt*), i. e., the sense (*Sinn*) of the statement; C) The Foundation (*Aussagegrundlage*), i. e., the actual fact (*Tatsache*) to which the statement is related. The relations between these three elements can be thus characterized: The sounds (*phonesis*) are the expression (*Ausdruck*) of the import, and the designation (*Bezeichnung*) of the foundation, while the import is the interpretation (*Auffassung*) of the foundation. In so far as the sounds are treated as the expressions of the import they are grouped with a statement (*Aussage*). In so far as the foundation is treated as the fact comprehended by the import, it can be called the stated fact (*Ausgesagte Sachverhalt*); or simply, the fact. The relation subsisting between the statement and the fact expressed is called meaning (*Bedeutung*).

I still believe that this discussion is basically correct, but I have already pointed to the fact that the import merely means that the individual is emotionally directed towards the object (the foundation). Of course, sounds of this type contain in themselves the fact that they mean more than mere sounds. One may easily call this the expression of the import. It is also true that the sound which for the dog has become a promise that feeding will occur is no longer like any other sound. It has gone through many more constructive processes. For the dog the sound has the import of feeding. The previous feeding experiences are the foundations to which the sound relates. We also understand why import is the interpretation of the foundation. I would state, however, that it is no longer so important to go into every detail of the relation between signal and fact, and that the general insight that we deal with constructive processes is of outstanding importance.

One sees that it is not so difficult to reach a biological and physiological theory of language if one considers the principles of the constructive psychic energies. Words and sentences have signal functions. They are signals for objects. Objects are not merely given to the individual by passive reception but in a continuous process of construction and reconstruction. The individual takes parts of the objects, puts them together, rejects other parts, molds and remolds the object. This remolding, reconstructing, rebuilding process is based upon a continuous interplay between sensory and motor functions. With the construction of the object, the first steps have already been taken towards using the object for the biologic purposes and aims of the individual, since the whole process of construction is guided by the biologic needs of the individual and later by the situation. When an object is signalized, the sensory motor attitudes connected with the construction and utilization of objects come into play. The meaning of a word and of a sentence is the sum total of the sensory motor attitudes concerning the expected objects. This sum total is unified in the preparedness to action, or in action as such. Words get their signal function by being by-products of the process of getting hold of food and sexual objects. Primarily, they were psychological phenomena of excess energy not immediately used for hunger and sex, and have primary directness toward leading to the satisfaction of urges from which they originated. Signal functions have an immense social significance. They are signal functions not only for one individual but for the whole community. Signal functions are at first inexact indicators of objects biologically important. By continuous testing they are reconstructed so that they become more reliable guides to action. The material for the signal function is taken from the vague background of continuous motor activity and unrest of the small child with its undifferentiated needs. The constructive process also gives motor perfection to language. The further elaboration of language takes place by trial and error, biologic satisfaction and disappointment, which lead from the use of single experiences as patterns for action to individualized action fitting specific situations.

THE PSYCHOPATHOLOGY OF LANGUAGE

Psychopathologists use language as their chief instrument. They listen to what the patient tells them, and then must achieve understanding of the patient's personality. This seems an almost impossible task if one approaches language from the point of view of the logician. The task becomes much simpler if language is considered

merely a sign, and a sign of varying reliability according to the definitiveness in the relation between sign and object or to the varying
degree of the constructive process concerning language. If one considers language from this point of view, it appears no less reliable
than other signs; for instance, drops of saliva. The objects in question
are complicated but it is still possible to reach them in approximation.

The meaning of a sign is the attitude towards the object to which
the sign points. Signs provoke attitudes toward objects and thus become the basis for actions which aim at the object (referent, in the
terminology of C. K. Ogden and I. Richards). Since sign, referent,
and action are so closely interwoven, it is justifiable to stress the importance of action and behavior. There is no fundamental conflict between our psychology and behaviorism. Imaginations and thoughts
are not entities in themselves but are connected with definite attitudes. One often speaks of the course from thought to speech. This is
as wrong as if one were to consider thought an independent entity.
Thoughts are linked up with images and images lead to motility, and,
as C. Hartshorne has pointed out, there is a socialized factor in sensations and, I may add, in imagination and thinking. This socialized
factor leads to expression, the foremost channel of which is language.
Language is, therefore, only a part of the socialized function of expression and only a part of the motor sign function. Owing to the
factors discussed above, language is capable of using a great amount
of libidinous energy and thus becomes superior to other signs. Since
thinking and imagination have so many social elements, and language
is the best socialized function, imagination and thinking always have
a direction towards expression in words, and tend to signalize themselves to the community. In thinking, therefore, we find a direction
towards verbalization, but there is a great difference between complete and incomplete verbalization. One again sees how useless it is
to talk about psychic elements instead of attitudes. Freud has developed the rather complicated idea that the difference between the
conscious and unconscious idea is not that they are different records
of the same content situated in different parts of the mind, but that

the conscious idea comprises the concrete idea plus the verbal idea corresponding to it, while the unconscious idea is that for the thing alone.

The relation between sign and referent is so fundamental that it is hard to believe it is not present in what Freud calls "unconscious thinking." Freud has not given enough attention to the sign function of words and language. He states that in schizophrenia words are subject to the same process as that which makes dream images out of dream thoughts. They undergo condensation and by means of displacement transfer their cathexes to one another. The process may extend so far that, because of its manifold relations, the single word may come to represent a whole train of thoughts. Freud is also of the opinion that the predominance of the word relation over the object relation gives to the substitute formation the strangeness characteristic of schizophrenia.

In aphasia there is an impairment in the signal function of language. In some of the cases the speaker is not able to give the signal; and, in other cases, he is not able to grasp the sign which another uses. The inability to give the sign may consist of more or less extensive mutilation of the phonetic structure of the verbal signs, or in using the wrong signs. In other cases it may merely be difficult to get hold of signs of specific objects. There is a relation between the inability to produce correct verbal signs and the inability to understand and react to verbal signs correctly. Still, in the so-called motor asphasia cases, the production of signs is chiefly impaired, whereas in sensory aphasia cases the understanding of signs is impaired. The sensory aphasia case is also unable to produce the correct signs and the correct grammatical sequence of signs. Henry Head's terms, "verbal aphasia and syntactical aphasia" are merely other names for the same types of aphasia. Head's "nominal aphasia" comprises cases with essentially defective use of names and lack of comprehension of the nominal meaning of words or other "symbols." The older aphasia literature calls such cases "amnestic aphasias." Head speaks about disorders in symbolic thinking. Kurt Goldstein emphasizes that categorical thinking is impaired in amnestic aphasia. Nevertheless, it is not the central function of thinking which is impaired in these cases. It is true that the sign-referent relation is disturbed in an important province of psychic life. This relation, however, is at least partially preserved in other fields of the patient's experience; his social relations are in many respects undisturbed. It is true also that there are aberrations which are not merely in the sphere of speech. The motor aphasic patient reduces his activities, keeps to himself, is moody and pessimistic. The sensory aphasic patient is outgoing, talkative, optimistic, and hyperactive. The core of the personality of these patients remains intact and the impairment in their social behavior generally is not very extensive. Have the moodiness, the pessimism, and the inactivity of the motor aphasic patient and the logorrhoea and hyperactivity of the sensory aphasic patient an inner connection with the speech disturbance and the disturbance in thinking? Or, in other words, is there one basic disturbance which explains the whole attitude of the patient? The disturbance in the sign function has no definite inner relation to the disturbance in the attitude of these patients. It merely has a relation to their difficulties in thinking; or, at least, our present insight into psychological problems does not allow us to deduce that persons who use the syntactic forms incorrectly should be euphoric and hyperactive and should not be aware of their defect. Apparently one type of thinking is closely related to the core of the personality and another type of thinking is less central. This latter type is closer to speech; or this type of thinking has closer relation to the formulation of words. In the aphasic patient this type of thinking is disturbed.

Henry Head characterizes the asphasic disturbances as disorders in symbolic thinking. The English language uses the term "symbol" in a wider sense than does the German language. In the American edition of the *Pocket Oxford Dictionary* (1927) we find the following definition of symbol: "Thing regarded by general consent as naturally typifying or representing or recalling something by possession of analogous qualities or by association in fact or thought (*white, the lion, the thunderbolt, the cross are ss. of purity, courage, Zeus,*

Christianity); mark or character taken as the conventional sign of some object or idea or process, e. g., the planet signs, chemical element letters, letters of the alphabet."

There are two types of signs. The one type is not connected by partial identity or by similarity with the referent. These are signs in the proper sense. As the first part of this discussion has shown, language belongs chiefly to this type of sign, although historically it may have developed in part from signs which were partially identical or similar to the referent. These latter signs are symbols in the narrower sense. The more conventional the sign, the simpler is its use. In primitive language, symbols in the narrower sense play a greater part than in more developed language. Symbols in the psychoanalytic sense are partially identical with, or similar to, the referent. In many of the symbols of psychoanalysis, the relation between sign and referent is "unconscious," that is, in the background of consciousness. In geometry, the sign used has something in common with the referent and we deal with a definite relation. The symbol in art and religion points not to a definite referent but to one which remains more or less vague. In allegory, the referent is definite; allegory is akin to the sign in geometry, but is chiefly based on the partial identity of the sign with the referent, whereas in geometry the sign is generally similar to the referent. If one uses the term "symbol" one should be aware that it means a great variety of sign referent relations. These distinctions may appear formal and artificial; nevertheless, they have significance even from a clinical point of view.

I have mentioned that in the course of development of language the word tends to lose its inner relation of similarity to and partial identity with the referent. It becomes a sign, and is not a symbol in the narrower sense characterized above. In schizophrenia the patient has lost the capacity of distinguishing which signals are reliable and which are not. Under the influence of overstrong instinctive drives, similarity and partial identity appear to him as reliable sign functions. Under the same influence he is ready to emphasize the partial identity between the sign (symbol) and the object and to take the sign for the object. In all of this there is a tendency to take the signal for the referent. The stronger our instinctive drives, the stronger is this tendency. It is particularly alluring to take the word as an equivalent of the object as such. The word initiates the constructive process which in the final outcome leads to the object. It has the same function as the light signal in Pavlov's experiments, which leads to salivation. This, characteristically, even starts a little prematurely when trace reflexes are examined. A patient mentioned by Freud, complains that her lover is pretending something (*verstellt sich*) because in church he stood first in one and then in another place (*stellt sich um*). Freud explains this instance by saying that in schizophrenia the primary process (condensation, symbolization, etc.) takes place merely in words. This is incorrect. As mentioned above, the disturbance in the sign-referent function in schizophrenics spreads over the whole field of experience, and the schizophrenic attitude towards the word is merely one instance of his general attitude.

The sign may become a substitute for the object as indeed it becomes in Pavlov's experiments and may even substitute for the object completely, as in belief in the magic power of words. We also understand why the name is so often taken as an object. The name provokes motor attitudes in the same way as does the object. One of my patients, reported in *Wahn und Erkenntnis,* said that one produces sausage by the word "sup." He himself can become godlike, hypnotic, by the word "susura." By this word a celestial body comes into him. Some celestial bodies give two or three words, and some thousands. The more words they give, the more valuable they are. He thinks that one can throw words into a basketlike object. Preuss reports that primitives consider the word not only as magic which originates from human beings, but as substance acting independently —an imitation of the objects which it names.

Difficulties in the use of words arise for the individual when words are not used as signs according to social tradition, because the social tradition is overcome by instinctive needs. Words, therefore, become very closely allied to emotional relations.

A woman thirty-five years of age, well-advanced schizophrenia, gave these three definitions of a puddle: (1) "It is a drop of water and

Scotch; a rosebud and soon it goes into four roses to be big enough for a battleship. (2) Mud and water makes most water. (3) That's where the transformation of an ugly duckling into a swan."

This certainly is not merely taking words for things, but represents an attitude of indifference to a complete perception of the world. Here, a constructive process stops before it has come to the final conclusion. Some difficulty in the emotional life is present; and a deeper knowledge of any case of this kind, as Jung has first shown, reveals that the arrest in speech development is due to an arrest in the thinking process in connection with emotional problems. As a result of this arrest, the object to which the thinking process tends remains outside its reach, while parts of the object, which otherwise are neglected, come into the foreground. This is especially important in the third definition. In the first definition the idea of mixture leads to Scotch, the queer formulation "a drop" leads to rosebud. Besides a change in the content, the grammatical construction is also disturbed. The third instance is characteristic in so far as the patient does not care to finish the sentence. In the analysis of speech in schizophrenics, one therefore has to add a further principle, namely, that the development of thinking remains incomplete, and with that, an arrest also takes place in the verbal formulation. The schizophrenic speech disturbances thus can be understood by three principles: (1) the signal is in part or completely identified with the referent; (2) this identification gives magic power to the word; (3) the referent and the words and sentences are products of incomplete development of the thought and language construction. The incompletely developed thought may find a correct expression, or the completely or incompletely developed thought may find an incomplete expression. The differentiation of disturbances of this kind from aphasic disturbance is comparatively simple, in the majority of cases, since in the aphasic case the sign function is chiefly disturbed, whereas in the schizophrenic case the disturbance is in the development of the thought process as such. The involvement of the sign function is more or less related to the deep arrest in the construction of the thought process.

One sees that in the speech disturbances of the schizophrenic the deeper problems of the personality will be revealed, whereas the sign-function disturbance in the aphasic will not lead to the deeper disturbances of the personality of the patient. It is characteristic that the aphasia patient, unless the destruction in the brain goes beyond the speech centers, shows in his whole attitude that his emotional relations to other human beings are not fundamentally disturbed. In contrast, the schizophrenic patient shows fundamentally central disturbances. This is the more remarkable because the aphasic patient certainly has disturbances in his whole attitude, but they do not affect his social human relations in a deeper way.

There are cases in which it is difficult to make such sharp differentiation. Frank J. Curran and I have ascribed such cases of mental confusion to a toxic basis. One patient said, for instance: "I never saw a bulldog eating feces of tulips, did you? I suppose it is supposed to be silly. If it is silly eating a piece of tulip you do hesitate naturally when you are used to your teeth every day. When I talk now I evidently go too fast for my own mind, don't you think so?" Another of our cases, in which a schizoid personality had a slight sensory aphasia, gave the following definition of a lecture: "A lecture is a subject telling about a certain subject, the theory and the publisher." Her definition of a puddle (in writing) was: "Mixture of thoughts, muddled water, other sand within his . . . puddle, mixture, ice cream soda, chocolate and vanilla soda."

The marked similarity between the various types of speech disturbances is ultimately based on the fact that we deal with human beings who strive towards the world. After all, signals are signals for objects, and speech is never completely dissociated from its original function; that is, serving the vital needs of the individual concerning food and sex.

Speech is our most important weapon in a psychotherapeutic approach. In almost every neurosis we see that particular words and phrases gain a specific significance for the patient. Specific words have become the signals for fundamental attitudes, and covered by these specific words the attitude remains unchangeable. It is an important task for psychotherapy to show what the word actually signalizes. When in one of my patients "beauty" has become the motive for his whole life, and the idea that he is unable to attain the love of a beautiful woman has hindered him from getting any satisfaction out of life, the analysis of the signal functions of this word must be made. In such cases one word and one concept sum up the early history and the libidinous situation of the patient. The word signals mean much more for this patient than for others; the analysis of the word and its referent becomes the psychotherapeutic procedure. One often sees that in neurosis the signal is taken as the referent, especially under the influence of emotions, and that processes are initiated which culminate in magic thinking as described above. These are a common manifestation not only in the life of neurotics but in every human life. Ogden and Richards and Alfred Korzybski are right when they emphasize the importance of the clear understanding of words, and demand an insight into the relation between the signal and the referent.

This relation is comparatively simple in the case of concrete objects. Difficulties usually start only when we deal with the so-called abstract, where the signal covers a multiplicity of referents. The general concept of "horse," for instance, includes all horses. Difficulties immediately arise, however, since in the psychological process only concrete referents can appear. The preparedness to action provoked by the word signal may then lead to actions which do not fit the referent. On the other hand, we cannot do without abstract thinking, and if we rely too much on concrete thinking and concrete language, we are also unprepared to act. I shall present a short report of a nineteen-year-old patient, probably a schizophrenic, who evidenced a decided greed for single facts and words with definite and concrete meanings.

The patient says he cannot say how many people live in New York, since there are too many high buildings and one cannot count exactly. He has very elaborate plans for his future. He wants to work as a messenger boy, then do evening work, and afterwards apply for a civil service job as a fireman or a policeman. He also has an idea of how much he wants to make when he is thirty years old—around fifty dollars a week. He says he grew too fast, and gives the exact figures of his weight and height. He says his father and mother drink and fight too much and want him out of the house. He says they told the policeman to beat him up, and gives height and weight of the policeman. There is a questionable story about smoking marihuana cigarettes. This is a patient who clings to the petty details of everyday life. He is absolutely concrete, has no confidence in abstractions and the magic of words, thus in some way fulfilling the ideals of semantics. But it is a question whether this clinging to reality is not really the expression of a fear. Mental health would seem to involve the possibility of leaving the concrete for a time. It means the freedom of choosing between the abstract and the concrete.

Abstract and concrete are words which probably stress too much the idea of polarity and opposites. The essence of language and thinking consists in being prepared for many possibilities, and we are only prepared when we have handled single situations and are ready to handle other new single situations.

There exist signs which regulate social behavior (see also Karl Buehler). The expression of anger is, for instance, a sign of social significance. The person experiencing the anger may or may not wish to express it; but signs are given both willfully and involuntarily. Words and sentences are signs which we give voluntarily. They point to occurrences in the outer world or to occurrences concerning the speaker. The melody of speech, the inflections, are additional involuntary signs to the listener. The word in its essence, however, is a sign voluntarily produced. As far as language carries with it involuntary expression, it transgresses its own realm. The sign must be chosen so that the listener can understand it, irrespective of whether it conveys an order, an assertion, or a question. The deliberate communication in social contact is the essence of language. This has nothing to do with the question of whether the words and sentences are symbols for the referent or whether they are signs for the referent in the sense discussed above. In language only a small number of signs are symbolic for the referent. There is a great difference, however, in whether a symbol is used as a symbol or whether it is used as a sign.

When I use a symbol as such, then I do not express the desire that the referent should be clearly known to the person to whom I communicate the symbol. Sign function and symbol function are different but they may occur in combination with each other. The soothing quality of white may be a symbol for peace, and may be used in flags as a wish for peace. I doubt whether primitive tribes would respect such a symbol, the sign character of which is not agreed upon. Symbols may easily lend themselves to sign function; but not every sign is a symbol nor is every symbol a sign. For instance, one distinguishes between symbolic magic and symbolic action. When a primitive points at the head of an enemy with a spear and expects the latter's ruin, we speak of symbolic magic. According to Wundt, it is a symbolic action when a human being expects a religious absolution by a cleansing ceremony in water. Directing a spear against the head of an enemy is not a sign. The primitive does not want to signalize that he wishes to destroy his enemy, but he actually wants to do so by means of an incomplete action. The ceremonial bath is a symbolic wish but not a sign. The social significance of symbolic magic and symbolic action is absolutely different from the social significance of language which is supposed to be a reliable sign system used for communication between human beings.

CHAPTER XVII

MEMORY

IN CHAPTER XIII, in the discussion of time, I stated that an experience which concerns the outside world or the body does not suddenly disappear from the field of consciousness but lingers on and gradually becomes paler. Its importance for the actions of the individual diminishes until it finally passes out of the present situation. Nevertheless, when I am standing in a room I not only know that the things behind my back are present as I saw them but they are more or less vividly in my field of experience. Even if I do not turn around I am conscious that I am able to revive the picture whenever I wish. I may revive representations which will be all the more vivid the more vitally interested I am in this past experience. If I revive them merely for the sake of experimentation, the reproduction will be far from complete. When I see a part of the room before me, something of its actual presence will make the representation of the other part of the room more vivid. As shown in Chapter III, the pictures revived will often be very incomplete, colorless, and even distorted. Moreover, they will not be retained for very long. The distortion affects the shape of the objects and their spatial relationships. We do not accept the reproduction as the actual memory of the room but rather we fit the individual sensual images into an anticipatory scheme, which is consistent with our total experience and the possibility of further action.

This elementary example demonstrates that remembering is far from being a mechanical and passive process. Memory is a dynamic process which is made up of a number of factors: (1) The interest and the tendency to revive the past experience, which arises only in connection with the present situation and with the aims of the individual; (2) the images brought forward do not constitute the remembrance but merely help in the reconstruction of the remembrance; (3) the remembrance is complete when an anticipatory scheme has been fulfilled and the individual representations are fitted into this anticipatory scheme; (4) the final remembrance is so constituted as to form a basis for a new action.

The term anticipatory scheme needs further explanation. Before I start the active process of remembering, the approximate goal to which the remembering will lead is known. Or, in other words, I must know in advance the part of the room which I am going to remember. In what way do I know about the things which I have not yet remembered? Is there merely a somatic "engram" present or is there also a psychic representation? The fact is that I have the knowledge. Part images continually come into consciousness, thus I also know the direction in which I must search in order to go further. But there is still more than that in my consciousness. I know that I shall be able to revive everything and I have, in my consciousness, knowledge which transgresses my immediate sensual data. These are the teachings of the Würzburg School on thought (*Bewusstheit* or *Gedanken*). I would prefer to say that we deal with an embryonic form of thinking, a "germ of thought" (*Keim*). Whatever this germ may be, previous experiences within psychic reach must be changed. These unchanged experiences which cannot be remembered are called preconscious experiences in psychoanalytic terminology.

I therefore conclude that an unchanged picture of past experiences is always present but not immediately remembered, and that past experiences are always present unchanged, in the form of thoughts or diagrams connected with the knowledge which will bring them into consciousness.

During the process of remembering, parts of the situation come up in the form of fleeting images. These fleeting images may be more or less different from what we actually wish to remember. The study of optic imagination (see Chapter III) shows this very clearly. Even these simple considerations indicate that we must have a double system of memory: one a complete and true copy of the actual experience; and the other incomplete, symbolic, and fleeting. The anticipatory scheme is, therefore, the complete remembrance about which we have knowledge and which we reach by diagrams and optic pictures, which have to be chosen and readapted. Thus through a constructive process we regain the memories of the past.

Symbols in remembering can be studied in pathological cases in which forgetting seems to be exaggerated. We may start with the study of the so-called Korsakoff syndrome, in which recent material is quickly forgotten and cannot be recalled. We may also speak of the disturbances in memory retention. This Korsakoff syndrome can be observed in almost every organic brain disease. It is seen in connection with polyneuritis of any etiology—head injury, hanging, carbon-monoxide poisoning, cerebrospinal lues, general paresis, brain tumor, senile involution, and arterio-sclerosis. The difficulty in retention is in the foreground, the memory of past experiences usually being better preserved. Disorientation in time and space is often present. Experiences of the past are frequently reported in distorted form or past experiences are reported which have never taken place (confabulation). Disturbances in immediate perception also occur. H. Buerger-Prinz and M. Kaila emphasize the disturbance in form perception. E. Gruenthal and G. E. Stoerring describe disturbances in thinking and attitudes. Some authors even deny that these are really memory disturbances, but apparently feel that memory is merely mechanical reproduction. H. Hartmann has shown that short stories told by Korsakoff patients are reproduced in a distorted way but that the substitutes are usually similar to the primary content or symbolize it. Indecent content was often reported in a symbolic way. Content which was known in one moment was not known later. Hypnosis sometimes brought forth forgotten material. Stories told to the patient often were reproduced in the way that the patient brought them into connection with himself and reported the events as pertaining to himself (see also discussions by S. Betlheim and H. Hartmann).

In the *Introduction to Psychoanalytic Psychiatry* I state:

It is much more difficult to determine the nature of the attention disorder as we meet with it in the Korsakoff symptom complex. But, aside from the fact that Brodmann and Gregor were able to show by means of the "economy phenomenon" that in the Korsakoff disorder the apparently forgotten also persists and leaves traces behind, clinical experience itself adds probability to this view. Thus one of S. Betlheim and H. Hartmann's patients who had forgotten the birth of a child, hallucinated children lying at her feet. On the basis of our experience with epilepsy we are already obliged to assume that the economy in learning is based upon a retained image; thus the attention disorder must also have as its basis something very akin to the phenomenon of repression. Betlheim and Hartmann have given us important information concerning this. They read to the patients some indecent text. The patients in reproducing the text read to them, changed it into a decent content. They read to a patient the following story: "A young girl went for a walk alone in the fields, a young man met her, fell upon her and threw her on the ground. The girl defended herself but it was to no avail. The man lifted her dress and forced his erect penis into her vagina. After the assault he left the loudly crying girl and ran away." The patient reproduced the story as follows: "Two girls walked up a stairway; two boys followed them up the stairs. They then married the girls because one was pregnant; the other went home." Another patient reproduced the text: "and he forced his erect penis" into the vagina by saying: "and put the knife into the sheath." In another patient, the words "erect penis" were replaced by the word "cigarette."

One sees in the first example that the content was changed into a decent text. The doubling of the scene is still more noteworthy because the one girl wasn't even made pregnant, while the other, while pregnant, was married. That a typical coitus symbol comes to light in the ascending of the stairs is as noteworthy as is the occurrence of the typical symbols of the cigarette and knife for the penis. Affective substitutions and symbols of course arise in the same manner, a subject into which we must not enter here in detail. The typicalness of the symbolism speaks here in favor of manifestations which are strongly rooted phylogenetically.

It is evident, therefore, that the confabulations of the Korsakoff patient depend upon an elaboration of existing memory material.

It seems, therefore, that the actual memory is present but transmits merely symbolic representations into the "consciousness." We are probably dealing with the preliminary stages of remembering. The outstanding points in these preliminary stages are: (1) the material is easily brought into connection with one's own person; (2) the events are, as in the instance given above, multiplied and every part is elaborated in a different way; (3) emotional distortions and elaborations play a particularly important part in the preliminary stages of remembering; (4) condensations are common; (5) there is a tendency to word decency and a happy ending which comes out clearly in these experiments.

It may be asked whether the primitive stages of remembering and of perception have any inner relation to each other. The tendency to multiplication is certainly present in both. Each item in the multiplication deviates from the other, thus showing an elaborating process. We also have found this trend in the study of perception. Furthermore we have found that emotional processes play a much greater role in the preparatory stages of both perception and memory in comparison to the final product. These analogies are not astonishing since the primitive workings of the sensory apparatus find their clearest expression in the images, which also play an important part in the process of remembering.

As shown in Chapter XIII, we localize specific events in a specific point of time by means of a constructive process. In the Korsakoff syndrome the patient not only has difficulty in producing the correct remembrances but he also cannot localize them in time and they undergo distortions and condensations. It is therefore one-sided for Horst to consider the Korsakoff psychosis merely as a disturbance of temporal local signs (*temporale Lokalzeichen*). The preliminary stages in memory development are more strongly under the influence of emotional drives than is the final product. The mere fact that Korsakoff patients bring their memory material in close connection with their own ego contradicts the opinion of Horst. I may merely mention in passing that memory disturbances in general paresis are very closely related to memory disturbances in the Korsakoff psychosis. The patient with dementia treats the present in the same fashion as he treats the past. He does not feel obliged to unify and integrate his distorted recollections.

It is easy to understand memory gaps which occur in amnesias of all kinds. In hysterical amnesia the individual merely wants to forget experiences which already have been fully elaborated, because they are too painful or disagreeable. It seems that these processes of repression occur more easily when the individual has weakened his ego system by intoxication. Apparently we dare not forget obvious material when our ego system is too well preserved. Alcoholic intoxication not only reverses repressions but also makes impressions paler so that individuals can more easily forget what they want to forget. In any case, the frequency of amnesias in alcoholics points to the fact that some repressions are due to a weakening of moral standards and of the superego. I do not deny the importance of the toxic factor, but, as R. Stern has shown, in the majority of cases amnesias due to pathological alcohol intoxication can be cleared up by hypnosis. In *The Image and Appearance of the Human Body,* I discussed the various possibilities for and types of repression. I shall return to this topic later on in more detail.

Attempts to reproduce memory material do not always lead to preliminary stages. The remembrance may remain suppressed and may not play an important part in one or another case. Symbolic confabulatory elements then also play a less important part. E. Gruenthal and G. E. Stoerring reported a case in which forgotten material was simply forgotten and not replaced by symbolic products. They came to the conclusion that an isolated function of memory existed, which alone may be disturbed, and they rejected the results of Buerger-Prinz, who emphasized the disturbances in the perceptive sphere as necessary correlates to the memory disturbance. They emphasized that the memory disturbance secondarily influenced most of the other psychological functions.

These authors were of the opinion that their patient, who suffered accidental gas poisoning, had completely lost the faculty of retention. All the other psychic disturbances he showed were secondary to the isolated loss of the faculty of retention. No continuous discussion with the patient was possible since he immediately forgot the questions put before him. It was necessary to repeat even short questions several times. If the questioning was stopped after he started to answer he either gave no further response or repeated the beginning of his answer. The patient still thought that the date of the examination was the date on which he was poisoned four years before. He did not know that he had married. The patient did not think that his memory was bad and considered himself perfectly healthy. Experimentally he was unable to retain the problem presented to him in consciousness for more than two seconds. Repetitions did not improve the results. The patient was helpless. He was always very glad to see his wife but he did not know that she had been with him before. He answered questions of differentiation comparatively well but it was necessary to repeat a question several times. His spontaneous utterances were chiefly related to the immediate situation. The patient sometimes felt that he should do something, even when he forgot what he wanted to do and that he wanted to do something.

This case is really of great importance for the general problems of psychopathology. Does an isolated function in the mind exist which deals only with the retention of material, and can this function be taken away without any definite impairment of other functions? If so we would have to think that psychic life consists of a mosaic of uncorrelated functions. This is just the point which Stephan Krauss stresses. The question is, however, whether this isolated case justifies such sweeping conclusions. It is so far the only case in which learning did not make any difference. In all the other cases described in the literature learning does take place, as Brodmann, Gregor, and others have extensively shown. The material learned always leaves traces. E. Gruenthal and G. E. Stoerring do not think that any traces remain in the experience of their patient. When one isolated case contradicts so many other observations the question arises whether the authors' interpretation is correct. If the patient's memory for the distant past is preserved, why should he speak in only very short sentences? Why should he forget the continuation of a sentence which he has started? Why should he talk so little? Why should he show so few impulses? In short the patient not only has disturbances in retention but in his whole attitude as well. The diagnosis of an impulse disturbance is at least very probable, and therefore the case is not one of isolated disturbances of retention only.

I do not doubt that the case has retention disturbances too, and I believe that H. Buerger-Prinz and M. Kaila present a one-sided view when they neglect memory disturbances in the Korsakoff syndrome. Memory disturbances are not isolated phenomena. When there is a retention difficulty, the attitudes of the individual towards the situation are changed. The average patient with a Korsakoff psychosis certainly has no particular interest in going deeper into the structure of reality. His emotions are flat. We are not justified in saying that emotional disturbances are secondary to memory disturbances or vice versa. Our categories, memory and retention, are after all categories which are very schematic, and do not correspond to reality. It is more or less artificial to say, as do Gruenthal and Stoerring, that the primary defect of retention is responsible for the disturbances in determination, will, and emotions seen in their patient. After all, patients with defects are different human beings with a different attitude towards the world. Their aims have changed not merely because they do not remember but because a deep inner change in their total attitude has occurred. Previously many investigators believed that confabulation and fantasy in the Korsakoff syndrome was due to the absence of memory, but more recent observations speak against such an assumption. The lack of control of recent memories is simply one factor. The patients are changed in their emotional attitude as well. They enjoy an easy and complacent attitude in their thinking and let themselves go in their daily life as well as in fantasy. It is very awkward to justify popular prejudice and say that one confabulates because a memory gap is present. There is no empirical material which would point in this direction. Unfortunately in psychopathology and psychology there is a rather widespread tendency to consider one disturbance as basic and the other sides of the picture as secondary.

E. Gruenthal and G. E. Stoerring also make use of such constructions. In other words their interpretation and discussion of the case is merely a repetition of a theory which they accepted before they started to examine the case. The general problem of primary and secondary disturbances in psychic life still remains. E. Bleuler also makes extensive use of the idea of primary disturbances in psychic life which he is inclined to connect with anatomic processes. He speaks of primary disturbances in the association of schizophrenics and is inclined to consider negativisms, hallucinations, and the rest as secondary. But in psychic life there is no such thing as a disturbance in association. Human beings change their attitudes and motives and revert to more primitive ways of existence when the more highly developed plane becomes too complicated or unsatisfactory. The correlation of such a change in attitudes with organic changes in the brain is far from being simple. Even in general paresis the dementia is not merely a defect but involves a change in the attitude of the individual. To a great extent we are probably mistaken when we consider symptoms merely as defects of functions which we seek in the patient and do not consider the positive functioning of the individual.

I have observed a forty-year-old man who tried to kill himself by gas—he felt that people were watching him because of an abnormal growth of hair on his face. The exact duration of his loss of consciousness could not be ascertained. Four days after his resuscitation retention difficulties were decidedly in the foreground. He was disoriented in space and time and very quickly forgot material offered to him. At 11 A.M. he believed it was four o'clock in the afternoon and that he had already lunched. He had no spontaneous tendency for confabulation. He showed a general unwillingness to talk but was rather humorous in his attitude. The story of the rape of a girl was repeated by him in the following way: "He was so taken up by this girl that he got the best of her. He couldn't get his mind on anything else. He just about ruined his life with the girl thinking of it. I don't know what he did about it." When asked immediately afterwards to repeat the story, he said: "It slipped my mind about this man and the girl. He offended her, insulted her and had intercourse with her. But he suffered for it. I suppose that was it." (How did he suffer?) "He had to go through the law with it. I suppose that's the way he suffered." In the ship test and the mannikin test the patient made minor mistakes so that his score corresponded to the six-year level. There was no proof that his imagination and representations had undergone any change. Despite this the patient showed no isolated disturbances in memory. He was rather indifferent towards his memory disturbance. He had no insight and his impulses were diminished. His disturb-

ances with optic construction were of a minor degree. His whole
world was a world of no importance. It was easy for him to be in a
humorous mood. This attitude was the more remarkable since he
was depressed before he tried to asphyxiate himself.

I have chosen this case for discussion since in many respects it corresponds to the observations of Gruenthal and Stoerring. Since the
disturbance in this case is not so far-reaching there is a better opportunity for analysis. The patient's changed attitude is not merely
secondary to his memory disturbance. There is an indifference
towards the world as well as towards the results of his own thinking.
There is no ambition to formulate a definite constructive picture of
the world. On the other hand it would be too far-reaching to deny
difficulties in remembering. The analysis also would be one-sided if
we stressed too much the changes in the quality of representation.
The difficulties in optic construction in this case are not very pronounced, and I have in my material cases in which they were completely absent. My rather extensive clinical experience does not contain any case in which there were no disturbances other than retention
difficulties. Although remembering and thinking are not entirely
identical, still they are very closely related to each other and are two
aspects of one basic attitude. Complete dissociations are not probable,
although dissociations between mechanical memory and judgment
have frequently been described.

Frank Curran and I studied the problems of memory by a method
which we considered to be new. We ordered our subjects to continue
to repeat a story which had been read to them until they were completely exhausted and refused to go on. This technique was suggested
by the experiments of K. Lewin and his pupil D. Karsten, who gave
simple tasks to their subjects and did not stop until the individuals
were completely exhausted and refused to continue. Primitive forms
often appeared in the course of such an experiment. There was a
deterioration of the configurations. No experiments had been made
with verbal material. We examined a great number of subjects, many
of whom were normal, brought to the hospital because of passing excitement, and others who had memory disturbances. Some showed

pronounced Korsakoff symptoms. After some experimentation the following story proved satisfactory. It was read only once to the subject and the patient was not supposed to repeat the title. The story was as follows:

HULA DANCE BURNS FATAL

Portland, Oregon. Olaf Nelson died here today of burns suffered when a match ignited his grass skirt in a hula dance comedy during the American Legion convention. District Attorney Brown announced that he would file manslaughter charges against Mr. Moore. Moore lighted a cigarette and tossed away the match. Brown interviewed fifteen witnesses who said Moore deliberately tossed the match to Nelson's costume.

The instructions to the subject were: Repeat the story as often as you can. We want to see how often you can repeat it before becoming exhausted.

One typical protocol of a normal subject is reproduced here:

1. Olaf died here today while doing a hula dance from a match that touched his skirt. The D.A. did something—

2. Olaf died here today while doing a magic dance, from a match that touched his skirt. The D.A. said he was witness.

3. Olaf died here today while doing a magic dance, from a match that touched his skirt. The D.A. says he has witnesses or something.

4. Worlof died here today while doing a magic dance from a match that touched his skirt while dancing for some kind of society or something.

5. Some district attorney or something. Worlof died here today while dancing a magic dance from a match that touched his grass skirt.

6. Worlof or Orlaf died here today while doing a magic dance from a match that touched his grass skirt. Some kind of D.A. or something—

7. Gracious—Orlof, whoever he is, died here today—no—yes—while doing a magic dance—no—yes—a match touched his grass skirt. From a burn—I didn't say that before. He was at a charity ball. The D.A. said something about witnesses. Twelve witnesses.

8. Orlof died here today from a burn while doing a magic dance from a match that touched his grass skirt. That's as far as I can go. I can't get in that about the D.A. and the twelve witnesses. I'm usually good at remembering things. (Subject interrupts continually to tell about troubles.)

9. I have to laugh. Orlof died here today while doing a magic hula-hula dance from a match that touched his grass skirt. Now, that's as far as I can go—D.A. and twelve witnesses—charity organization—

10. Orlof died here today from a burn while doing a magic hula-hula dance from a match which touched his grass skirt. The D.A. says that he has twelve witnesses as far as I can remember.

11. (Sulks) Orlof died here today while doing a magic hula-hula dance. The D.A. says he has twelve witnesses.

12. Orlof says—Worlof died here today while doing a magic hula-hula dance. The witness says he has twelve witnesses. (Subject weeps.)

(The following day—without repetition): Orlof died here today while doing a magic hula dance from a burn from a match which touched his grass skirt. And the D.A. says he has twelve witnesses that saw him burned.

Such a protocol gives deep insight into the workings of memory. In the first repetition the patient not only omitted a great part of the story but for certain phrases substituted other similar ones. Words of a general meaning replaced those of specific meaning. Instead of a rare word a more common one was used. In the second repetition words which had been omitted reappeared and words of similar meaning were added. Whole sentences reappeared, which were not repeated in the previous repetition. A mistake once made perseverated. Changes in the position of a word or of a whole sentence took place. Finally a primitive version crystallized. This preserved many of the mistakes and perseverations, which were not much changed by further repetition. It is as if the patient reached a comparatively stabilized state after a period of active elaboration and construction. It was easy to see that we were dealing with a very active process.

On the basis of our material we could say that the following are the most important changes which occurred in these experiments:

1. Substitution of a phrase by a similar phrase.
2. Addition of phrases to the story.
3. Addition of phrases expressing attitudes of the subject: (a) impatience. (b) disgust and uncertainty. (c) jokes. (d) rebellion. (e) garrulousness.
4. Substitution of a word by a synonym or by a word of similar meaning.
5. Substitution by a word with a more general meaning.
6. Substitution by a more specific word.
7. Substitution by a more common word.

8. Substitution by a less common word.

9. Perseveration.

10. Substitution by an emotionally stronger word.

11. Substitution by an emotionally weaker word.

12. Depreciation.

13. Colloquialism (vulgarity).

14. Substitution by a word having greater moral connotation.

15. Substitution by a word having lesser moral connotation.

16. Newly added words which do not substitute; change in individual names.

17. Items omitted.

18. Perseveration of mistakes in individual names.

19. Correction of mistakes in individual names.

20. Reappearance of omitted names.

21. Reappearance of omitted sentences.

22. Changes in the location of a word: (a) anteposition; (b) postposition.

23. Reversal of two items.

Preliminary insight into the large variety of changes is gained if we consider that during repetitions all these changes appear in various combinations, until an approximate equilibrium is reached. These studies show that the forces which are important for memory are also important for the fate of words. There is a clear-cut leveling tendency in language. It is interesting that in organic cases with an organic memory defect this leveling process is speeded up.

A forty-two-year-old woman with severe memory disturbances of organic type on an unknown basis showed very little tendency to confabulation. She did not think she had memory defects. The story was read to her twice and the patient reproduced it as follows:

1. Olaf Nelson died from burns from a lighted match from his skirt.

2. Olaf Nelson died from burns from a lighted match from his skirt.

3, 4, 5. (Repetitions are identical in spite of the urging of the experimenter.)

6, 7, 8 and 9. Olaf Nelson died from burns from a lighted match to his skirts. (Substitution for "from his skirt.")

10. (After the ninth repetition the patient complained): It is hard to repeat it when you merely hear it. (The patient was then ordered to read the story herself aloud. The tenth repetition was still identical.)

11. (At the eleventh repetition the patient added): Moore died from the burns of a match lighted in a dance comedy hall.

12. Wilson, what's his first name, Olaf, Odolf, Wilson died from burns from a match that lit his skirts.

13. Odolf Wilson died from burns of a match that lit his skirts in a comedy dance hall.

14. (Identical.)

15. (Identical, but omits "in a comedy dance hall.")

16–17. (Identical to 15.)

18. Olaf Wilson died from burns from a lighted match to his skirts.

19–24. (Identical.)

25. (The examiner told her: "Take your time, tell the whole story." The patient repeated and added): That occurred in a comedy dance hall. (Asked whether her report is correct, she said): Wilson comes in somewhere.

26–27. (Identical to 24.)

28. (She added): In a comedy dance hall. (When asked whether the story was complete she added): Who is this? Who was produced? Manslaughter; he was charged with manslaughter?

29. (Identical. Patient added): I was thinking who was charged with manslaughter. Wilson was it, was it not? He was, because of the matches; manslaughter that is more of a—more of a fight. (The patient was permitted a pause of half an hour and then repeated the story as follows): Adolf Wilson died from burns that set his skirt on fire. It occurred in a dance hall. (How did that happen?) He evidently had something explodable about his clothing. The matches exploded and the skirt got on fire. That occurred in a dance hall academy. (What did the other people say?) Wilson was charged with manslaughter. (Who charged him?) Officials, I presume.

One cannot deny that this pathological case showed the same fundamental characteristics as those found in the normal. There is a continual process of testing. Emotional factors continually interfere. The individual protests against the continuous effort by making the whole process more or less mechanical. In every repetition the total situation plays a part. The patient obviously utilizes much less of her remembrances than she actually possesses. The conditions of a memory experiment determine the amount of material which makes its appearance. When a wrong solution has once been found it has a tendency to persist.

This method has also been systematically employed in cases of Korsakoff psychosis. The following protocol comes from a severe alcoholic Korsakoff, a newspaperman:

1. Nelson, a miner of Hoover Dam project, died today when a guy named Moore threw a cigarette case into the encampment. Why he should die so suddenly after his burn is puzzling the prosecutors. Further details will be published as they progress. The Grand Jury will sit in today and go on with further details.

Now that's the way a newspaperman would write it and I'm a newspaperman and a good one. (Patient proceeds with details of his life story.)

2. Nelson, a laborer in a dam, was badly bitten or stung by a bird. He couldn't catch the bird; I don't know why. No attempts were made to catch the bird. They cauterized the wound and found it was a peculiar gash. After treatment—it was of no avail—the man died. I don't think this differs from the other version.

3. I'll do as you want me to—I think you are trying to catch me. The name was Nelson who was working on the bla-bla dam. He was bitten by a huge bird whom he tried to strike down. He was taken by surprise and the bird took a large piece out of his buttock. He collapsed from pain. He felt the hot blood trickling down his leg. He eventually died from burns. The breed of the bird was not determined. Scientists who know the countryside say that they had never been attacked by such a huge monster. Nelson is expected to live but will be maimed for life. The government is taking severe steps to prevent repetition of what had happened. All hunters in the neighborhood will be of no value until they get new ones—by order of a God-damn fool lying in a hospital bed. That is enough —everything should be short, concise and to the point; otherwise it is no good. (Patient insists on telling more of his life.)

4. Nelson went to a doctor and complained of a bad burn. The burn became larger and larger. The origin of the burn was as follows: some chorus girl in her anxiety to get on the stage threw a cigarette on his straw suit which gave him a severe burn. Three or four operations did no good. They thought they had success but they didn't. Then they sent him to the hospital. Then he came out and came back to die of internal injuries. I hope this goes with the rest of the story.

5. Now listen—you don't want me to repeat that God-damn story any more. I'm not a smart or fresh guy. I'm what they call one of New York's best editors. I can look at a story and judge just how much space it will take.

6. This fellow Nelson was building a fire; he was a hunter and he was

making some food for himself. He heated chestnuts and one stuck in his esophagus. It was never proved by science just how he died. On post mortem they found nothing. It is a case that had always puzzled scientists. However, something new and startling is promised—watch for further details. That's enough for today. Say, you promised to get me something to eat. . . .

7. Nelson led a very hard life, of course. In the misty weather he slept out, down cleaning the ground away from his traps. By this manner he captured many valuable wild mink and other animals known to the neighborhood. He died from a wound. He never knew about it till the day of his death. Until the day of his death Nelson continued to worry about his wound. He couldn't recall how he got it. Was it a friend or an enemy? The cause of Nelson's death is still a mystery. His comrades entered the service and avowed that some day—somewhere—they will bring to earth the man who caused their friend's death. The man disappeared just like a shadow. Many in the neighborhood thought they saw him and named several, but under investigation it was found that these men knew nothing about it. Federal, state and local police are still working on the strange case of Nelson's death. As if they would give a good God-damn who did it! I shot crap with five Pennsylvania state troopers and they all had loaded dice. Of course, they didn't cheat me because I had a pair of loaded ones myself.

The patient was eager to talk and it seemed as if he could go on forever giving new versions of Nelson's death. The patient also said he knew the examiner's brother: "He is a great kid! Does he still play football?" He went on with tales of the examiner's brother.

Following the procedure of S. Betlheim and H. Hartmann we told the rape story to another severe case of Korsakoff psychosis and let him repeat the story over and over. Since we have presented similar material above we shall not give the details here. In the first repetition the rape scene was already changed into a scene of seduction and the pregnancy motive was omitted. In the second repetition the passion of the American girl was particularly emphasized. Then the patient spontaneously added:

Then I heard of another girl—how she was in the part—was very passionate—she always was held down—she saw two boys swimming—they were just coming out swimming and she and this girl, a friend of hers—they were reserved—tried to conceal themselves. The American boys hol-

lered—the two girls who saw these two naked boys—they started to yell
—the average American girl wouldn't have done so—guards came—the
girls almost collapsed, the boys of seventeen and eighteen almost fainted—
the poor girls fainted." (The original story contains the motives of the
nakedness of the men, the crying of the girl, and her pregnancy.)

In the third repetition two European girls are shocked when they
see a boy coming out naked from swimming. The patient, however,
made very many variations in this story. In the fourth repetition, the
boys were frightened because they saw the girls naked. In the fifth
repetition he again said that the boy hollered because he saw girls
naked and that the man or woman acting as a guard came around. In
the seventh repetition he said:

I'll tell you a story. Here a few weeks ago one of the classes in high
school where I teach went into the country and four teachers were asked
to go along. We went along and two older girls and two older boys made
up to play a little trick on the group. They know the whole group but
one pupil they did not know so well. He came from Italy about three
months before. They had planned a little trick. They went into the woods
and this one girl she was a cut-up. The other teachers were not interested
at all and all of a sudden this girl gave a scream: "Oh girls, that Italian
boy is all naked out there." European girls and boys would not notice it
but the American girl said, "Oh where?" . . . Some of the American
boys were naked and one of the teachers said, "Oh there, they are all
naked again." Well, this American girl who had been in school in Europe
just fainted and passed out on the ground. The American boys who had
gone to European schools I suppose wanted to look but their European
training would not let them so they screamed.

(The ninth version is as follows): You said, "Oh run, here come two
naked boys." If you had said that the two American school boys would
have said, "Oh where?" . . . I don't know what the girls would have
done. I cannot speak for them.

(At the time of examination, several nurses, some of them colored,
were present. Instead of the final twelfth repetition, he said): When we
started this second session you said, "Go ahead and make it a good story"
and I tried to make it a good story after all I went through today. (What
was that?) The court trial. They wanted a story repeated. There were
some specialists there who wanted to get the reaction. They were all colored but they could not get them to change their story. (What story?)
On a second trial sometimes they try to get them to change their story

but they did not succeed. They were marvelous girls on the stand. I think it was a commencement episode and at first it had to do—I got so excited later on I just forgot what they said in the beginning. The teacher in this room was involved. It was decided that each of the pupils answer on the stand. The pupils had—there was one pupil who acted as a ventriloquist and this pupil would give the answers instead of the person on the stand. At first crack out of the box a colored girl was on the stand and she was very bright and they could not confuse her. These were Americans. She did not beat around the bush. She did not want to confuse these Europeans but she said, "we know she is a very bright girl and you are trying to get her to say 'yes' to something that was not true." (What was not true?) They tried to get her to say that two men spoke to her on the street and asked her to go along and have a good time. This girl, you could not confuse her one bit and she answered every question in a "yes" or "no" manner. This man thought he had this case in his hand and said, "Are you satisfied now? These are good girls and would not go out with these men, these pickups."

We can very easily see that in this case we are dealing with the same motives encountered in the previous cases, including the normal ones. According to the character of the story, however, the formal modifications which occur are in close relation to the individual life of the patient. The repressive tendency comes out in this way: the rape story becomes more decent as the element of peeping comes into the foreground. Different versions appear and multiplications take place. The present situation and the situation in the story are mixed together, and the patient starts to play some part in the whole situation. His occupation as a teacher has already colored the whole situation.

The so-called pathological changes in memory deal basically with the same processes as in the normal person and show the following characteristics: (1) The processes take place in a similar way but show larger swings. (2) A state of equilibrium concerning the final formulation is not reached, or is reached much later. (3) In some extraordinary cases there is no definite use of the material which has been presented. Due probably to the incompleteness of our methods we cannot demonstrate in all cases the existence of the finally formed habit. (4) In another group of cases the habit formation was premature and the habit or the final scheme was primitive and expressed only a more general attitude.

Our experiments show therefore that the original story undergoes a continuous process of organization and reorganization which not only brings forward different parts of the original story but brings it into connection with similar material. In this process of organization and reorganization specific attitudes are acquired and a definite pattern is developed, which puts a specific final scheme at the disposal of the individual. We may speak of definite habit, or better of attitude formation. Even when a definite habit is established, it cannot be maintained but falls into disuse, and the individual refuses to use that pattern any further.

The results in this respect are similar to the results D. Karsten obtained with actions in drawing patterns. We have studied the problem in Korsakoff cases with gestalt tests. One trend becomes particularly obvious here and that is the inner logic of such a development.

It is to be expected that the same form principles which appear in the repetition of stories will also come out in the repetition of drawings. We used as material the gestalt drawings which have been so extensively studied by L. Bender. The patient was ordered to repeat the same gestalt several times. The first two series came from the first Korsakoff case reported. The patient was ordered to copy Bender's Figure 4 (from Max Wertheimer). The first page was drawn after the pattern was shown to him once. (See Plate III.) One sees that despite the fact that he can see his previous copies, the tendency still persists to make the curve flatter and to bring it nearer to the base line of the other part of the figure (Copies 1 and 19). This tendency becomes pronounced when he turns to the other side (Copy 21) and the forces of memory can develop in a freer way. In this second series the drawings are covered after one line (four pictures) is completed. The curved line is now seen under the open quadrangle. One further sees that the curve becomes still flatter and the beginning and the end of the curve are specifically marked (Copy 28). In the third line the curve has become completely flat and the beginning and end are conspicuously marked. It separates completely from the quadrangle falling back to a more primitive gestalt principle (L. Bender). At the same time a closing of the open quadrangle takes place. It is interesting that at first the patient feels the urge to close it, and with the first attempt asks: "Shall I close it?" (Copies 31–42.)

In the second series the patient copies Figure 3 (Plate I). The primitive tendencies substitute a circle for the point and a straight line for the angle. In the second repetition (Plate IV) the straight line turns into a curve and the circle gets a central point. In the third copy there is a marked tendency to contract the figure. After covering up the first three attempts, the patient draws the fourth copy. A straight line again substitutes for a curve and the contraction gradually reaches the ultimate degree. That we are not dealing with mere chance is obvious in the next series in which the same original is again shown. After a series of three repetitions is completed the figures are covered. The extreme tendency to contraction comes out again. The fifth copy of the second series is reproduced. In the course of these drawings the patient asked: "Do you want them free or links?" On another occasion he said: "Do you want them chained or loose?" One sees that a unified pull is in the field which goes through the whole picture.

In another Korsakoff case the same patterns are transformed in a different way. In pattern 3 the patient substitutes straight lines for angles and crosses for points and reduces the number of the vertical lines to one. In pattern 4 he persistently tries to make a staircase out of the curve and this staircase motif is the only one which finally remains (Plate V).

It is important to see that in this pattern we find the same tendency to come to some kind of equilibrium on a primitive level as was found in the development of stories. In some Korsakoff cases at least there is a primary involvement of form principles and this involvement is similar to the one in the sphere of memory. It is impossible to understand these problems from the point of view of a mere defect.

There is one pull which goes from the first figure to the last. The

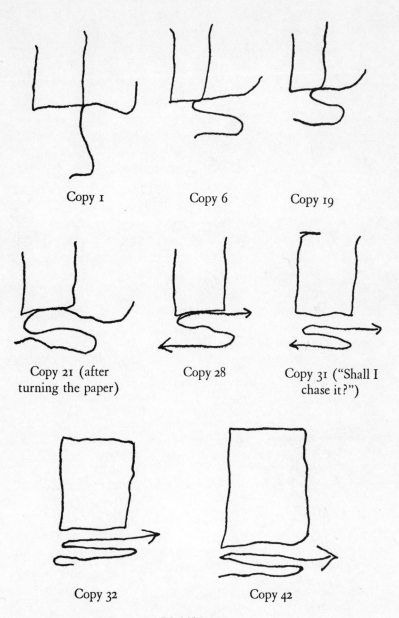

Copy 1

Copy 6

Copy 19

Copy 21 (after turning the paper)

Copy 28

Copy 31 ("Shall I chase it?")

Copy 32

Copy 42

PLATE III
Copying of Bender gestalt Figure 4, by a Korsakoff patient

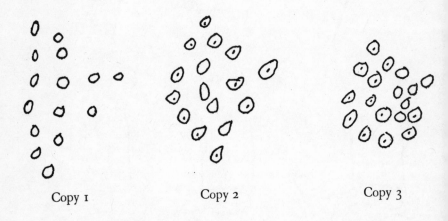

Copy 1   Copy 2   Copy 3

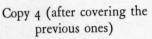

Copy 4 (after covering the   Copy 5 of another
previous ones)   series

PLATE IV
Repeated copies of Bender gestalt Figure 3, by a Korsakoff patient

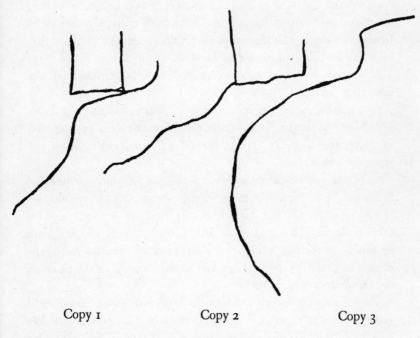

Copy 1   Copy 2   Copy 3

PLATE V

The Bender gestalt Figure 4, copied by another Korsakoff patient

basic constructive principle remains the same from one repetition to another. One definite tendency of force or pull directs a whole series. The attitude formation is identical in the repetition of stories and in the repetition of drawings. The drawings show more clearly that with repetition a more primitive pattern may appear and more definite forms make their appearance. Thanks to the investigations of L. Bender, we are able to identify these primitive forms with the earlier stages of development that may be observed in children.

A general theory of memory must take into consideration the following factors.

1. A psychic experience once conceived does not completely disappear from the psychic field. Proofs of this assertion are (a) the facts of psychoanalysis; (b) experiments in hypnosis, especially in epileptic dreamy states.

2. The primary experience becomes paler in the course of time and is less available to recall, in proportion to the amount of time elapsed. It can be evoked when the immediate situation demands it. This takes place when the immediate situation is partially identical with or similar to the past situation. The amount of partial identity, the degree of similarity and the urgency of the demand of the situation are the determining factors.

The fact that memories cannot be destroyed is one of the basic facts of psychic experience, which cannot be further reduced. We might ask to which physiological function this fact is correlated. One of the theories offered is that of the deposition of engrams. However, it is better to think less in terms of a static entity and more in terms of a dynamic process of configuration involving the total brain. The focal points in this process must be in close relation to the centers which are necessary for the maintenance of life, otherwise the tenacity of memory could not be explained.

3. A psychic experience (memory) during its construction is brought into connection with other psychic experiences which are partially identical with or similar to it. Psychic experiences represent the result of a construction guided by the biologic situation. When a psychic experience becomes a memory the constructive proc-

esses continue. The constructive processes are directed by the biologic needs. Memories are therefore present not only in their original form but also in relation to the other experiences of the individual. The proofs consist of the facts of dreams and errors in everyday life (Freud), and the symbol-like changes in the reproduction of stories by Korsakoff cases.

4. Repetition [1] of a psychic experience increases its availability for further use. It also tends to make a more definite pattern out of the psychic experience, which now can be better used in its totality than in its parts. If such an experience is called forth it is used more as a total pattern and loses in flexibility. Bergson has discussed this point clearly but he draws the incorrect conclusion therefrom of the existence of a metaphysical difference between the two phases in the learning process.

5. The process of learning is successful when the pattern has reached some stability without becoming completely inflexible and rigid.

6. Memory and learning can be understood only from the point of view that the past is used for the present. By a process of trial and error those parts of the past are used which are related to the present situation. If we want to remember, we reconstruct the past for the one or the other purpose. If we want to learn, we try to form a pattern which is useful from one or the other point of view. We want to learn only when we have the formulated or unformulated conviction that the pattern acquired will be of use for the solution of a task.

It cannot be denied that repetition increases the availability of psychic experiences. One might raise the question whether the repetition merely acts as a repetition or whether with every repetition the constructive psychic processes progress. There can be no question that repetition cannot be simply mechanical repetition, that constructive processes which are not identical continue with every repetition. Every repetition establishes the reliability of a sequence which as shown in the experiments of Pavlov has a very real mean-

---

[1] Repetition means here the repeated experience of one situation, whereas in the experiments reported above the situation (stimulus) was offered only once and the reproduction was repeated.

ing. The dog's expectation of being fed is well grounded after he has received the food six, seven, or eight times following the ringing of the bell. Regularity of a sequence makes psychological and physiological adaptation possible. It is to be expected that the reliability of a sequence has some physiological correlation and that repetition means some actual change in the organic correlations. The mere fact that no psychic experience disappears completely from the psychic field makes it probable that repetition increases the availability by digging deeper traces into the physiologic organization.

Even in the very artificial conditions of a laboratory, true repetitions do not exist. The very fact that time elapses between two repetitions makes the time factor of paramount importance in the total situation. In addition, small differences exist between every single repetition and the individual must make decisions as to which of the differences are to be remembered. In other words an organization of patterns takes place even in the most mechanical learning process. Learning is not a mechanical increase in traces of experience. Doubtless repetition has some effect on the traces. This has been denied by gestalt psychologists and it has even been denied that traces exist. Unbiased observation, however, makes it clear that traces do exist and that they are increased by repetition, whatever repetition may be. The experiments of Pavlov give us valuable help in demonstrating the process of organization by what we call differential inhibition. In every repetition the individual organized the new experience with other experiences and pieced the experiences together by trial and error.

K. Lashley doubts whether the law of exercise is of fundamental importance for the theory of learning. He does not doubt of course that repetition of experiences in contiguity leads to associations between these experiences. He thinks it possible that overlearning multiplies the number of associative bonds rather than strengthening those first formed. Even if this formulation were in all respects completely correct (in some respects it is) multiple associations based on repetition help learning. The primary contents are more accessible after a repetition has taken place. Since we know that the muscle which has been used often becomes stronger and since we further know that an action becomes easier the more it is repeated, I think it is vain to deny that traces increase by repetition. It is true that with each "repetition" manifold dynamic processes take place.

7. The result of learning is a simple and schematic pattern which can be used in action, and which may be achieved after one experience. Habit formation is not dependent only upon repetition but upon what an individual wants and whether he gets it by the habit developed. The study of memory has to take into consideration that the development of a habit does not mean that the possibilities for other actions (memories), although they may be obliterated, are not present. The possibility of changing the method of approach to a given situation is always present. Among other factors it depends on the effect of our actions whether we maintain a habit or not.

8. It is artificial to say that pleasure and displeasure or pain play an important part in this learning process. Whenever we isolate elements in psychic life great difficulties arise. Satisfaction arising out of insight into a situation can hardly be separated from insight as such. Insight in itself is not merely an intellectual process. Whole chapters of psychology (psychoanalysis included) should be rewritten with a better grasp of this fundamental problem. We try to retain those habits which have led to actual progress in handling a situation. It is indeed the effect of psychic experience (which always implies action) which determines how much of it we want to repeat and how much to use for further actions. Edward Thorndike's formulation, which stresses the effect of our actions as the basis for learning, is therefore basically correct from a purely psychological point of view. However, when an individual knows what is right and wrong he is better able to act correctly the next time if he has enough material which can be used for the construction of the right answer. (See also the studies of M. H. Trowbridge and of H. Cason and John Eisenson.)

Cason is right in his criticisms of Thorndike's theory when he protests against the formulation of the law of effect "that what comes after a connection, acts upon it to alter its strength." The result of one action merely makes it possible to be more successful in the arrangement of our next action, but there is no strengthening of hypothetical connections. Whatever the physiological correlations of this process of having more insight for future actions may be, they must be of a very complicated type, and cannot be simply a strengthening or lessening of hypothetical connections. Cason is right therefore when he writes: "A general law of learning is necessarily independent of the incentives that may or may not be present while learning is taking place." It has been the trend of present-day psychology to emphasize emotions to too great an extent as if emotions and feelings were independent powers. A situation should be defined as a total situation perceived to which an individual reacts according to his insight and needs. Insight, as well as perception as such, is determined by motility and by needs. Isolation of any of the parts of the situation is more or less artificial.

Max Wertheimer concealed familiar forms, such as letters of the alphabet, in complex configurations and found that it was often difficult to see the letters even when the observer knew of their presence. He concluded that past experience was ineffective, since presumably the letters were more favored by past experience than were the complex and relatively strange configurations in which they were concealed. The experimental study by K. Gottschaldt sought to determine the extent to which the perception of form is a function of past experience. His method followed Wertheimer's suggestion. Gottschaldt submerged the impression figure into the test pattern. The impression figure was recognized within its test pattern in only 2.9 percent to 6.6 percent of the cases, and even they were only recognized when a searching attitude was present. W. Koehler felt that these results prove that experience has no automatic influence upon our seeing definite forms. As the result of a careful experimental study, K. W. Braly drew the conclusion that a properly designed impression series influences the perception of visual stimuli. In the experiment of Gottschaldt the impression figures were so carefully hidden that they were present merely from the point of view of the synthesis and not from the point of view of perception. In Gottschaldt's experiments simple forms were woven into a complex maze of lines which actually destroyed the simple figure as a perception. The influence of the impression series in Braly's experiments was not due to searching but was exerted without the conscious knowledge of the subject.

It seems that the newer development of gestalt psychology is much more inclined to acknowledge the influence of experience. Kurt Koffka in his new book emphasizes the influence of traces on later processes. According to him every process is in some respects a learning process. It leaves traces which may lead to an improvement in action. We have to eliminate the idea that the trace is a mechanical residuum and must give up the idea that the so-called memory material is dead material. Traces and memory are potent processes which influence those processes going on in the present.

CHAPTER XVIII

THINKING

AS A basis for the discussion on this subject I shall use a case history, although the subject was not completely analyzed. The patient was a twenty-three-year-old boy who entered the clinic for treatment because of torturing shyness and feelings of guilt and inferiority. He had obsessive thoughts of intercourse with men, women, and children. In the street he felt the urge to touch their sex organs and also had obsessional ideas about kicking them in the genitals and on the shins. The patient's father, who had been a court attendant and carried a pistol, died of pneumonia when the patient was about seven years old. The patient recalled that, when he was three years old, his father bought him a set of electric trains, and that at night he would put candy in the children's half-open mouths. However his mother told him that his father had a bad temper and was hard to get along with. It was his mother's custom to undress in the patient's presence, which provoked a nervous sensation in his penis. There were quarrels between the parents as both apparently strove for superiority. He had a brother two years younger than himself, whom he considered homosexual and who wanted to have intercourse with him. About the time of the death of his father, he stole silk underwear from his mother, and bathed in it daily. He would urinate into these clothes and wear them soiled. "I either wanted to wear little girls' underclothes or my mother wanted me to wear them." The patient also exhibited curiosity concerning the underparts of automobiles and trains and would say he could see the underclothes of these vehicles. At thirteen the patient had passive homosexual relations with older men. Since then he had felt an urge to do the same thing to others and to kick somebody in the anus as well as the penis, but never carried those ideas through. Before this time he had slept with his brother and mother, and analysis revealed that he felt that his mother had a sex organ similar to his own and wanted to have intercourse with him. Up to the last phase of treatment his knowledge concerning the female sex organ was incomplete. He felt particularly ill at ease in crowds, since he experienced continual sexual urges. Once he dreamed that a baby killer of newspaper fame wanted him to steal one of the swords from the museum. He went so far as to take it but returned it and felt angry at the man. The sword was like a duelling sword, made of ivory, and had a wide guard. Somebody gave him cigarettes because he did not steal the sword. After the death of his father the patient used to steal, for which his mother would strike him.

At seventeen or eighteen he wanted to stab his mother in her sex organs. The sword is a symbolization of the penis as a violent weapon. It is the penis of the father which is murderous. He felt the need to preserve his own penis (cigarettes) which he could only do if he did not try to get his father's penis. In another dream the dangers of sex activity were symbolized. There were hollow spaces, secrets, a gun set in the wall and, finally, a fear associated with making cavities in the male sex organ. Sex relations for him were seemingly a fight between two penises.

The life of this patient was dominated by his mother. He had to defend himself against her throughout his life. It seemed that his personal connotation of "mother" was comparatively simple. But it is worth while to keep in mind that the word "mother" is an object with an almost unlimited number of qualities which undergo objective changes. The mother at the time the patient was five was not the same as she was later. She wore different clothes, she had aged, she had gone through a variety of experiences which must have changed her. Is a mother the same, dressed and undressed? Is she the same when she protects health and gives nourishment as when she attacks, punishes, and hits? She is also different as an object of sexual desire. To unite all these different experiences into a unified connotation of "mother" represents the final difficulty in the construction of an object.

Our patient feared his mother. Did he fear her because she hit him, or did he fear that she carried a sex organ which could be pushed into his rectum? Even if it were possible to decide such a question, we have to keep in mind that his adult attitude and the attitude he had as a child are not identical. Furthermore, if he once felt that his mother had a threatening penis then at that time she meant more to him than any chance individual. She was for him a general connotation, similar to a tone of 400 vibrations per second in Pavlov's experiments, which is not merely this particular tone but sound in general. It is therefore extremely difficult to come to any psychological definition of what "mother" means for this patient. If it should be true that our patient endowed his mother with a penis and feared her, although he wished to be used by her anally, was the fear of castration and the wish for and fear of anal sensations the final meaning in this case? Or was this a problem of aggression by an irresistible force to which he wanted to surrender although he was afraid? Furthermore, would the surrender itself express the hope of additional adaptations expressed in this patient by his wish to kick others in the shins or genitals, or by pushing his genitals into the genitals of others?

The problem arises as to whether the projection of a general problem into an organ which is either the sex organ or allied to it is really the only significant aspect of the situation, as psychoanalysis emphasizes. There is no isolated problem involving the anus alone. The anus must always be considered a part of the total organism to which the whole motor system belongs since it has so close a relationship to the problem of overpowering and aggression. Moreover it must not be forgotten that the problem is described not only in the language of the body but also in the language of interest in the outer world, as Alfred Adler has shown. Both will eventually lead one to the same conclusion, both expressions belong to each other. What goes on in the body is a part of the total situation in which the outer world as well as one's own body are involved. We still have not approached Carl G. Jung's formulation when he contends that the formulations of both the psychoanalysts and the individual psychologists represent particular types of thinking and for this reason are limited. I think that we have overrated the differences in types. The typologist always assumes tacitly that he himself is above types and has the total experience, but he should be liberal enough to concede the same possibility to others. E. R. Jaensch and Jung both make the same mistake in establishing themselves, and themselves only, as superior to the limited types of others. We see that causality is not the only way in which one may consider the total situation, and that aims and goals are not opposed to causality but are its very essence. It seems that our patient did not finish the construction of the object "mother." The separate parts did not fit together. In his thinking he retained attitudes towards his mother which were relics of his earliest attitudes in childhood.

Similar considerations are necessary in order to reach an understanding of this patient's obsessional impulses. He wanted to kick one person in the shins and another in the genitals, or use a knife or his penis for the same purpose. He would have liked to use his weapon against the vagina or against the anus. Foot, penis, and dagger assumed the general connotation of weapons of aggression. Shins, vagina, and anus may be combined under the heading of areas accessible to aggression. In general we are dealing with a general connotation in the sense mentioned above. We have the right to believe that these connotations are the same as those used by children. William Stern found that his daughter first used the word "dolly" to mean a real doll, and a little later to mean also her toy dog and rabbit, but not her silver bell.

It is important to realize that we find in the speech of children the same imperfect construction we meet in symbolism. I may add that in the dream cited above, this symbolism appears in the same way as in the patient's impulses. Sword and cigarette both symbolize his sex organs. We therefore conclude that symbols are relics of earlier stages of construction or of thought development.

W. Stekel has spoken about symbolic similes. In our case, leg, sword, dagger, cigarette, and phallus would form such a symbolic simile, but of course this relation is not really an equation in the logical sense. It would be more accurate to say that the individual does not care to differentiate further within the general category of weapons of aggression. Once again we find a situation similar to the reaction to sound in the conditioned reflex experiment. In the discussion of conditioned reflexes in Chapter X, I emphasized that transference from the original conditioning signal to another one is possible and that the original signal may even become ineffective. This is practically the same relation as discussed above. Coördinated pictures or connotations may be substituted for each other. It would be inexact to say that only general connotations are of importance. The connotation "weapons of aggression" has similarities only to a general connotation. It has the same structure as the sound in the beginning of the conditioning experiment. It has some similarity to what William Stern considers pluralistic connotations. It is characteristic of this type of thinking that the relation between signal and referent is rather loose and is not the distinct relation which exists between the well-differentiated signal and the referent. One should emphasize the characteristics of a signal with a clear meaning, and should not call such a signal a symbol, as Henry Head does.

It is even questionable whether we should say that the sword is a symbol of aggression for our patient since he has no knowledge of it. A symbol should be called an experience only when it leads to the thing symbolized. If such an experience does not exist we should speak of thinking as similar to symbolism or of symbol-like experiences. There is another important difference between the signal and the symbol, namely the signal has no inner relation to the referent whereas the symbol has. This inner relation is the relation of contiguity, partial identity, or similarity. Therefore we must distinguish between meaning, symbol, and symbol-like picture. The question arises: how are these different experiences represented in psychic life? When we hear a word, or when a triangle is drawn upon a blackboard in order to represent the ideal qualities of a triangle, we deal with a sign or a signal. The sign has to be experienced somehow. It must not be a perception but it can be a representation. Kuelpe, N. Ach, and K. Buehler have spoken about thoughts (*Bewusstheiten*) which are not representations but specific elements in psychic life.

Of course this is a completely introspective problem and therefore exposed to all the doubts connected with introspection. The present point of view is not so much that thoughts are independent experiences without sensual representation, but that they are only comparatively vague sensual experiences (perceptions and representations). The vagueness of this sensual material is in sharp contrast to the decisiveness and clarity in thinking.

Perhaps this whole argument is more or less senseless and is caused by the fact that until now we have reckoned too much with isolated elements in psychic life. Perception, representation, and thoughts, all of them, are only phases leading to action. With this reservation we are free to say that there exist experiences in which sensual material plays a comparatively unimportant role. There are no perceptions of representations which are isolated; they are always in connection with other experiences. When something has been combined with other experiences it always leads to attitudes which fit not only the present perception but also other perceptions connected with it. There are no isolated experiences; every experience points to something else. The universal character of signal function is related to the fact that we are in a continuous state of preparedness not only for the present impression but also for what the present impression may signal. When a word or a representation or a perception is a signal, we have to try to learn whether this signal is sufficiently distinct. But we go back to the descriptive problem. The word, the perception, and the representation and thought are, as stated earlier, the result of a constructive process, but they themselves provoke attitudes and tendencies to actions which must be more or less definite.

We know very little about the introspective qualities of the readiness to action. The readiness to action, as we know from physiology, involves the whole body. It induces changes not only in the muscular system but also in the glands of external and internal secretion, and in the whole vasovegetative system. I think that what we call "attitude" is connected with the experience of these physiological changes, which are also closely related to what we call thought. Attitudes are continually changing until they find their final expression in the action which is the crowning point in the constructive psychological process. Attitudes are always concerned with something, and therefore changing attitudes are associated with an ever-changing wealth of pictures, which are more or less complete. The whole process is a process tending toward simplification. When we have reached a definite meaning, simplification has progressed considerably toward definite action. The meaning therefore is the last step before the final action and already it has comparative simplicity.

The study of neurotic cases and the symbolism of such cases give us further hints regarding the manner in which development in thought takes place. At first the individual has a general attitude concerning the aggressiveness of his father and mother, both endowed with the weapon of aggression, the phallus. This general aggressiveness finds a passive subject. Later on he starts to defend himself by becoming aggressive. The aggressiveness is partially that of a total person, partially that of a specific organ. In the beginning, the aggressiveness remains in the general sphere and is not fully differentiated. The whole attitude is in some way an instance of neurotic thinking, which does not come to definite differentiation. It is true that such cases may come to one or another action, but such action is a differentiation which has been completed too early and is comparable to a primitive gestalt formation on an undeveloped level.

I have avoided the use of the word "emotion" in the description of these processes, but there is no question that we could have characterized the whole process as an emotional procedure. If we ask ourselves why the patient never achieved a final attitude towards the world, we see that he was continuously checked and hindered by other influences and interests. When he sought complete submission to his mother, his urge for activity and his fear of castration hindered him from complete surrender. When he wished to express his masculinity toward his mother, his fear of her obstructed him. Instead of the sexual act there appeared kicking or stabbing. In other words, symbols or symbol-like pictures appear when an urge towards reality is checked. The check expresses an attempt to attack another part of reality. So, in this continuous process of adaptation to reality, check and countercheck occur. Symbols are in some way the remainders of these fights and represent various phases in the attempt to come closer to reality. Such symbols appear as the result of the struggle and point in two directions. They are unreliable signals since they are directed toward two disparate parts of reality. There is some restlessness therefore in every symbol, which I have called in German "schwebend" (swinging or wavering). The relation of the finished product of thinking to the object is comparatively clear. Actions based upon symbols are not sufficient to deal with reality. The probability is that what we see here in the neurosis is only an enlargement of what we see in the course of every process of thinking in normal individuals. There is a development of thought and a development in thinking in every single act which takes place.

ON THE DEVELOPMENT OF THOUGHTS [1]

In our psychic life sequences play an important role, in which the sensual material of representations serves as a bridge to a sense and a meaning. Experiences of this kind I call "thought processes" and the goal towards which they are directed "thoughts." Representations are aids to thoughts. They should be considered with great care. It is an acknowledged fact that representations and thoughts go through different levels before they achieve clear formulation. A good picture of the course of this process is given by a patient of Anton Delbrueck who suffered from pseudoreminiscences of mistreatment. The first reminiscence brought the event into his consciousness in unclear outline. The second remembrance brought the main points into the right order, while the third recall provoked very clearly and decisively the total event from the beginning to the end, with all details.

According to G. E. Mueller,[2] representations undergo a development which can be directly observed; they unfold from a state of blurred indistinctness to more and more obvious configurations.

[1] This is a rewriting of my article, "Uber Gedankenentwicklung," *Zeitschrift für die gesamte Neurologie und Psychiatrie,* LIII (1920), 250–64.

[2] The description of the development of representations uses the results of G. E. Mueller's book *On the Analysis of Memory and Representation* (Leipzig, 1911). Mueller has also given a complete bibliography.

Mueller leaves it undecided whether every representation goes through this developmental process, as in some cases the process cannot be observed. I do not consider this doubt as unjustified. If a psychic process takes place quickly and without inhibitions, the observation of it becomes as inexact as the observation of free-falling objects outside the Atwood falling machine. A preliminary orientation concerning the development of thoughts is possible in those cases in which a new goal in thinking need not be reached but in which previous knowledge has to be brought back to consciousness.

In this respect cases in which the act of remembering takes place without hindrance should not be used. Nagel's subjects could not find a certain syllable in reproducing a series of syllables; they would pronounce a syllable which seemed similar to the one sought, continually changing with great speed the vowels and consonants until they felt they had found the correct one. In other words, they went through clang associations which lead to the syllable sought. Giessler tried to make more efficient the memory of a word sought by pronouncing at random a word which might have been influenced by it. By frequently repeating this experiment, he succeeded with the help of test words in coming closer and closer to the right one, finally finding and pronouncing it. In several experiments this search was very indefinite. It follows, from a series of experiments by Mueller, that the desired representation appears if it includes parts of the experience which are contiguous in space and time. From the preceding I draw the conclusion that the development of representations takes place through representations associated according to similarity and contiguity. Clang associations and associations to incidental stimuli are predominant. According to the investigations of H. Piéron this seems to be an oscillatory process, and it appears that one is sometimes nearer to the words sought and sometimes farther away.

To this description the objection might be made that the derailment to representations associated with the goal is merely the result of an inability to reach the goal. We might ask whether the uninhibited development of a representation really goes through a circle. It must be decided whether "the representation of passage" has anything to do with the one really desired, of which a vague presentiment is present from the beginning. At any rate the circle traversed before the final product appears is a product of the individual life experiences and coincides with the structure of reality. The construction in the development of a representation is connected with those elements in which it dissociates in the association experiment. This whole constructive process of the representation is not limited to one sense. Transpositions from the field of one sense to that of another take place. These transformations also partially affect the contents.

It must be emphasized that the process of representation mixes different spheres with each other. According to G. E. Mueller, "part mixtures of contents" take place. In association experiments the stimulus word "penny" may provoke a written image in the color of a penny. In other words the development of representations is constructive with the material. In Mueller's experiments one subject, when reciting a series of numbers of different colors, saw the red numbers not only as more glowing but usually as bigger and closer to the subject than the other numbers. F. Fraenkl's subjects, when learning and reciting, declared that, of every group of a series of letters read to them, they saw the first letters more heavily written than the others. We are dealing with affective reconstructions of the reproduced material. Whatever may receive attention (the red numbers, the letters) changes its form. We have found two new essential items in the developmental process of representations: the preparatory process of the representation first melts associative material together and, secondly, rebuilds it according to affective points of view.

I especially emphasize that in the last cases mentioned the byproduct which is affectively rebuilt remains even after the representation has gone through this phase. These phases can also escape introspection if the process of representation occurs with great speed. The affective reconstruction of a representation is closely allied to symbolization. According to G. E. Mueller any given object which is perceived provokes the perception of another object, which in its turn is accompanied by a similar by-impression, state of feeling, or emotion and can therefore become its symbol of the first object. During learning and reciting, symbolic complex pictures occurred which indicated by their appearance the value and importance (or the degree of connection) of the single parts of a complex, in addition to the intended representations (memory image of numbers, and the rest). When the center of a triadel complex was more impressive than the sides, the symbolic picture had the shape of a triangle with a horizontal base.

We have herewith gained some definite ideas of the development of representations in normal individuals. Representations develop from a stage of unclearness and indetermination to more and more sharply defined pictures. They go through a series connected in an oscillating way by similarity and contiguity. Fusions take place between these parts. The single parts are reconstructed according to the affects or in a symbolic way. Phases of this developmental process of the representations may remain in consciousness even after the final representation is reached. Two instances related to the pathology of the individual may be mentioned. In both cases we deal with optic agnosias. I take from a case of Stauffenberg's the following instances:

The picture of a mouse was shown. "It is not a cat." (Casket?) "I know what it is; it is not a bottle." (Snake?) "It is rather like a cat." In the field of perception we find the fact that only the sphere, the general circle of perception comes into consciousness. The cognative function tries to find its way in this sphere. According to H. Liepmann a case with mind-blindness can substitute for an object one related in meaning and, for instance, call spectacles a spy-glass.

A case of Otto Poetzl was shown a bunch of flowers out of which protruded the stem of an asparagus. He saw a red rose in the bunch, which was then taken away. When asked the color of the lapel of an officer present, he said it was like a green tiepin. The mixture between two spheres was obvious. The pathological perception corresponds to what we have called in imagination "mixture of part contents."

After this diversion I continue with our main theme. Thus far I have consciously restricted myself to sensual (*anschaulich*) experiences. Doubtless, when we think, we are not interested in sensual representations. On the contrary they are only aids which would hamper us if they remained too long. In most cases we do not want representation, but we do want thoughts and knowledge.

Kuelpe, N. Ach, K. Buehler, Messer, and others deserve credit for proving that these experiences are not based on pictures. Even the sharp critic of their opinions, G. E. Mueller, states that subjects can only operate easily and quickly with unclear representations. This obviously proves that the emphasis in thinking cannot be placed upon these unclear representations which are merely an aid to the meaning, to the experiences of knowledge and insight. Whether we consider these unpictured parts (knowledge) as quantitatively large or merely as a small group of experiences, they are at any rate of paramount importance for the experience of knowledge and thinking. K. Buehler at the present time considers the knowledge that something is valid as the main function of knowledge, and knowing that something exists can be deduced from the former. Lindworsky holds that primitive and general sensual schemata are coördinated with insight, unillustrated by pictures. These general schemata are connected by way of association with more special schemes, which finally lead to individual representations. It is thus possible to reduce the essential part of our thoughts to a minimum (the insight into relations). All authors who believe in the assumption of essential elements in thinking note the close relation of these essential experiences to the "act." We should ask ourselves whether the developments found in representations are valid also for "thoughts" (*Bewusstheiten*), and "meanings." Karl Buehler, one of the pioneers of this theory, asked his subjects questions to be answered "yes" or "no." When they understood the meaning of a question a protocol of the inner experiences of the subject was taken. Such experiments were, for instance: "Do you understand? If a vermin makes you feel disgusted so that you ascend one step more quickly, does that give it the right to exist?" The subject reacted in the following way: he represented a staircase on which somebody stepped upward, without seeing anyone else. The thought which led to the understanding was included in this picture. Stepping upward was taken in a general sense. This meaning was perceived by way of a picture which was not at all fully adequate for the meaning. In the development of thought a symbolic picture was used. It is true that the question comprised a part of the symbol. It is astonishing that such a complicated thought was satisfied with so primitive and inadequate a representation. Kinesthetic word representations were not present according to the remarks of the subject. Such representations, even if present, could not contribute to the understanding of the way in which the meaning of the sentence was grasped.

Two further instances will complete what we have said: (Do you know how many steps are on the staircase to the main entrance of our university?) "No. When hearing about steps I thought quickly about the steps of some philosophical system. At the same time I was conscious that I couldn't solve it." In this instance it is certain that at first symbolic representations appear for the experience of meaning. Finally, the third instance: (Do you know where our stop watch is now?) "Yes—I have immediate representations of the flight of rooms in the Institute with the big chest in the middle. I wandered quickly through with my eye and then I thought—probably there." The representation appeared here immediately like an automatic reaction except that the "probably there" thinking occurred. It was as if the picture had got its meaning only by this.

A symbolic or symbol-like experience in the narrow sense did not exist here. In spite of this I would like to emphasize that pictures and word fragments are only a help for the meaning. This help is in a similar relation to thought as the symbol of what it symbolizes. These remarks give us some insight into the development of representations. Basically it is not the representation that develops, but a thought which develops with the help of the representations. In the instances cited we also are dealing with thoughts, which are sought and become real with the help of representations. The relatively essential experience connects itself with single partial phases of the development of thought and finds its realization in a picture which is relatively adequate for the desired meaning. One might suppose that the essential knowledge was present before the development of thought began, and invested itself in representations. Experience speaks against this view since it shows that one has only a presentiment of the thought up to the moment one finally reaches it. We might say that the meaning suddenly jumps out of the representations. Even then we are dealing with a development that makes the sudden appearance of a thought possible. It seems that it is not merely accidental that there is a thought in the representation. Picture and meaning are in an essential inner relation. This justifies the fact that we started our discussion with an attempt to describe the development of representations.

H. Silberer's results on autosymbolic phenomena might be mentioned at this point. In the state of sleepiness, pictures arose without any immediately recognizable connection to an intended thought but which could be considered as a symbol of the thought. The intention to improve an uneven place in an article appeared as the picture of a board being planed.

The development of thoughts goes through a stage of symbolic and symbol-like representations. The representations are partially similar to thoughts, are labile, can easily be suppressed, and disappear very quickly, whereas the result—that is, the thought—remains. For the thought itself, the representation is only a passing stage. The representation is very often symbolic. It is appropriate to consider the word "representation" as a transition stage, since it is truly a mediator of meaning. There also exist more direct hints that the development of thought takes place in this way. K. Buehler noted in one of his protocols: "Remembrances of the past (thoughts) came into my mind but I did not know what it was. . . . The direction towards it came immediately but I couldn't perform it."

Karl Buehler cites the Kantian proposition that the connotation "dog" signifies a rule according to which the power of imagination is able to formulate in the abstract the shape of a quadruped. There exists a general consciousness of the rules according to which thoughts are formed. It must be emphasized that again we are dealing with a close connection between the psychic function and thoughts. This "consciousness of the rule" and this "direction" are very often connected with spatial schemes, with diagrams, and the like. The quantitative relation between sensual and asensual experience is of no importance. The latter is the supporting pillar of thinking. The objection may be made that these are only isolated observations but such observations have forced themselves upon various investigators, even in research directed toward other goals. (Michotte and Ransy, K. Buehler, G. E. Mueller, J. Lindworsky, and O. Selz.)

Undoubtedly the appearance of symbolic or symbol-like pictures is not rare in the process of thinking. The cases in which such pictures are clear are signposts for the appreciation of a great number of similar occurrences, which I have described. In view of the large number of similes and metaphors in language, we may attribute to the indicated development the general significance that it concerns every thought occurring in any individual. Finally the general relation of a picture and its meaning is very closely related to the connection between the phases of development and its final product.

To sum up: representations and thoughts go through a development in every individual. Every representation and thought has a history. The points of development for which a preliminary fixation is possible are as follows: (1) Representations develop from a stage of unclearness to clearness. Thoughts develop similarly. (2) The process of development of representation goes over associated fields. Objectively related and personally connected material is drawn into the picture. (3) The undeveloped representation unites fragments of various layers of representations. (4) It is especially accessible to affective rebuilding. (5) It often has a symbol-like structure. (6) In thinking, the sensual content very often plays a small part in comparison to the nonsensual experiences of thinking, which, to be sure, are connected with fragments of representations. Further, thought goes through a development in which symbol-like pictures are of great importance. The sensual elements are perhaps themselves merely symbols of meaning. Let us underline the point that meaningful experiences are poor in representations and the underlying representations are less clear. I wish to reëmphasize that an

essential characteristic of those representations which play the greatest part in thinking is their poverty of sensual qualities.

Let us take the word representations as an example. The fully
developed thought is simpler in this sense than in its preliminary
stages. We have to complete it. Such a development of a thought
has a unified act of will as its basis. It is an intention and every
one of the phases of development of this thought has originated in
the same affective soil and carries its characteristics. The development of a thought originates in a unified instinctual attitude of the
individual, in a unified intention directed toward a part of reality.
It has been emphasized that the normal passage or phase of the
thought goes through a region of affective reconstruction. The different instinctual tendencies, constructions, and determinations create
labile pictures which generally are overcome by the urge towards
objectivity. Near the clear thought with conscious meaning stand
the dark multitude of developmental phases as a vague halo. Only
out of this dark mass does the fountain of original psychic life
originate. Here exists the possibility of remolding rigid experience.
It is the maternal soil out of which the thought develops by continuous resetting. If the original intention could succeed without inhibitions, unchanged through intentions directed towards other object situations, the goal reached by thinking could not do justice to
the richness of motives which have to be considered. The passing
phases of thought become manifest when the intentions towards
different parts of the objective cross—that means when new object
relations become obvious in the act of thinking. The value of thinking consists in the utilization of object relations. The intercepting
of intentions directed towards objects manifesting themselves in
pictures are, according to this opinion, essential for fertile thought
process. I am inclined to define thinking as an act directed towards
objects, the performance of which has been intercepted by acts directed towards other objects. This interference appears in pictures.
It is characteristic of the fertile act of thinking that it reaches its
goal, insight into its object relation, in spite of the breakage. Some

thought processes are intercepted prematurely. Minor causes are sufficient to interrupt the development of thoughts before their completion. I point to the experiments of E. Stransky who found perseveration, contamination, and clang association in speech when attention was relaxed. According to our analyses in normal persons these products are also preliminary stages in the developmental phases of normal thinking.

A fertile field in which we find such preliminary stages of thought are schizophrenia and paraphrenia. I will reproduce shortly the results of the examination of a paranoid case of this group, and remark here that, since I can rely on a rather extensive experience, I consider these findings as typical. Freud, E. Bleuler, and the Zürich school have repeatedly pointed to similar mechanisms.

The patient, Aloisia D., a paraphrenic for many years, developed an extensive delusional system which was based on psuedo-reminiscences and on reminiscences of hallucinations. This delusional system had no influence on her everyday life, which was that of a good poorhouse inmate. The content of her delusional system was as follows:

Clover seeds got a soul from a human being who has been boiled into a juice. They penetrated into the blood stream and developed into worms. These worms built a magnet child according to a plan which had been drawn in the body. It was also necessary that air be blown into the genitals. At birth, "slava" fire come out of the genitals which burned everything to gold. With the magnet child one could draw treasures to oneself. The "slava" gold kept the world together. The patient had had five magnet children. She created besides this anthropogony, a queer cosmogony and a still queerer fairytale world which will not be discussed here. Between her fantasies and her delusions there existed very close inner relations. Worms and "slava" appeared in various different forms as representatives of the masculine and feminine principle.

I would like to discuss only the various formal disturbances which the patient showed. Condensations of manifold type were present. I cite merely one instance without analyzing it: "Under the name of Vanderbilt (she called the firm of her uncle by this name) many millions were deposited. Ten millions were in the country bank.

The patient had to sign the peace in the Franco-Serbian war in the year 1892. Everything had to be done with Vanderbilt's money."

Parts of different circles of experience and knowledge are mixed together and molded into one. We deal with condensations. Since the nature of condensation is well known I go to the next point. The patient said that her second boy had a big "bone head," which her uncle wanted to use in order to cure himself. The child had a rubber suit into which it grew. The limbs of a child which has grown in this way can be used for medicinal purposes. Those cured in this way say that they had a bath. The basic series of ideas is seemingly a penis enshrouded in a condom and in this way protected against disease. This is substituted by the idea of a child with a bony head, the limbs of which serve to protect against disease. In my opinion it would be incorrect to say that the patient symbolizes the penis in the child. We may say, however, that the process of thinking offers symbolic substitutions. At this change in thinking the penis to be protected is changed into a child which cures. It is worth while mentioning that activity and passivity coincide almost completely at this stage of thinking.

The "slava," the subterranean fire-gold (that slava and genitals are identical cannot be doubted) has to be served (the patient's term for intercourse) twice a week, by a Czech. The Czech was with her, Aloisia, and served her. Slava, which is the soul of the woman, sees two human beings through the earth. In reality she sees only the phallus of the man and sees it as a whole human being. The whole procedure lasts only a few seconds but the slava was contented. If somebody other than the Czech intruded into her, the slava then felt like thorns.

This passage is worthy of attention. The act, namely intercourse, is twice thought of by the patient. Once in a correct way and again in the symbolic sphere (as satisfaction of the slava). Slava is a fire-gold coming from the genitals and stands for the female genitals. It is humanized, since it sees, and it sees the male sex organ but sees it as a whole man. The psychological analysis of the transpositions, condensations, and playful repetitions which go hand in hand with the reduplication of the events in the symbolic sphere is not necessary for our purpose. I have already mentioned that the thinking of the normal person knows a symbolic prelevel of the results of thinking, and that this pre-product cannot be blotted out. Here we find the analogy. In the normal, total experience is summed up in a unified meaning, but not in our case. In psychopathology such duplications of experience are not rare. It would be worth while to consider "autoscopy" from this point of view. The individual doubles his body image and projects it outside. This second appearance may be transformed according to affective points of view. One of my patients who leads a very unhappy family life saw herself in a medieval costume far away from the present (*Selbstbewusstsein und Persönlichkeitsbewusstsein*). The individual also projects bodily defects, delusions, and hallucinations without losing the consciousness of her own defect. During this projection the defect increases. One of my patients who had a crippled arm saw persons opposite him with not only a crippled arm but also with a crippled leg. This corresponds to the point of view of the psychology of the normal in which we learned that important things are exaggerated.

But, let us return to our patient. Fertilization and birth appear in symbol-like pictures in an almost unlimited number. The scorpion originates, according to her, from the semen of the man which enters the woman (fertilization). The poison of the scorpion makes a juice out of another human being. Being made into a juice is again a symbol-like representation for intercourse and fertilization. The human juice fertilizes clover seeds (fertilization). These seeds enter the blood (fertilization) and grow into worms. The worms can also penetrate into the body (fertilization). Children are put into the woman by liquefaction of the abdominal wall. The slava gold is pumped into the body as air. We see here that the great number of symbol-like representations mean the same thing. Another one of my patients does not differentiate between the representations "Tom Thumb," snake, and worm. In the background is the connotation of a phallus. This reminds us that in the psychology of the normal, helpful representations of various kinds can be used in order to reach the meaning. When one thinks of a general subject, instead of a single representation a whole series of images appear (K. Buehler). It is known from child psychology that various names can be given to the same objects. The counterpart of the disturbance now described is as follows: Aloisia does not differentiate between the brother of her mother and the brother of her father. The personality of her uncle is equivalent to the personality of her father. They have the same fate. They have lost their heads. An idea remains which we have to formulate in the following way: Father—uncle—man of whom the head is the only remnant—old man. The final result of the process of imagination is treated, in a way, as if it were a transitional phase in the process of thinking. The individual representation represents here the general connotation. This is connected with a leveling of individual representations.

I have discussed only the most obvious formal disturbances which our patient showed, and I believe that I have demonstrated that these disturbances can be understood as malformations in the process of differentiation of thoughts. I would like to emphasize that, whatever we find in the paranoid forms of schizophrenia and in paraphrenia in representations, hallucinations, and scenic experiences particularly can be found in a compressed way in the so-called verbigeration. As proof, I refer to E. Stransky's paper on speech confusion in which he states that verbigeration and utterances in schizophrenic patients show a repetition of sentence-like complexes and representations which compete with each other and which perseverate irregularly as if turning around an imaginary axis in a monotonous but erratic dance.

I feel justified on the basis of formal analysis to state that, in a large number of cases of schizophrenia, as a final result of thinking, pictures occur which are passing phases in the normal process of thought. The far-going understanding of these products is possible under the point of view that there are inhibitions in the development of thoughts.

With these formal changes in the course of thinking, typical contents of thoughts are connected. Thinking gets its direction towards reality, its respect for facts, only in the last phase of its evolution. The stages of affective rebuilding and symbolization precede it. If cognition takes place according to this stage it would seem as if the world were subject to the wish (Freud's "omnipotence of thought"). If the wish operates directly, it follows that every effect is an effect by the use of a wish, and there exists an action by wish only (phase magic). If the evolution goes from the schema to the single object, a phase must exist in which only the generalities are of importance, and differentiation in the sphere is of less importance. The sphere, power, authority, will not be differentiated. It is a general connotation on an affective basis. The connotations affect, nature, sexuality, and the like, will be experienced as large units. Since, as stated before, affect and thinking have to be considered as one, matter will have the quality of a magic substance, that is, every part will have the same significance as the whole. It will also show an almost infinite indivisibility, which is otherwise a characteristic of matter. Since affectivity predominates, the ambivalence [3] of affectivity connected with the predominance of a schema and sphere will distribute the connotation into the two large realms of good and evil. As Lindworsky and Selz have pointed out it will find a place in these great circles of good and evil in accordance with the inclination of spatial symbolization. Finally, because of the equivalence of concepts of one spherical region, masculine may stand for good or right, and feminine for evil or left, and so forth. The predominance of instinctual life and of affectivity will bring into effect mechanisms of appropriation and rejection (projection, identification, and appersonization) in the undeveloped thought material, and the relation between subject and object will show fluctuations on an affective basis.[4]

These conclusions from the results of the psychology of the normal person are proved by the facts of psychopathology. The study of schizophrenia and paraphrenia is also of great importance for the psychology of the normal person. In a previous book I have partially shown, in accordance with Freud and Jung, that the characteristic con-

[3] The term is used here merely descriptive. In contrast to Bleuler I do not consider ambivalance as an innate characteristic of emotional life.

[4] See my papers on "Hallucinations" and "Identifications," and my book *Wahn und Urkenntnis.*

tent of the unfinished thoughts of schizophrenics is also characteristic for the thought processes of primitives. I want at least to indicate the analogies in the development of the thinking faculty in children. The circle is now closed.

I have tried to show that every thought goes through an evolution in the process of thinking. Stages of this evolution are to be found in the thought processes of the primitive, the child, and the schizophrenic. Although what so far has been found may be incomplete, and the knowledge of these genetic processes imperfect, the facts entitle us to surmise that every single act of thinking recapitulates the phylogenesis and ontogenesis of thinking. Every thought is at first thought by us in the way of our primeval ancestors. This is *vita ipsa*. Every thought runs through the natural history of creation and we experience in our thought the genesis of the organic world.[5]

I have not much to add to this description written more than fifteen years ago. I would merely be more emphatic in saying that this development of thought is not a passive development but an active one, a process of construction with continuous testing and differentiating in contact with the world. In the meantime, the experimental material at hand has been enriched by investigations of Auguste Flach. When she asked one of her subjects how to characterize the relation between purpose and motive she got the answer: "They are threads which extend from motive over the brain to elaboration. . . . I see the picture of a higher and of a lower standing object. . . . Threads extend from the lower to the higher. . . . The threads mix with each other, are interwoven and thicken towards the end. . . . The end is at the upper end. . . . The motive is below and the purpose above. . . . The threads which go from the motive to the purpose go through the brain interwoven as they are."

Another subject was asked what she meant when talking about barter. She experienced something in the shape of loops which signified the circular symbols of bartering. Curves represent the action and the movement which take place during the barter. The

---

[5] Similar thoughts can be found in Nietzsche's and Weininger's works. This whole sphere of problems has been outlined by Schelling.

movement must be in the form of a spiral, since one person loses in the barter and the other wins.

According to Flach these pictures get their significance merely from their ability to exemplify a thought. The visual picture is simply a system of relations, a help for thoughts. She emphasizes that the symbolic schemata are very often concerned with spatial relations. She also emphasizes that in many of these schemata, motor elements are present. In the pictures preceding a solution to thinking, we see the individual go back to the basic relations of actions to spatial relation and motion. Flach thinks that the symbolic schema is different from schematic representations as described by Messer. "It was neither lion nor tiger but only the curly fur was in consciousness." She thinks that the symbolic schemata are not incomplete but contain the basic principles of an objective relation. In an attempt to react with understanding to the meaning of a symbol, we see that the symbol is merely the first attempt to come into relation with the object, and it seems that spatial relations are an aid to orientation. Messer believes, as does R. Allers, that optic representations are insufficient for relation to thought and are simply an illustration of thinking. For instance, with the stimulus word "hearing" the optic representation of one's own ear appears. I do not think, however, that he and Flach are right in believing that these optic illustrations are meaningless. They are first attempts in the constructive process of thinking which takes up all sides of the reality before it arrives at its final conclusion. Every side of reality is in the preliminary stages of thinking and is as general as is the sound before the differentiation in conditioning has taken place.

There is no definite difference between the illustrating optic associations and the symbolic schemata and the more elaborate diagrams which are described by Golden, H. Flournoy, G. E. Mueller, Schanoff, H. Henning, and many others. Flach writes that there are specific types of representations which make a relation in thinking perceptible, substitute for it, and which are described by the name diagrams. These are the cases in which relations in time or of another type—for instance, a certain series of numbers, the days of the week, the months of the year, the epochs of history—are graphically represented by geometrical figures. Flach correctly emphasizes that we deal with a localization in space, which helps as a definite point of orientation in memory. Flournoy believes that all diagrams go back to early childhood. Indeed, when with G. E. Mueller one analyzes a diagram in a case of Le Maitre, one sees that the diagram is connected with and based upon actual experiences in childhood, and that the spatial relations remain. One is justified in seeing in these diagrams remainders of early constructive processes. Before falling asleep similar experiences take place, as H. Silberer has shown. Here is an instance: "I think about the essence of judgments which are trans-subjective; that means valid for everyone." He sees a powerful circle (or a transparent sphere) soaring in the air and human beings reach with their heads into this circle.

Flach is inclined to differentiate between illustrating pictures and symbolic schemata. Only the latter contribute to the process of thinking. I do not think that they are different. In both of them the individual goes back to a more primitive way of acting, in which the concrete infantile experience reappears, which was present before the differentiation took place. Flach justly points out the relation of symbolic schemata to the knowledge that experiences belong to a definite sphere of human experience. This general knowledge corresponds to our general attitudes, which are to a great extent of a motor character. The elaborations in the motor and psychological spheres are strictly parallel to each other and it is therefore of great importance to emphasize the spatial and motor character in the symbolic schemata.

CHAPTER XIX

THE PLEASURE AND REALITY PRINCIPLES IN THOUGHT AND ACTION

THE PROCESS of development of the use of the principles of pleasure and reality is guided by satisfaction or dissatisfaction, as the experiments of Pavlov prove. Another way of formulating this is that the process is guided by the goal represented in the anticipatory scheme and ends when we achieve that goal. One might simply ask: "Which typical signals lead to satisfaction, and which do not?" As has been previously stated, even moderately severe pain may become a signal for food which is biologically needed. However, if the situation is changed so that the dog feels the necessity to defend itself, the preparedness for food as expressed by the salivation ceases. The animal will accept the dangers involved in the acquisition of food if this danger involves only its skin, but if its bones are broken it must for the time being neglect the furtherance of its nutritive goal in order to preserve itself from total destruction.

Freud himself stated that there was no fundamental dichotomy between the pleasure and reality principles. The reality principle demands only the postponement of an immediate satisfaction for the sake of more lasting and more complete satisfaction at some later time. Pavlov's experiments show that reality consists partially of regular sequences to which we adapt ourselves. We have to be prepared from the point of view of the organism. This preparation is partially a muscular attitude. It also expresses itself in secretory and other vegetative processes, such as salivation or the secretion of gastric juice. External reality consists of regular sequences as well as of configurations, which are only comparatively unified occurrences in the sequence.

Thinking is a continuous attempt to secure the satisfaction of biological needs; this is accomplished by a closer reality and a better handling of it through learning the signals which promise satisfaction. The first part of the sequence evokes the expectation of its continuation. The signal may be absolutely dissimilar to the object signalized. One side, one aspect or quality of an object, may signalize the full presence of the object. For instance the smell of food indicates the presence of food, its optic qualities, and its special consistency. An object may signalize the presence of another object, but the relation between sign and referent is independent of any similarity between the two. Signals are not reliable before they have been tested through a process of gradual differentiation of satisfaction and dissatisfaction. One of the chief functions of thinking is to establish the reliability of signals. This process of testing is not confined solely to actions. We test in thinking which, as Freud has correctly stated, is a trial action with only small quantities. These complicated processes have to be constantly checked and rechecked. This checking up and thinking might also be called "self-observation." The problem of self-observation has been unnecessarily complicated by the idea that observation of one's own inner process of experience is different from observation of the outer world. One not only observes continually what is happening around one's self, but also what is going on inside one's self. In order to understand the process of thinking we must understand the process of self-observation.

In this book we have been concerned with psychological problems. In speaking here about sequences in reality, objects and configurations, I imply without hesitation that such sequences, objects, and configurations which have been established through action by the process of trial and error are indeed a part of this world. Our insight into the structures of the real world is as incomplete as are the successes of our actions, but by a gradual process of successful action we come closer to a reality which consists of objects and their relations, configurations, and sequences.

Before discussing the question of self-observation in detail I should like to present an illustrative case history.[1]

The patient was a twenty-one-year-old medical student. In the course of the first two weeks of the analysis he formulated his difficulties as follows: "For the past year I haven't been able to talk, to say what I think. My thought and my speech are not correlated. There is always something stiff in me when I talk with people. I must make them feel ill at ease. Most of the time nothing goes through my mind. There is only mental activity without direction. I am manufacturing things in my mind. I often say things just for the sake of saying them. I am afraid I won't remember everything."

He continually complained that he had lost the power of imagining anatomical relations, and felt compelled to try repeatedly to see whether he could picture them correctly. He had particular difficulty in imagining the anatomy of the pelvic region. When he finally succeeded in picturing this region to himself he found that it had been turned around and was distorted. He also had difficulty in imagining the topical relations between the stomach and liver. It was as if he tried to pull up the liver so that he could look into the deeper parts. (His mother had a gall bladder operation about a year earlier.) "In my thinking, I think seventy per cent about the pelvis and thirty per cent about the stomach and liver. . . . I feel blank—everything is futile. I never could do anything without thinking of myself. I always try to think what I am thinking. The knowledge I had was temporary. I never had lasting knowledge."

This condition had developed gradually in the course of the four months preceding the beginning of treatment. It had become so severe that he no longer dared continue his medical schooling and was afraid to face his schoolmates. He felt that everything was futile and he laughed at the idea that he would ever recover. He sat at home in despair, moaning and groaning. He said: "I feel I would like to be a dog; I would like to be a robot—a mechanical thing."

The patient was the eldest of three siblings. His sister was two years

[1] Reprinted from "Self-Consciousness and Optic Imagination in a Case of Depression," *Psychoanalytic Review*, XXI (1934), 316–28.

younger and his brother six years younger than himself. His parents always bestowed on him a great amount of admiration and love. The father, a rather successful business man, showed his admiration in a more restricted and indirect way, the mother was always effusive in her praise. She not only admired his physique and spoke about his royal appearance and features, but she called him a "noble character." Her praise for his intellectual faculties was unlimited. She very often said that he dropped pearls out of his mouth and what he was saying was pure gold. His remembrances of this maternal attitude go very far back. It had never changed. The admiration of the family increased markedly when it was found he was gifted at school. He failed twice in college because he was not very much interested in his work and preferred to do other things. However, following this there was an unbroken series of scholastic successes which culminated in his receiving a gold medal for his achievements in pathology during his second year at medical school. He became more and more accustomed to everyone's admiration. He was considered witty and unusual. Everybody predicted a great future for him and he regarded himself as a superior being. His ambition was to be the best medical student in the country. At the beginning of his illness he was at the height of his success but the moment he got the gold medal he started to doubt whether he actually deserved it. A disappointment in his love life had occurred a short time before this event. A girl with whom he had fallen in love married someone else. At the same time he began to worry about his strong sexual urges, which he felt interfered with his studies. He felt that a person of his superior ability should not have such feelings and tendencies; they did not fit into the idealized picture his parents and friends and he himself had formed.

Further analysis revealed a great deal of relevant material concerning his sexual life. His attachment to his mother became mixed with feelings of disgust at a very early age. He realized that she didn't close the door when she went to the toilet. At the time of analysis he felt that his mother's hands had an unpleasant fecal smell. He was very much ashamed when his mother came into his room half-dressed. It embarrassed him greatly to undress in the presence of his mother. In the course of the analysis he recalled that following a throat operation in his fifth year he was sitting on the toilet with his buttocks exposed while his mother was with him. Once he had a fantasy that he was a baby sitting on the toilet seat and defecating. Another fantasy which he reported at that time was: "What would happen if I were to find out that I had looked under the skirt of a nurse and she had urinated in my face?" He recalled that when he was six years old he had been lying in bed with his sister while his mother lay screaming in the next room as she gave birth to his younger brother and he buried his face in the pillows and cried.

Two other important early recollections only came out later in the course of the analysis. The first event occurred when he was less than two years old. He was riding in a carriage with large wooden wheels, drawn by a Shetland pony. His mother was sitting in the back and he was sitting between her legs. He also recalled the driver with a whip, and the road of red clay. At a slight rise in the road the sky over the hill looked like a sea of rolling water and he was afraid they would fall in, but his mother quieted him. The second recollection concerned the period between his third and fourth year. He had had the measles and he remembered the dark room with green shutters. A recollection of his fourth or fifth year concerned another boy who showed him a long rifle.

The two most important features of his psychosexuality come to the fore in these recollections. First, his enormous interest in seeing and secondly his disgust connected with the anal function, which probably changed his attitude toward sex. His mother's interest in his appearance increased his interest in seeing. She was interested in the size of his penis. He himself later compared his penis with those of other boys and also wondered about his father's penis and what it looked like. He had a great curiosity concerning his sister's sex parts, but only remembrances dating from his eleventh and twelfth years could be brought back clearly into his memory. His mother justly considered him good-looking and throughout his whole life he was very much concerned about his appearance. He worried because one of his teeth was missing. He wanted others to admire him. At the age of ten or eleven he worried because he thought he was too fat and the other boys would laugh at him. In the course of the illness he also felt that he was too fat and should diet. In addition he reproached both his mother and sister for eating too much and being too fat.

At the time of prepuberty a long series of both active and passive homosexual experiences occurred in which mouth and anus were used. In his masturbation fantasies he imagined a man and woman having intercourse and tried in vain to take the man's place. A great fear of being detected was present. At sixteen he had a heterosexual experience which was later repeated once. In the following years he indulged in incomplete heterosexual activities until about one year before the onset of his illness. He had rather frequent intercourse with a girl for whom he did not care. After the first week of the analysis he started another heterosexual relationship but found the girl ugly and unattractive.

With these facts in mind we can now come to a better understanding of the symptomatology of this patient's illness. He still had a great interest in his appearance, and although he considered himself good-looking, when he began to distrust his abilities he found that even his features had become common and ugly. He also thought that his body smelled badly and that he perspired too much; that his clothes no longer fitted him, and that he had never had a well-fitted suit or a smart-looking hat. It is obvious that his interest in his own body was strengthened by the enormous attention his mother paid to it. His narcissistic interest in his appearance is the direct continuance of the love his mother displayed for his body. The doubt concerning his appearance started at the same time as his doubt concerning his mental capacities. The edifice of his narcissism broke down under his erotic disappointments. His attitude towards his body was now the reverse of his extreme narcissism. However, it is and was a particular kind of narcissism closely related to seeing and being seen. He finally felt so ashamed that he did not want to go to school any more.

His attitude toward his own thinking was a continuation of his attitude toward his own body. He had become narcissistic concerning his thinking because his mother praised it so much. The same factors which wrecked his confidence in his appearance wrecked his confidence in his thinking. He looked at his own body and his own thinking with the eyes of his mother. His self-consciousness concerning both was directly related to the introjection of his mother (and to a lesser degree of his father) into his superego. The undermining of his self-confidence, which followed the extreme expansion of his somatic and intellectual narcissism, coincided with an increase in self-observation and self-consciousness. He observed himself continually through the eyes of his superego. He expected the same admiration he got from his mother from all other persons around him, and his mother had become the exponent of human society. He wanted to be admired by his mother and by himself, his superego and by everyone in the world.

There is a continual interchange between the superego and the persons of the outer world. In patients of this type one has the impression that the relation between the superego and the outer world has remained flexible: when our patient despised himself he felt despised; when he admired himself he felt admired. I have shown that the knowledge of one's own body is in many ways a product of the social relations to one's group. The same is true concerning the knowledge of our own thinking. We think about ourselves what others have thought about us. Self-consciousness is a social phenomenon. This phenomenon never would have occurred in the same way in our patient if he had not had a strong tendency to visual observation from the start. This tendency has, as these scattered remarks show, undoubted libidinous roots. He has an extreme visual curiosity about sexual matters. His optic imagination serves his sexual curiosity, as demonstrated by his attempt to imagine the pelvic region and the abdomen of his mother. He observes his own process of thinking with the same curiosity. His self-observation and self-consciousness are directed towards his faculty of optic observation. He wants to see everything. He is not satisfied with knowledge which cannot be visualized. He wants his whole knowledge in the immediate present.

His self-observation is therefore based upon visual libidinous components and upon the introjection of his admiring mother as a distinct part of his superego. Therefore we are dealing here with a type of narcissism which is closely related to optic tendencies. When in the course of the analysis the patient improved, he said that he had never believed he had lost all his knowledge and all his power of imagination. His continual self-depreciation had provoked frantic assurances of appreciation from his mother.

He depreciated himself in order to get more appreciation. He humbled himself intellectually in order to be appreciated more by his mother and others. The self-depreciation made it unnecessary to prove his enormous narcissistic claims. He would have been the greatest man if he had not been afflicted by the disease. This is a mechanism similar to that which S. Rado has pointed out in depressions in which the ego depreciates itself in order to get new assurances of love from the superego and the parents from whom it is derived.

The picture cannot be understood unless we take into consideration that sadomasochistic tendencies express themselves in the tendency of continual self-observation. The patient observes himself in order to punish himself. Self-observation has, as T. Reik has pointed out, a sadistic tendency. The parents see in order to control and to punish. The omniscience of God enables Him to punish.

The phenomenon of self-observation and self-consciousness has therefore the following roots: narcissism; sadomasochistic tendencies; optic libido.

It is important to see how the relation of the patient to other individuals is changed by self-observation. He thought that everybody was interested in whether he was witty, clever, successful in his work, good-looking or not. It did not make much difference to him whom he impressed. The result of his narcissism was not the disappearance of object relations, but rather a quantitative increase, which resulted in a general leveling that did not take into account the separate individualities in his surroundings.

All these tendencies found a clear expression in the sexual relations which started during the analysis. He found the girl ugly. He thought, "Why do I allow her to be so familiar with me?" and went into a rage when she called him "Honey." He ordered her to assume queer postures during intercourse. He examined her vaginally and found she had a retroflexion of the uterus. Thereupon he insisted on having intercourse without protective measures because he wanted to confirm his opinion that she could not conceive. Actually she represented only a vagina to him. He felt that it did not make any difference to him with whom he had intercourse. Every girl was the same to him, and he would have liked to have had intercourse with every one. With the progress of the analysis the personal relation to his love object awakened.

A still clearer reflection of this tendency became apparent in the transference situation. He was curious about what the analyst thought of him. He was very proud when he said something which the analyst considered witty and clever. He wanted to impress the analyst, but he also wanted to be loved and appreciated by the analyst. While he confessed to a high regard for the analyst he also felt that the analyst was in the last analysis inferior to him because he had to serve him. He thought the analyst would not ask for money. Particularly in the beginning of the analysis he often felt that the analyst was sitting very far away from him on a wooden chair. To this chair he had the associations of throne and electric chair. (When six or seven years old he had a fever and people had seemed to be very far away.) Once he thought that he smelled the flatus of the analyst, and on another occasion he found that the analyst's cigarette had a very bad smell. Once, when he had to wait, he developed the fantasy that the analyst was masturbating. He also wondered whether the analyst had intercourse with his female patients. Thus he projected his own desires and concerns into the analyst and then introjected the analyst into himself. If the analyst lived in the low instinctive sphere, if he smelled badly and also masturbated and had illicit sex relations, then those things could not be so bad after all, because they did not hinder the analyst in his intellectual capacity. There was then no reason why he could not be as good as the analyst. With progress in the transference situation he gained a new appreciation for his father and mother. In a discussion of the money situation many hostile tendencies toward the analyst appeared. The patient felt that the analyst should be only too happy to treat such an interesting case without any fee. After discussing the money situation with his parents he began to feel that they wanted to shirk the financial responsibility and started to blame himself in a similar way. Some of the reproaches he directed against himself were primarily directed against his parents, especially his mother. It can easily be seen that his mother was twice introjected. First, she was a part of the observing and appraising superego which continued in the tendency to self-observation. He felt that the analyst should admire him as much as his mother did and as he wanted to admire himself. Sometimes he would say to himself, "Was it not clever? Am I not witty?" or "The analyst would certainly admire my clever remarks." Secondly, his mother was also a part of his ego and id, in that she represented the gross sexual and anal side of his personality. When he had almost completely recovered he summed up in the following way: "Will I know that the desire to see has left me? . . . If I should, then I shall have it back."

The analysis resulted in a complete recovery in six months. The process of cure followed this course: Ego and id features were projected into the analyst who apparently tolerated this part of his ego. A part of the analysis consisted in the undoing of introjections by projection. After the process of projection had taken place, the analyst was taken back by identification into the patient. Introjections, identifications, and projections express themselves therefore in a circular movement. There are two different movements, one in the ego and the other in the superego, which mutually influence each other.

Clinically, the case belongs to the group of manic depressive psychoses. It is a type of depression in which the emotions of grief and sadness do not enter. The patient stated correctly: "I am not sad, but my thinking is paralyzed." He complained chiefly about his inability to think and to imagine optically. This inability forced him to continual self-observation, which was similar to that found in cases of depersonalization.

Our patient never complained that his thoughts were mechanical, automatic, or not his own. He complained about the inhibition in his thinking but attached his thoughts to his own personality. He also felt his body as his own, although he said he would like to be a dog or a piece of wood. In other words, the inhibition in thinking and imagination was much more in the foreground than in cases of depersonalization. But he also completely lacked the feelings of estrangement which characterize depersonalization. His difficulties were more circumscribed than those found in depersonalization. He withdrew less from his experiences concerning his body and personality and therefore still retained the feeling that his acts were part of his own personality. There is no question that these descriptive differences are due to differences in his libidinal development and in the structure of his ego and superego. Still, there is no doubt that both pictures might belong to the manic depressive group, in spite of the considerable differences they show from the classical types of depressions. Oral sadistic features did not play any part in the case here described. We are far from a deeper understanding of the differences in the various depressive pictures. The studies of Karl Abraham, Sándor Rado, and others are merely concerned with the classical group of depressive psychoses, and we do not have the right to transfer their findings to the great variety of so-called depressive pictures found in the manic depressive psychosis.

I do not believe that we have the right to consider this case as merely a neurosis. I am convinced from experience in similar cases that the patient would have recovered without treatment, but in an indefinite time. His personality, however, would have remained distorted.

When I discussed this case before the New York Psychoanalytic Society at the end of the third month of analysis, there was an almost unanimity of opinion that it was a case of schizophrenia. The self-observation and the leveling of the object relations were considered as proof of this diagnosis. I do not think that there are here any of the characteristic dissociations of schizophrenia, and the course of the case strongly indicates the diagnosis of a depression, under which title I presented it.

Since that time the patient has gained a fuller appreciation of his love object. He deeply felt the incompleteness of sexual relations in which he had no feeling for his love object. He assisted the girl with whom he had sex relations, when she became pregnant. He made a complete adjustment to his family and to his studies.

An observation like this, incomplete as it may be from the analytic point of view, leads to important general problems. The patient continually observed his own psychic processes. He had a particular way of observing his inner experiences. W. M. Wundt says that the "inneren Sinn" is different from consciousness—a subjective action in consciousness. Comte (cited by Arthur Kronfeld) states: "The thinking individual cannot be divided in two, one of which is meditating whereas the other sees it meditating. The organ which observes and the organ which is observed are identical. How could an observation take place?" But there was no question but that subjects observed themselves. Self-observation is a fact and not a theory.

F. Brentano (cited by Arthur Kronfeld) is of the opinion that every psychic act includes the knowledge of this psychic act. In the very act of perception the knowledge that one perceives is included. Analytic observation shows that we observe ourselves in the same way that we have been observed by others, especially by our parents. Self-observation and self-consciousness are therefore acts of a social nature and are the expression of the fact that human beings are basically social. T. Reik has drawn the conclusion that self-observation is not based upon the primary qualities of the human mind. I would not draw such a conclusion. I think that the human mind, and especially the function of consciousness, is the expression of the essential social quality of human existence. The experiences of the individual life, the attitude of others towards our actions and thinking as far as it expresses itself in words, belongs to the very nature of our acts. I think that Brentano is right when he states that the knowledge that we are perceiving is an integrated part of the perception itself. But

I would add that this knowledge of one's actions is the expression of the social character of the psyche. The individual experiences of our patient only exaggerate trends which are present in every individual.

As I have shown in *The Image and Appearance of the Human Body,* we build up the knowledge of our own body not only by self-observation but also by observing others. Furthermore we are interested in those parts of our body which provoke the interest and actions of other persons. I spoke of the socialization of the body image. Our observation above clearly shows that the same principle holds true with regard to mental processes. Thinking is always socialized thinking. Herein lies the importance of the word since the word makes the socialization of thought possible.

Also from another point of view, one's own thinking has close relation to the body image. In the construction of the body image, optic factors play an outstanding part. We may say that observation generally is to a large extent observation through the eye. Whenever we want to observe, we use vision and optic imagination. Curiosity is to a great extent visual curiosity, and the latter is closely related to the visual curiosity concerning sex. Self-observation and optic curiosity are closely linked to each other not merely from a phenomenological point of view but from a dynamic point of view as well. Here lies the explanation for the fact that depersonalization so often starts with the complaint of inability to imagine things visually. Optic perception and imagination are basic not only for the socialized knowledge of one's own body but also for the socialized knowledge of one's own thinking.

We come to the following general formulations: (1) The knowledge of one's own psychic acts belongs to the characteristics of psychic life. (2) This knowledge is the expression of the social character of human existence. (3) The differentiation between ego and superego is the basis for socialized acts. (4) The body image and the knowledge of one's own psychic acts are closely related to each other. Optic interest and curiosity are basic for both of them.

In the course of our discussion we encountered the problem of narcissism and we saw that the narcissism of our patient did not consist of a lack of relations to other persons. On the contrary, in the course of his disease his relations to other people were more in the foreground than they had ever previously been. The objection might be raised that this was only an attempt to regain object relations and to have closer contact which was primarily prevented by the increase in narcissistic tendencies. But this interpretation cannot be accepted, since we saw in his early history that the increase in his narcissistic attitude was due to the enormous investment of libido from his parents. The narcissistic attitude in this case was the result of object relations of special intensity and character. In a study on blushing and other social neuroses I came to the conclusion that in these cases the so-called narcissism is the expression of the oversocialization of the body image. Self-consciousness in regard to thinking is the over-socialization of the thinking process. Narcissism in this respect does not mean disappearance but rather the leveling of object relations.

From this we may arrive at some further general formulations: (5) Narcissism, at least in special cases, is not due to the disappearance of object relations, but to an oversocialization and resultant leveling of object relations. (6) The relations between superego and people in the environment retain a special flexibility. Federn has studied the ego feeling in several interesting articles. He speaks about the sense of the boundaries of our ego: "Whenever an impression impinges, be it somatic or psychic, it strikes a boundary of the ego normally invested with ego feeling. If no ego feeling sets in at this boundary, we sense the impression in question as alien. So long as no impression impinges upon the boundary of ego feelings, we remain unaware of the confines of the ego." We can reach a much simpler and clearer formulation if we study the psychology of the body image and the investment which is given to the different parts of the body image in connection with the reactions of others to our body and their actions concerning our body. Federn also believes that the ego feeling is the original narcissistic investment of the ego. I have shown in *The Image and Appearance of the Human Body* that we do not gather knowledge about our own body unless we have contact with other persons and with the outer world. It is a mistake to believe that we have an immediate knowledge of our body image. As stated above, it is built up in the course of the socializing process and this socialization is already present at the most primitive levels. I therefore do not think that Federn is right when he says: "As such, it (the original narcissistic investment of the ego) has no object at first. I designated it intermediate narcissism. Not until much later, after the object libidinal cathexes have reached the ego boundary or have invested it and again been withdrawn, does reflexive narcissism arrive." I insist that in even the most primitive experience psychic acts are socialized. Psychoanalysis should give up the idea that we have an immediate and primary knowledge of our own body and should consider that human beings actually are socialized in their body image and socialized in their process of thinking.

A final theoretical question presents itself, namely, what is the essence of the so-called conscious act? According to Brentano's formulation, perception and action are conscious in themselves. Our discussion shows that this formulation has to be enlarged by adding that the knowledge of one's own psychic act is at the same time the expression of the social character of human existence, which finds its final expression in the superego but is based on the first construction of the body image which needs the world, the other persons in it, and their actions. We may therefore come to certain additional conclusions: (7) Consciousness is a social function which is reflected in the superego. (8) Overconsciousness (self-consciousness) is the result of oversocialization with a leveling of object relations.

I know that some of these conclusions are not in accord with current psychoanalytic formulations. Therefore I should like to emphasize them by repeating them again.

1. The knowledge of one's own psychic acts belongs to the characteristics of one's own psychic life.

2. This knowledge is the expression of the social character of human existence.

3. The differentiation between ego and superego is the basis for socialized acts.

4. The body image and the knowledge of one's own psychic acts

are closely related to each other. Visual interests and curiosity are basic for both of them.

5. Narcissism, at least in special cases, is not due to the disappearance of object relations but to an oversocialization with a leveling of the object relations.

6. The relation between superego and persons outside retains a special flexibility in cases of this kind.

7. Consciousness is a social function which is reflected in the superego.

8. Overconsciousness (self-consciousness) is the result of oversocialization with leveling of the object relations.

The chief difference in these theoretical formulations lies in the denial of an objectless narcissistic stage. This denial implies a greater stress on the social character of human existence. I consider as an addition to psychoanalytic knowledge the fact that this case shows that, as we have noted, self-observation has three specific roots: dissatisfied narcissism; sadomasochistic tendencies; optic curiosity. The observation demonstrates further that increased narcissism is the result of "self-sacrificing" love on the part of the parents.

The formulation that consciousness is a social function should be acceptable from an analytic point of view. It leads back to very early formulations of Freud concerning the nature of repression, but it approaches the problem from the positive side. The continual interplay of identifications and projections which take place in the ego as well as in the superego are the expressions of the primary social function already present in every psychic act, which can never be an isolated psychic act but the act of a person who lives in a social group.

CHAPTER XX

THE NATURE OF CONSCIOUSNESS

THE TERM consciousness is generally used in a rather vague way and without a very definite meaning. We may consider the term in its clinical sense. When we are awake we can see the context of our experiences. We observe events taking place in the outer world and see them in a specific context. We then turn to our inner experiences and again find a context. We compare the two and construct. We then have possibilities for actions which are adapted, or at least are adaptable, to the structure of the outer world. As we grow sleepy it becomes increasingly difficult to retain insight into the context of outer and inner experiences and to act in such a way as to cope adequately with the more complicated structures in the outer world. Thinking becomes increasingly difficult. In the next stage, when action has become almost impossible, primitive forms of thinking appear, in the form of hypnagogic hallucinations. The investigations of H. Silberer throw some light on the nature of these forces. In sleep, the contact with the outer world is further diminished. The dream world is a world which does not lead to successful thinking and action; the context of its pictures is not obvious, and from them the context of our inner life is not easy to learn. From the state of wakefulness to the state of sleeping and dreaming there are various transitions representing different states of consciousness.

A similar series of phenomena, having a slightly different direction, leads from the state of wakefulness to the state of deep hypnosis (see P. Schilder and A. Kauders, *Hypnosis*).

Another angle of the problem is revealed when we study cases of head injury in which the patients have lapsed into deep coma followed by complete flaccidity. These cases show no interest either in the world or in their own experiences. In the next phase toward recovery, defense reactions against painful stimuli come into the foreground. Grasping or sucking reflexes appear, and flexor reflexes are present. Stages of deep clouding of consciousness follow, in which the individual is unable clearly to perceive what is happening in the world around him; the perceptive function is deeply disturbed, as a result of which there are disturbances in imagination, fantasy, and memory. Even when consciousness has become clear in relation to the outer world, and the context between the diverse inner experiences can be reconstructed, the memory function may still remain disturbed, and the construction of the memory continuum may be completely unsatisfactory, as the Korsakoff syndrome shows.

Still another aspect of the disturbance in consciousness appears in the cases of mental confusion which have been studied by Heinz Hartmann and myself as well as by W. Mayer-Gross; in these the individual had particular difficulty in really establishing complete insight into the structure of the outer world. However, changes in the consciousness in sleep, hypnosis, after head injury, and in mental confusion are in no way identical.

The helplessness and bewilderment of a case showing mental confusion is very characteristic and corresponds to a specific inability in the perceptive function. It is probable that a much greater variety of various stages of consciousness can be found. The awakening from alcoholic intoxication or from anesthesia to full consciousness passes through characteristic stages.

These superficial clinical descriptions permit us to come to some conclusions concerning the nature of consciousness. By consciousness we mean, then, that constructive psychic work which goes on continually, which tries to bring the data in the outer world into a context, and which helps us to a deeper insight into the structure of our psychic experiences. Consciousness becomes clouded when the work of construction becomes incomplete. The completeness of the constructive work can be measured by the efficiency of our actions.

The problem of consciousness is therefore, as E. G. Boring has emphasized, the problem of a context. The context has to be worked out as a continuous process of construction. Where no complete construction is possible the context remains incomplete. When one field of experience is more or less excluded from the context of the general construction we speak of the system of the unconscious. When there are difficulties in any endeavor of construction we speak of lack of consciousness, clouding of consciousness, or bewilderment. There are no isolated experiences. Even when no complete construction occurs, there is material for construction in the background, and the individual must try to correlate this material. Consciousness is therefore necessarily connected with self-observation, as Franz Brentano has correctly stated. When constructive efforts are diminished, self-observation may be less apparent but it will always be present. Self-observation therefore is one of the inherent qualities of consciousness. Consciousness is in this sense readiness for action. Self-observation may be increased when the individual is not sure whether he should go on from the construction to action. Self-observation is also increased when individuals observe themselves through the eyes of others.

The person who is unconscious is not only excluded from the outer world but is immediately changed in his social relations. He becomes isolated from other human beings. The complete construction of an object is possible only on the basis of full coöperation with other people. Consciousness, thus, is in its essence a social phenomenon. The farther construction progresses, the closer our world approximates the world of others. Clearness of consciousness makes us social human beings, and only on the basis of the social action as measurement can we have a clear consciousness. Impairment of consciousness leads us immediately from a social into a private world. Consciousness is only one side of our social context but it is an important one.

The problem of the localization of consciousness received a new impulse by the discovery of C. von Economo of a sleep center in the periventricular gray matter of the third ventricle. Further important contributions have come from A. Adler, Luksch and O. Poetzl. Von Economo is of the opinion that the posterior portion of the central gray matter near the wall of the third ventricle is concerned with the maintenance of the state of consciousness, because a lesion in this region produces sleep. The anterior portion of this center near the sub-thalamic region is supposed to produce awakening. This hypothesis, however, is not very well founded in fact. E. A. Spiegel believes that a bilateral lesion in the thalamic region produces sleep, and that a lesion in the posterior wall of the third ventricle has no influence in animals. Clinical evidence speaks very strongly for the significance of the posterior wall of the third ventricle. O. Poetzl tried to localize the region very sharply near the nucleus of Dankschewitsch. Karl Kleist has enlarged the concept, and partially following Reichardt, speaks of different centers of consciousness from the medulla ob-longata up to the thalamic region. According to Breslauer-Schueck and Reichardt, lesions of the centers in the medulla oblongata pro-voke deeper degrees of disturbance in consciousness.

My own experience makes it seem probable that lesions which are close to the hypothalamic region do not provoke sleep but rather con-fusion. Such at least were the findings observed in a tumor case by myself and Max Weissmann. S. W. Ransom reviews the newer litera-ture and comes to the conclusion that extensive lesions in the region of the mammillary bodies cause catalepsy and somnolence in a cat. He also reports that it is possible to produce profound somnolence in monkeys by damage of the hypothalamus. The experiences of W. R. Hess point to the importance of lesions closer to the posterior wall of the third ventricle. Whatever final detailed investigation will show, there is no doubt that the sleep mechanism can be disturbed through lesions in the region of the third ventricle.

Under the influence of Pavlov the older cortical theory of sleep has gained new adherents. Pavlov showed that animals in which a con-ditioned reflex has been inhibited become more and more drowsy, and finally fall into a more or less deep sleep. This is especially true if the so-called trace reflexes are not satisfied. For example, after the establishment of a conditioned reflex in which food follows the light stimulus at an interval of five or ten seconds, if in further experiments the food is not forthcoming, the animal may fall asleep. Pavlov ex-plains this on the basis of an inhibition which spreads over the cortical region and finally affects the deeper centers and produces sleep. O.

Nachmansohn and others have drawn the conclusion from these experiments that sleep is due merely to cortical function.

It is the consensus of opinion that the decorticated animal shows something like sleep and awakening. In Gamper's case in which merely the brain stem including the *nucleus ruber* was preserved a decided sleep rhythm was present. One might say, of course, that a rhinencephaly is connected with very great changes in the function of the brain and that under normal circumstances the midbrain may not be able to provoke the sleep rhythm. One might also doubt whether the rhythm observed in this child may be exactly the same as that observed in normal sleep. At any rate the case proves that rhythmic functioning of consciousness takes place even when the cortex is not developed. The dog without a forebrain also shows a rhythmic change in consciousness. It is a matter of course that sleep in the absence of the cortex must be different from sleep in an individual with a cortex. As long as the unity of the brain is preserved, the brain and the whole organism function in their totality and one cannot isolate the parts. There can be no doubt that independence of single parts does not exist and that localization cannot be understood in the sense that part functions lead an independent life in isolated parts of the brain. The experiments of Ernst Pick and his school have shown that specific drugs act on different parts of the sleep mechanism. Whereas paraldehyde attacks chiefly the cortical part, the barbital group and chloretone act specifically on the subcortical part of the sleep apparatus.

One must not forget that rhythmical functions are present in all parts of the organism. The sleep rhythm is one of them. Von Economo justly differentiates between body sleep and brain sleep. After all the brain is only a part of the total organism. We are here concerned with sleep merely from the point of view of the function of consciousness. There seems to be an organic urge to withdraw from the outer world from time to time. Our knowledge of the mechanics of this withdrawal is incomplete. There is no question that the relation to the outer world is very important. The phenomena of hibernation in animals are sufficient proof for this contention. The relation of sleep to day and night also cannot be contested. As it is incorrect to study the organism in parts, it is also incorrect to study the organic function of the organism except in relation to what is going on in its surroundings. The outer world and the organism are closely correlated to each other. The organism seems to need rest periodically; this periodicity is closely accommodated to occurrences in the outer world. The state of awakening represents action and interest in the world. Sleep represents withdrawal from the immediate problem. It is an escape mechanism and a withdrawal. We should have a clear understanding that strictly physiological problems are also problems of the organism and are concerned with the fundamental relations between the world and the self.

William A. White has developed a theory that consciousness appears when resistances are present. In Chapter XVIII on the development of thinking I discussed the occurrence of images when the individual does not immediately reach his biological aim. In other words the pictures occur when tendencies conflict with each other, or when the reality is so complicated that a continuation of renewed efforts is necessary. Consciousness is therefore one phase in the constructive effort to gain insight into the world, and it is a sign that a great effort is being made in order to solve specific tasks. The individual goes to sleep when there are either no specific tasks or when evasion of these tasks is biologically advisable. Consciousness builds itself up in a great variety of levels.

CHAPTER XXI

PSYCHIC ENERGY

THE TERM psychic energy is often used not in the descriptive sense but in the physical sense of energies involved in the psychological processes. There can be no question that energy in the physical sense is involved whenever psychic processes occur. Physical, chemical, and also electrical processes take place during psychic activity. The question arises whether the energy processes connected with the psychic function are sufficiently distinct from other processes to enable one to speak of a special psychic energy. One of the cornerstones of modern physics is that diverse forms of energy may be transformed into each other. Mechanical energy may become thermal or electrical energy. The separation of energies into different types is basically a practical one. The energies connected with the psychic function are, in my opinion, sufficiently well characterized so that one is justified in speaking of psychic energy when referring to them. This does not mean that these energies are different from the known physical, chemical, and electrical processes; it means that they serve a distinct entity of events.

Various attempts have been made to measure the energies connected with psychic life. S. Bernfeld and S. Feitelberg state that a potential exists between the brain and the body, which can be measured by physical methods and which increases with the state of rest and decreases with the activity of the individual. They call this the potential of the individual. During the process of perception, the individual's potential decreases, that is, perception occurs at the expense of the potential. They believe that this potential is approximately identical with libido. They also hold that the energy expended is identical when the threshold of perception is passed and when the threshold for the perception of differences is passed. I cannot decide whether these investigations can lead to sufficient insight into the energy processes in question. They are merely quoted as a modern attempt to approach the problem. Physiological investigations have not progressed sufficiently to tell us whether the amount of psychic energy available is a constant or not.

It is one of the tenets of modern psychology that the amount of "psychic energy" as far as it is manifested in the amount of psychic experience is much more constant than has been previously supposed. When we sleep, less energy is expended in perception but a greater amount of psychic energy is given to one's own body and to dreaming. A similar theory has been proffered concerning catatonic stupor, in which the patient seems to be stiff and unanimated and does not show any obvious signs of interest in the external world, although he lives an energetic life in fantasies and interests directed towards himself. The depressive patient who does not move is occupied with intensive self-torture. With these formulations we have made several assumptions. We have identified the connotation of physical energy with the psychological connotation of interest and have assumed that the amount of interest appearing, consciously or unconsciously, is an indicator for the energy of psychic processes. Even if these assumptions are true we still have no reliable method of measuring the energies involved. We might perhaps compare the energy of sexual fantasy before and after castration and seek to establish whether other psychic processes in the castrated individual are not endowed with greater vividness, but it is doubtful whether such investigations could be made with any degree of reliability.

The observation by Henry Head on vigilance seems to contradict the theory of a constant psychic energy. He recalls Sir Charles S. Sherrington's work on the transected spinal cord, showing that the reflex response is dependent on the total state of preparation of the organism. Immediately after the operation very little reflex activity is present, but it increases after some time has passed. Similar phenomena are observed in human beings whose spinal cord has been severed. When fever or gastrointestinal disturbances develop, the activity of the spinal cord may decrease. "When vigilance is high, mind and body are poised in readiness to respond to any event, external or internal."

Kurt Koffka adds that the energy at the disposal of the nervous system is variable. If this contention were true, "psychic energies" would not only be in a continuous interplay with the other energies of the organism but might undergo great changes in relation to processes which are extrapsychic. In spite of this I am inclined to believe that the psyche maintains a comparative independence from the point of view of energy. Only in extraordinary circumstances are energies added to or subtracted from the nervous system, as far as it is concerned in psychic activities. Decrease of vigilance under severe somatic shock may be one of those instances, although even such an assumption need not be true. The seeming decrease of vigilance may be due to a deflection of energy to psychic provinces more difficult to observe.

The question of whether the supposedly stable amount of psychic energy remains constant or varies during an individual's life is even more undeterminable. The average motor output, as well as the fantasy processes, of the child and his vigilance toward the outer world seem to be much higher than in the adult and senile individual. They seem to steadily decrease throughout life. The child seems to expend (and reconstitute) great amounts of energy. His energy seems to be more liquid, whereas in the adult a greater amount of psychic energy seems to be bound in the personality. The potential energy of the adult seems to be greater.

At any rate, it would be difficult to disprove such a contention. It is possible that this attempt to maintain the idea of a specific amount of psychic energy in an individual's life may be merely a remnant of the conception of the soul, flattering the self-love of human beings. In spite of the fact that little has been proved objectively, psychic experience may constitute a particular province of energy; the conception of a specific amount of energy in the life of a person is nevertheless not abstruse. The energies of the total organism are in a continual interplay with psychic energies, and, even if we believe in a relative constancy of psychic energy, it can only mean that regulatory mechanisms exist. There is constant interplay with the mechanisms of the total organism and a certain amount of energy is always available.

Possibly we should be less ambitious and, returning to the realm of facts, measure the motor output and the motor activity as C. Richter and his co-workers have done. With Guttmacher, G. B. Wislocki, and G. H. Wang, Richter recorded the motor activities of rats. They found diverse rhythms of activity: one of one and a half hours; a four-day rhythm in females dependent on the ovaries; one of twenty-two days; one of nine days to one hundred and twenty days. Adrenals, hypophysis, and ovaries have a decided influence on this rhythm, whereas the thyroid has no effect—that in humans the thyroid has a great effect on the motor output is generally recognized. Experiments thus show that rhythms exist in motor output. Is there less psychic energy at the time of less output or is it merely hidden and used for other purposes? At any rate, these experiments based on reliable observation open the way to a more definite approach to the problems of energies connected with psychic processes.

CHAPTER XXII

THE PSYCHOLOGY OF GEOMETRY AND PHYSICS

GEOMETRY

OUR investigations permit us to postulate certain formulations concerning the psychology of geometry. As our previous discussions show (Chapter IX), the psychological unit is not a point. In drawings by children, points appear at a rather late stage. The primitive units are the loop, the circle, and the ellipse. The regular circle is comparatively late in appearing. Frequently, also, the disc is substituted for the point. In a case reported by K. Goldstein and A. Gelb the patient was unable to achieve the concepts of straight and curved. Experience with children clearly shows that the curve precedes the straight line. These primitive units are sensory motor. It seems to be questionable whether optic impressions as such make the step from the curved to the straight line possible. The operated blind person seemingly has no definite idea of form (Chapter IV). As mentioned it is difficult to understand how Von Senden can come to the conclusion that these cases prove space perception is simply due to optic impressions. These very cases make it probable that optic impressions alone are unable to produce adequate spatial impressions. It is very probable that the vertical line gains its preponderance and importance solely in connection with the forces of gravitation, which act particularly on the vestibular apparatus. It also seems that neither angles nor crossings belong to the primitive optic perception, since they do not appear in primitive perceptions and primitive motility. The principle of curved lines probably has close relation to the fact that arm movements are related to a curve. One often sees children at play with outstretched arms moving an object in a curve.

It is well known that an angle cannot be drawn by a child under four or five years of age. In the Stanford-Binet test the ability to copy a diamond is considered as belonging to the six-year level. The tendency to separate definite and distinct units occurs very early, so that the tendency to see separated configurations appears to be a very primitive one. It is characteristic that proximity between a circle and a quadrangle is often artificially symbolized by drawing a connecting curve between the two separate entities. Direction in space is decidedly a product of later development. Reversals of 90 and 180 degrees are the rule. Whereas the one form may be copied quite correctly, other configurations may be completely out of reach of the child. L. Bender cites the case of a three-year-old child who could very clearly differentiate units of two, but was able to copy only three separate form units from units of two (the second figure of Bender's gestalt test). For a child of this age, three constitutes a multitude. The number of single units perceived in the multitude is irrelevant. The child is interested only in the "multitude." Whereas crossing and contiguity are only incompletely represented, enclosure plays a very important part in the child's geometry. These results are deduced from Bender's study of visual motor gestalt patterns. The importance of these findings is increased by the fact that very similar laws can be deduced from the study of optic imagination and of tactile after-effects and imagination. I have mentioned that in V. Benussi's experiments the impression seems to wander over the air in a curve. In optic and tactile sensation, at least, the vortex, the loop, and the curve are primitive units. It is of particular importance that, in the cases of V. von Weizsaecker, H. Hoff, myself, and others, vestibular disturbances distort the perception of the vertical line. At the same time the perception of crossings was severely impaired. There can be no doubt that the integrity of the vestibular apparatus is necessary for the creation of definite optic forms with angles and crossings. It is at least probable that tactile kinesthetic impressions also play an important part in the final elaboration of gestalten. One might have the opinion that the interaction between the senses is merely due to physiological maturation and that no actual experience is necessary to coördinate the experiences of the different senses. Again, it is astonishing how little the operated blind individual perceives the visual world; only through a gradual process does he come to an appreciation of it. It is difficult to believe that this coördination occurs without any active effort on the part of the individual. When we talk of the maturation of optic perception we may again ask what part motility may play. Of course, motility matures too. There must be provision in the central nervous system so that the sensory impressions and the motility can develop by active exercise, interaction, and construction. This experimentation takes place with every action in everyday life. It is probably not possible to remove from the growing organism the opportunity for continuous experimentation. There must be an interrelation between the maturation principle and the principle of experience. If we could restrict an individual in his experimentation the result would probably be an agnosia, as is clearly shown by the reports of congenitally blind persons. It is probable that maturation in itself takes care of the better coördination of the senses, but this latter is finally guaranteed by the action which addresses itself to the object. We see that in the organism several principles are working towards the same goal. The unity of the senses and their direction towards one definite object is not only guaranteed by maturation processes but also by the actions of the individual himself. In agnosias due to lesions of the cortex this principle is disturbed from the organic side. Maturation alone would not be able to make the final adaptation. However maturation certainly tends to a more unified perception of objects.

We thus return to the problem of the unity of the senses. It has become more and more accepted that the lightness-darkness element is inherent in all sense perceptions and that there is no fundamental difference between lightness and darkness in the optic and in the acoustic field. I mention particularly the experiments of E. M. von Hornbostel and Charles Hartshorne. It is difficult to prove experimentally that lightness and darkness in the optic and acoustic field are actually identical. These authors merely prove that one can compare them, but even this comparison is not always reliable. I rather think that while there is something in common to all sense perception there still remain certain specific differences. At any rate, in the optic perceptions of configurations—a prerequisite to geometry—experiences of all the senses are represented. The vertical and the horizontal are not merely optic. The point, the curve, and their derivatives are visual motor. Furthermore, the perception of movement is not merely a sensory visual phenomenon. Our motor attitudes toward moving objects are entirely different from attitudes toward objects at rest. These motor tendencies are inseparable from perception. The varied gray experience of a certain course in time as described by F. L. Dimmick and the perception of the object in its various positions form an inseparable unit with the motor attitudes. The question is whether one should consider human beings endowed with two independent faculties, impression and expression, sensibility and motility, or whether one should emphasize the necessary connection between the two as the basic fact of life. Gestalt psychology, which emphasizes the unit of perception, has thus far artificially separated impression and expression, and has considerably undervalued the influence of motility on sensory impressions. Geometry is, after all, a part of physics. The discussion of motility and motion belongs more suitably in a discussion of the psychology of physics.

PHYSICS

In *Gedanken zur Naturphilosophie* I tried to show that conceptions of physics are based upon psychological fundamentals and psychological experiences. Physics is concerned with objects, and we cannot understand physics unless we understand by what complicated psychological processes the object is built up. I tried to show that physics is based primarily not upon optic impressions but upon tactile and kinesthetic experiences of pushing, pulling, and balancing.

The concept of mass depends either on the pressure which an object exerts on the skin or on the muscular effort required to lift an object, or on a combination of both those factors. We perceive our own bodies as heavy masses. The concept of motion has already been discussed. The concepts of energy and force also have a close relation to pushing and pulling and to the kinesthetic and muscular sensations connected with them. The ideal of classical physics was to explain all physical relations in terms of mechanics. This ideal is easily understandable. The senses which come into immediate contact with the object seem to be more reliable than the distance receptors of the head. These senses permit not only a clear distinction between an object and one's own body but also those clear-cut sensations in connection with one's own body. I may see a color and an external object, but my eye is not red. Even smell does not lead to a sensation as a quality of the body itself. I perceive the odor of something in my nose, but I actually do not experience the sensation of smell in the mucous membrane of my nose. With the sense of taste it is not my tongue which is tasty, but the object touching my tongue. When we consider the sensations connected with the sense of touch, however, we find ourselves confronted with quite a different situation. Touch is a sensation connected with the skin itself. Muscular effort is experienced directly in one's own muscles. The very sensations themselves help build up knowledge of one's body.

It is no wonder then that physics has tried to rely more upon the primary senses as the term was used by Locke, who believed that these primary qualities led directly to the object itself. Kant showed the fallacy of this way of thinking and substituted for the object with primary qualities an object with no sensual qualities at all. He eliminated the reliability of subjective experience as such and replaced the world as we perceive it through our senses by a world without any qualities whatever. Less radical physicists were content to reduce the world to tactile kinesthetic-muscular qualities in which the concepts of mass and energy were of prime importance. But there were also forces in the world. The situation in physics began to change when the phenomena of electricity assumed increasing importance. Electricity certainly gives tactile and muscular sensations but these sensations lack the definitiveness of those one gets by touch and pull. These vague and indefinite sensations probably relate to more primitive tactile impressions. Modern theories of physics finally led to the concept that mass does not exist and is merely an expression of energy. Or, in other words, modern physics finally arrives at a denial of reality similar to Kant's. From a psychological point of view this formulation is meaningless. The conception of the world in physics is in the long run in closest relation to a primitive world filled with motion and vortices but without definite objects. There is no reason why we should believe that these primitive perceptions are actually reliable guides to the essence of experience. Objects and forces exist, and energies without objects are meaningless from a philosophical point of view. Physics does not lead to any reliable picture of the world; it merely gives technical help in the simplest problems of life. Modern physics has worked out the concept of relativity. Still, it maintains one constant—the velocity of light. The concept of constant velocity without a unit of measure is more or less meaningless. Velocity is also something which takes place in time.

It is arbitrary to consider the velocity of light as invariable and time as variable. The statements of modern physics have no claim to philosophical correctness. Physics remains a system of calculation and measurement, a system which remains incomplete since it neglects the fundamental human problems. Euclidean space conceptions and Euclidean physics make possible action which serves many biological purposes. The problems for which non-Euclidean geometry are of importance are comparatively limited. Of course Euclidean and non-Euclidean space in the geometrical sense do serve to explain a limited number of problems. It has been shown in previous chapters that space exists psychologically in connection with our relation to other human beings. When we study various theories of space we should ask "What is this particular space good for?" Space is, in the last analysis, our relation to objects, and it cannot be independent of objects and our actions towards them. Theories of spatial relations represent specific crystallizations of certain phases of the constructive process by which we come closer to the real world. This constructive process has definite and specific aims. The question of whether space is finite or infinite in this way loses its importance from a psychological point of view. No situation exists in which human beings are devoid of the possibility of acting, hence space must be unlimited. On the other hand, since individuals sometimes are paralyzed by conflicting possibilities and do not see "a way out" there must also be an idea of a limited space. Whatever progress physics may make, the physicist's theory must finally come back to the fundamentals of human experience. On retracing its steps back to the fundamentals of human experience, physics goes through a wealth of variable data, but, even so, physics cannot contribute to the fundamental problems of human life, which consist in the relations of human beings to each other.

In discussing time (Chapter XIII), the psychological factors which influence our perception of time were considered. The close relation between time perception and individual needs has been sufficiently stressed. The physicist's conception of time helps unified action and is the product of a constructive tendency directed toward specific aims. Physics no longer believes in forces. It aims at a mathematical formulation of what is going on in the world and tends to develop into a system of exact prediction. Whereas it is possible to arrive at fairly accurate predictions in the physical world, the problem of how to come to an exact prediction in the moral and psychological field has remained unsolved. Since there is no practical possibility of predicting beyond a certain degree of reliability just how human beings will act in a given moment, it is obviously difficult to extend strict determinism into the psychological field. If the principle of determinism is not valid, or at least not demonstrable, in the moral field, it cannot have universal application. It is seemingly one of the fundamental habits of the human mind to assume that a principle which has been proved valid once should be applied to other situations without any further testing. The principle of determinism apparently belongs in this category. Perhaps it is fundamentally wrong to try to formulate general principles that will be valid for every situation. It is possible that the tendency to uniform explanation is a more or less primitive way of thinking and that actually pluralistic thinking is much more appropriate.

The principle of absolute determinism is insufficient not only in psychology but also in microphysics. In 1927, Heisenberg introduced the principle of indeterminancy, which stated that the velocity and position of a particle cannot be ascertained at the same time. Herbert Shuey wrote that measurement and increased knowledge of position leads to increased ignorance of velocity, as it implies a static condition, a given momentary rest of activity, a destruction of fundamental relations. A particle in motion is changed at the time of measurement, otherwise there could be no situation created which would permit accurate study. When position is measured, therefore, velocity is lost.

In other words, predictions in nature are possible but not with absolute accuracy. We might also add that sequences in nature do not show any absolute reliability. After all, our reactions are the same reactions as in the conditioned experiment. Our organism reacts after a certain number of repetitions as if the sequence had been definitely established. We call this conditioning. But nature too consists of sequences, and we have tried to find out the reliability of the different sequences. This testing process is called cognition.

The testing process also reveals what the real units of experience are. These units of experience, or gestalten, crystallize only through this process of continuous testing. Part of the testing process consists of the creation and breaking down of configurations. We thus come to the general conclusion that nature consists of sequences of some regularity which condition us to specific reactions. Since there are no sequences of absolute regularity either in the physical or organic worlds, the laws in these spheres may be compared with the conditioned reactions of the organism. A dog conditioned to salivate after a light signal reacts as if to a law that the particular light will always be followed by food, whereas we know the dog may easily be disappointed. Quite in the same way the scientist and the philosopher may be disappointed when they propound a general law.

We may raise the question as to whether it is not possible to come to a solution of the problem of probability in a similar way. Keynes (quoted by Bertrand Russell) takes it as a fundamental logical category that certain premises make a conclusion more or less probable (but not certain). Improbability is a relation between a premise and a conclusion. A proposition does not have a definite probability but on its own account is merely true or false. Mere observation does not refute reliability of a proposition, for improbable things may happen and probable things may fail to happen. The whole subject of probability therefore, on Keynes's theory, is strictly *a priori* and independent of experience.

Bertrand Russell states that there is still a justification for the so-called frequency theory of probability. In a conditioned reflex experiment it is at first only probable that the unconditioned stimulus will follow the conditioned one. After a great number of repetitions the probability increases and becomes a "certainty." Probability from a psychological point of view is merely expectation. In the objective world the irregular sequence corresponds to it. In general, philosophical problems take on a different aspect when approached from the empirical psychological point of view. The regular sequence in nature never has an absolute regularity. Certain exceptions are invariably present. The painfulness of these exceptions leads to an attempt to establish the same definitiveness in the mental process which human action has, and we come to the theory of absolute evidence, which is in some way preposterous. Human action is never general, but merely decides the particular instance. The very generality of a theory often renders impracticable its application to a particular case. Action implies action not on the basis of general insight but on the basis of a particular situation. Only the action itself is definite and final. Thinking is simply preparation for action and can never attain the final completeness of the act itself. Here probably we encounter one of the most basic difficulties of philosophy and of science in general. Abstract concepts receive their final value only when utilized in action based upon repeated tests in relation to the reality situation. In every theoretical construction it is this natural process of using the abstract in the particular situation which leads to a correction of the general abstraction. Knowledge is therefore not merely a static agglomeration of data but is a process which involves both the concrete situation and the generalization and the testing of this generalization through new experiences. Physics in this light is no different from any other part of human experience.

In modern physics two problems play an important part: first, the problem of field and quantum, and second the problem of action in distance and action by mere contiguity. In the final outcome these problems are identical. It is the problem of continuity and discontinuity that has its counterpart in the psychological problem of transitive and intransitive parts in psychic life as emphasized by William James. The problem of contiguity and action at a distance has as its basis the fact that even when we touch an object there is always, psychologically, a space between the object and ourselves. This space disappears only when we make the touch so slight that it is merely a "sensation" but then it no longer refers to the outer world but merely to something going on in the body. In spite of the space between the object and the body, we still have the feeling that we are in immediate contact with the object. In other words we are dealing with an antinomy, but this antinomy is only verbal and disappears when we consider the total situation of the individual. We are in contact with the object but there still is something which separates us from it. The analyst will suspect that this problem of the psychology of the senses may exist in deep relation to the more human problem of how closely human beings can approach each other.

The problem of whether there is a field or whether there is action at a distance seemingly has been decided by modern physics in the sense that there is no action at a distance and there is merely action by contiguity. The electrical field seems to be the ideal according to which all action is conceived. According to our general theory we must expect that, when a fundamental psychological principle exists, the theories in physics will sooner or later come back to this principle. This occurred with the presentation of the quantum theory. The quantum is a distinct entity which acts like a bullet; it acts at a distance.

In the modern development of psychology, gestalt psychology emphasizes the distinct entities that are somewhat separate from the surrounding field. I have previously emphasized that the gestalt does not originate without testing and experimenting: it is based upon natural patterns prepared in the organism and in the outer world. Gestalt psychology speaks of factors of coherence. These factors of coherence or the natural structure of the patterns of experience are certainly of very great importance, but if we go into a general theory of psychological experience we should not overvaluate the stream of experience in comparison with the formed elements, since both are important. The habit of thinking in opposites has certainly been detrimental in this field too. Thinking in polarities is one of the fallacies of merely verbal thinking. There are no opposites in nature.

The problems of contiguity, action at a distance, quantum and field, transitive and intransitive elements, configuration and sum become sham problems if one considers them from the point of view of opposites, and if one thinks that because the one is true the other cannot be true. Opposites indicate important parts of experience. In the majority of cases the expectation that both opposites are true is justified.

According to psychoanalytic theory the ego has the function of uniting the different data of experience. It is worth while emphasizing that the ego, as shown by Freud, fulfills this function rather incompletely. In thinking, we harbor in our minds contradictory opinions, without particular concern. In regard to perception and sensual experience the different data very often are not correlated. V. von Weizsaecker especially has pointed to this "antinomy" of the senses. The problem of antinomies is one which has found its clearest expression in the Kantian antinomies of pure reason. Kant deduced from these antinomies that no experience is possible. He overlooked the fact that thinking in antinomies is in itself a fallacy. In the following chapter we shall discuss these antinomies in greater detail.

CHAPTER XXIII

ANTINOMIES

KANT'S antinomies of pure reason are as follows:
1. Thesis: The world has a beginning in time and is limited in space. Antithesis: The world has no beginning and no limitation in space; that is, the world is infinite in time and in space.

2. Thesis: Every composite substance in the world consists of simple parts and nothing exists anywhere but the simple or what is composed of it. Antithesis: No composite thing consists of simple parts and nothing simple exists in the world.

3. Thesis: Causality according to the laws of nature is not the only thing from which the phenomena of the world can be derived in their totality. It is necessary to assume a freedom from causality in order to explain them. Antithesis: There is no freedom but everything in the world occurs merely according to the laws of nature.

4. Thesis: Existence of the world depends upon a being necessary in itself, either as a part of it or as its cause. Antithesis: No being necessary in itself exists anywhere as a part of the world or as a cause of the world.

It is easy to see that the first three of these antinomies concern problems which are still of vital importance and which form an important part of the discussion of this book. One also sees that these problems cannot be solved by verbal definition alone. As stated previously, thesis and antithesis are only verbal forms of thinking and neglect the real meaning of the structure of the world. Israel Latif, quoted by L. W. Lockhart and C. K. Ogden writes that the classical view of opposition is fundamentally wrong, because logic starts with verbal abstractions, and terms often contradictory, such as black and not black, are treated as mutually exclusive, instead of considering the organism as reacting in a definite situation. Between black and white there is a series of intermediate values, there is a series of grays. Ogden in summary states that opposites are "directions and areas diagrammatized by the local stretches of either side of the cut." He further states that "in front of" and "behind" give us also the opposition of "before" and "after," while future and past stand in horizontal diagrammatic relation to right and left, as expressed in the position of the body facing either to the right or left, and of a progress along the line. Up and down represent movements from one extreme of the vertical scale to the other.

In our discussion of time (Chapter XIII) it was emphasized that only verbal habits constrain us to consider the past as the opposite of the future. Also the terms finite and infinite are treacherous when removed from the grounds on which they have grown. Even the terms space and time as such are probably verbal to a large extent and do not very often carry a concrete meaning. Mathematical thinking is particularly liable to lead to mere verbal thinking. One is in danger of taking signals for what they signalize.

The second antinomy is after all the problem of the gestalt expressed in the language of the logician. Only empirical investigation can give the final answer to this question. The third antinomy dealing with the problem of causality also requires the empirical answer we have given above. The fourth antinomy has lost its significance at the present time. It may be regarded as a purely verbal formulation.

Kant wanted to express in his antinomies the impossibility of interpreting nature by pure reason and categories of the mind alone. We may agree with him in this regard. But we cannot agree when he then tries to deny the possibility of coming to true objects, and opens up the way for the return of all those ideas which he had discarded in his *Critique of Pure Reason.*

V. von Weizsaecker speaks of antilogic as a phenomenological characteristic of sense perception. In his cases of vestibular disturbance quoted above, objects change their form according to their position in space. In these cases the patients had optic experiences which, according to von Weizsaecker, are antilogical. He mentions also as antilogical the experiences provoked by vestibular irritation. Objects may be seen moving but return to their position in space. His patient sees the direction of turning of an optic object correctly, but he sees an effect of turning which is contrary to the direction perceived. He sees the contradiction theoretically but is not able to remove, by this insight, the paradoxical impression in vision. He says: "I don't know how that is possible."

Logic is in large part verbal thinking. The world of experience offers many conflicting data. They have to be united in a constructive process. The way in which those who are born blind learn to see offers very important experimental evidence in this respect. It is a common experience that the individual who is born blind and is operated on does not care to have these new contradictory experiences. He tries at first to shut them out, but gradually they become incorporated into his psychic experience. It is of great importance to consider from a similar point of view the experiments of Stratton and Wooster quoted in *The Image and Appearance of the Human Body*. In these we find that there are always two series of experiences which do not fit together, but through a process of gradual adaptation these contradictory experiences eventually become correlated. From the excerpts quoted in my book there is no doubt that even then minor discrepancies are still present. In other words, the process which leads to the construction of our experiences is never absolutely complete. Our sensual experiences do not lead to absolutely clear object impressions. There is always some part of the experience which has to be corrected, which is incomplete, and in which the construction has not led to a final result. It is interesting that this incompleteness in the construction of the sensual world has its counterpart in Freud's observation that many conflicting tendencies remain in spite of the "synthetic function" of the ego.

In the sensual field it is better to speak of the incompleteness of construction rather than of antinomies and antilogic. For this final construction the vestibular apparatus is of particular importance. Careful examination of everyday life experiences reveals to an increasing extent that parts of the experience remain isolated, and although perceived are not utilized for the final total perception. Double vision is very often neglected. Otto Poetzl has strongly emphasized that hysterical phenomena frequently utilize impressions which are also present in normal reactions but are not utilized in experience. It is impossible to explain these facts unless one visualizes the individual actively engaged in the process of gaining control over the world for the purpose of action. The small actions of everyday life lead to the completion·of the sensory experience as the basis for successful action. The unified object, as especially shown by Stratton's experiments, is the result of motor activities. I. Latif quotes from an unpublished paper of E. B. Holt to the effect that Holt believes all concepts and ideas, even all mental contents, to be actual motor responses, a part of the response in each case being a re-creation by motion of some configuration of objects in the environment. "This the object or connative part and the rest of the response being merely a personal posture or attitude, this the subjective emotional or affective element of the idea or concept."

One may object to this formulation on the gound that it neglects the sensory part of experience too much, and that it makes too sharp a differentiation between subjective and motor experiences. The motor and the other organismic reactions are not separated. The salivation in conditioning is as important as the motor reaction. What is objective or nonobjective are merely outcomes of the constructive process. Motility is also present in subjective experience, but has simply not led to decisive action.

CHAPTER XXIV

CONCLUSIONS

PERCEPTION has frequently been considered treacherous and unreliable. Behind the senses, something else seemed to loom, either a mysterious object *per se* or the will of God, which creates ideas and representations for which there is no actual basis. It is fundamentally wrong to identify perception with imagination, representation, and ideas. We perceive something in the outer world. By imagination we mean something going on in the outer world. The relation between outer world, body, and self, is a fundamental human relation. There is no reason to believe that any kind of thinking and logic should lead beyond this fundamental principle. In this world we experience the whole scale of emotions, tensions, directions, and attitudes. Our behavior takes place in this world. The opinions of Kant, Berkeley, and Hume neglect this fundamental relation and overrate the power of reasoning and self-observation in comparison with behavior, attitude, and perception.

It is of fundamental importance to recognize the most primitive forms of perceptual experience. One might try to find this most primitive experience in the intermodal experiences of the senses, for instance the idea that brightness is an experience which is common to all senses appears in modern psychological literature (E. M. von Hornbostel, C. Hartshorne, L. Szekely and W. Boernstein). L. Szekely remarks that the perception of brightness is a part process common to all sensory perceptions. It may indeed express a fundamental attitude which goes into every perception, but just because of that, it cannot be a reliable guide to the fundamental laws of perception. Human beings possess a variety of senses and the experiences of these different senses cannot be reduced to a common denominator. Qualitative differences still exist, even if we insist with C. Hartshorne that all qualities have something in common and even if we stress to the utmost the idea that there are transitions. Even if we consider, for instance, the color red as the color of activity in life and so come to a better understanding of why blood is experienced as red, we still deal with a distinct experience, and this distinct experience is not identical with wishing to progress, to do something, to have strength. We must try to find another way to reach the fundamentals of perception.

The fundamental principles of perception have often been sought in motion. According to M. F. Washburn's theory imagination originates in motion. Pálàgy stressed the point of view that motion is of extreme importance. C. Stein speaks of a "sensory movement" common to all sensory experiences, and emphasizes its creative power. E. Storch emphasized the myopsyche as the fundamental substratum for every experience. The merits of these ideas are beyond doubt, but they frequently overlook the existence of sensory-motor units which are fundamental. The further elaboration of the unit may tend more toward the sensory or more toward the motor aspect. There is no fixed equilibrium between the sensory and motor aspects. The concept of the relation between the various senses becomes much clearer if we conceive of motility as the intersensory element common to all senses. Even this is insufficient; the various innervations of vegetative organs which accompany every sensory-motor unit, better called a sensory-vegetative-motor unit, are of no less importance. These are not merely physiological innervations but individual experiences. The vegetative experience is continually present. Sensations come from the heart, the intestines, and other viscera. Although the "organism as a whole" has often been discussed, the deep connections between the diverse functions of the organism have been almost neglected due to the fact that it was sometimes advisable to study these functions in artificial isolation.

These discussions are strictly psychological and the brilliant discoveries of physiology concerning the nature of irritation during perception are therefore not fully discussed. I merely give a short review of the work of E. D. Adrian.

The impulses in sensory fibers are of the same type as those of motor fibers. There is an "all-or-nothing" relation between the stimulus and the impulse. By stimulating one end organ of the small cutaneous muscle in the frog, the impulses return at regular intervals with a frequency in the neighborhood of thirty per second. The end organ has the same properties as the nerve fiber but differs in its rate of recovery and in its rate of adaptation to the stimulus. With constant stimulation, the discharge from the end organs in the skin declines in frequency much more rapidly than from a muscle or a pressure organ. The end organs may be classified as postural or phasic. The impulses produced by a pain stimulus are of the usual type and have the usual range of frequency. But the discharge must have a certain mass (duration and intensity) if it is to evoke the pain reaction. The impulse discharge from the eye differs little from that from the simpler sense organs. Owing to the decline in the discharge with a constant stimulus, a movement in the visual field gives a stronger excitation than a steady pattern of light and shade. But here, too, the effects of adaptation can be counteracted by movements of the eye. The sensation at any moment turns out to be proportional to the frequency of the impulses in the sensory nerve fiber.

Injury can set up a rhythmic discharge in the nerve fiber. The injured and the active state give the same potential change, since both involve a breakdown of the polarized surface membrane, though in the intact fiber the breakdown is promptly repaired. The injury discharge is of high frequency. Firm pressure on the surface of the limb will stimulate some of the slowly adapting endings. The receptors for light touch adapt very rapidly. It is considered unlikely that pain is always due to specific pain fibers. Rather the sensation produced by a given type of nerve fibers becomes a closer approach to pure pain in proportion to the slowness of conduction of the fiber and the lack of sensitivity in the end organ. The more sensitive tactile endings with their rapid nerve fibers do cause pain; the slow nonmedullated fibers with their endings which respond only to noxious stimuli can cause little else than pain, but the smaller medullated fibers may give both contact or pain, according to the magnitude of the discharge.

Studies in the auditory field have increased our insight considerably. E. G. Weaver and C. W. Bray showed that the sound oscillations in the cochlea were translated into electric oscillation in the circuit leading to the amplifier. According to Hallowell Davis, the nerve impulses in the auditory nerve reproduce the frequency of the stimulating sound waves, providing they are not too great. In the cat, the reproduction is almost perfect at all intensities of stimulation, up to a frequency of perhaps 1,000 per second. At higher frequencies unsynchronized impulses up to the frequency of 3,000 per second were observed, but it is not probable that this frequency of impulses is due to the stimulation of a single fiber. At frequencies around 3,000 per second, the fiber responds only to every third sound wave. This description applies not only to the auditory nerve, but probably to the secondary neurons which lead to the impulses to the central nervous system. Davis and Saul find that if the brain substance is explored with a needle electrode, the potential changes are much more intense when the auditory tract is reached. The response in the auditory tract cannot go higher than 1,000 per second, whereas that of the cochlea may reach 6,000 but the tract response covers the frequency of the sound below 1,000 and speech can be recognized as such, though the words are unintelligible. Synchronized impulses, however, cannot be detected in the medial geniculate body, which is a relay station on the sensory pathway to the cortex. The temporal region of the cortex of the cat under avertine anesthesia shows relatively slow (5 to 30 per second) rhythmic intermittent spontaneous activity. This rhythm changes under the influence of the action currents which are connected with acoustic stimuli. For hearing, it is therefore at least probable that the frequency of the action currents is coördinated to pitch, and amplitude to loudness. According to Adrian's work the frequency of the impulse is in close relation to intensity in other fields of perception.

One may of course ask what are the relations of these rhythms to perceptions. Boring writes that according to the frequency theory an increase in the frequency in the impulses in each of the nerve fibers increases the intensity. Adrian and his associates have demonstrated this in the peripheral nerve. A short abrupt stimulus can also arouse different intensity in perception. The frequency and amplitude of the stimulus on the total auditory nerve may still exist by implication. The theory of intensity as a total potential must be accepted, according to Boring, because we cannot get rid of the multiple fiber theory. Evidently adjacent fibers act together in producing a cognitive response. It must also be supposed that successive impulses, required by the frequency theory, can also act together. Summation of rapidly successive impulses at a synapse is known to occur and probably frequency becomes a difference in potential effective for cognition.

One should differentiate between the action currents of the cortex which occur with sensory and motor activity, and the rhythm discovered by C. Berger. He has shown that one can record a slow rhythm from electrodes connected in the brain. This rhythm is particularly clear when consciousness is reduced but not completely abolished. It increases in amplitude during *petit mal* attacks in which there is a deep clouding of consciousness. As it was possible to detect the current through the intact skull, it was possible to make experiments on humans, and it was shown that the Berger rhythm was disturbed and reduced when there were experiences in the visual sphere. Whereas Adrian is of the opinion that one deals with a rhythm originating merely in the optic cortex, Berger holds that the rhythm is represented all over the brain.

There is no question that, as mentioned above, action currents occur during activity of the cortex. The available material leads to the general assumption that rhythmic electrical activity, as exemplified in the Berger rhythm, continually occurs in the central nervous system. Conscious mental activities transform this spontaneous electrical rhythm. It may disappear and action currents will be observed. Of course one cannot anticipate future experimental results with any degree of certainty. The psychological evidence is against any important electric quality restricted to the optic sphere alone. Lately, E. A. Spiegel and Ralph Gerard have shown that a rhythm akin to the Berger rhythm can also be found in the optic thalamus and in the cerebellum. Nerve cells seemingly manifest a spontaneus rhythmic activity everywhere. Psychology favors the assumption that the

Berger rhythm exists not only in the optic sphere but over the whole cortical region, as Berger himself states. Fully conscious of the vagueness of the analogies, it is still worth emphasizing that speech, motility, and sense experience develop out of diffuse activity which has in part a rhythmic character. The phasic action is a product of later development. The relation between Berger rhythm and action currents in the cortical region reflects the basic relation between the primitive and the fully developed experience of the senses. A. E. Kornmueller finds that every field in the cortex and in the subcortical centers has a specific individual rhythm. Some centers react with action currents to sensory stimuli.

We must go back to psychological formulations. The optic field is the best one for study. It seems to be primarily in a state of continuous, almost rhythmical, motion. This motion fills the whole visual field. Color phenomena are almost regularly connected with it, but color is not absolutely essential to the primitive field. In this field of motion the vortex is the outstanding configuration. This result can be deduced from the experiences with the idioretinal light, in which color impressions so often are included. It is difficult to determine which are the primary colors: red, green, and blue may appear. The experiments with mescal and marihuana intoxication lead to similar results. The contour of lines is very often wavy. Primitive optical experiences are not fully differentiated with regard to the objective and subjective parts of the experience. They are in space and indeterminate in reference; that is, sometimes it appears as sensation referred to the self, sometimes it appears as primitive object-perception. Emotional attitudes decide the attribution either to subject or object.

We may better understand the perceptual process by studying imagination. Imaginations seem to belong only to the subjective side of life. Still, they point to something outside of ourselves. Experiments of V. Urbantschitsch and E. R. Jaensch, and my own experiments, have shown beyond doubt that there are many things in common between perception and imagination, especially in those vivid imaginations which Jaensch has called "eidetic images." In these eidetic images movements appear. These movements may be appropriate to the imagined object, but also they may not be. Jaensch has emphasized that many of the properties of perception can be especially well studied by the method of willfully produced imagination. There are two fundamental types of functioning in these images. The subjects may picture an object essentially correctly and organized according to gestalt properties. The other type of picture is without regard for similarity to the object. The picture is distorted, higher forms either become disorganized, or may appear only in pieces. The configurations are disrupted and may be replaced by a more primitive organization. Angular contours and crossings disappear, and circles, ellipses, loops, and vortices are substituted. All these processes are accompanied by motion in the pictures. Motor processes are connected with every one of these sensory activities, although one should not overrate the importance of eye movements as Wundt has done. Eye movements certainly are important, but so is the motility of the whole body.

Every tonic and phasic activity in any part of the body may gain importance from the formation of perception. The disintegration of imagination suggests that optic imagination develops from an indistinct vortical movement with vague color impressions, to loops, ellipses, and circles, and finally to distinct crossings, angles, and definite shapes of all varieties.

This preliminary impression is supported by L. Bender's studies of visual motor patterns. These visual motor patterns develop in stages which can be observed by following the development of the drawings of children in the first few years of their lives. The observation of these stages proves the development which has been suggested by the observations quoted above.

Tachistoscopic experiments demonstrate that the stages in the ontogenetic development in the visual motor pattern of a child are recapitulated in the individual development of every sensation, imagination, and perception.

The development from the primitive stages of experience to complete experience is connected with the process of active reality testing which participates in the creation of gestalten. The testing process is a motor process; tonic and phasic motility lead to repeated contacts with the outer world. In connection with this process, a better differentiation takes place between what belongs to one's own body and what belongs to the outer world. I do not think that sensations are projected into the outer world and so become perceptions. The division between outside world and body is always present. The decision as to what belongs to the body and what belongs to the world is based upon testing and constructive efforts. The primitive object is at first variable in its orientation in space. The early investigations of William Stern and the newer work of L. Bender show that children are insensitive to changes in the orientation of objects, especially in regard to right and left, and below and above. In copying they very often change directions without being aware of it. In the imagination of adults similar transpositions in space may be observed. Definite forms other than loops and vortices are finally conceived, in their correct spatial relations. Primitive form principles are often exaggerated (L. Bender). Primitive gestalten develop into more complicated ones. A whole may also be created by piecemeal gathering of single pieces, as observed by Kluever and myself in eidetic images, by Freud in dreams, and by Poetzl in experimental dream studies and in optic agnosias. I think that collecting and adding of pieces, putting pieces together as in a jigsaw puzzle, plays an important part in the psychology of the senses. A continuous testing, changing, and rechanging process occurs until the final shape is reached. The same process cuts wholes into pieces without any regard for form and configuration. Optic experience has two principles at hand: piecemeal construction and destruction, and organization in definite configurations which may mature from primitive to higher stages of development.

We do not live in an optic world, alone. We are directed toward a world which appeals to all senses. When we see an object, we anticipate that it can be grasped, smelled, and tasted. Every object has an appeal to all the senses. This principle expresses itself in the phenomenon of synesthesia. Primitive experiences very often are rhythmical; they repeat the same object, and instead of one object, several pictures may appear. We may say primitive experiences have a tendency to multiplicity. In primitive experience the size of objects is variable; the localization of the experiences is uncertain. Changes often occur in a rhythmic way. Variability in size, number, direction, space, distance, and rhythmicity is probably the most important characteristic of experiences in the primitive visual field. These primitive experiences remain in the background of the fully developed experiences. Primitive shapes in motion can be prematurely stabilized. Hallucinations show many characteristics which we otherwise find in primitive experience. Investigations of this type give the basis for a better understanding of hallucinations.

Similar principles, but with characteristic changes, are valid for other senses. Sound travels in space. It has a tendency to repeat itself, which comes out clearly in hallucinations. We turn toward the sound and we begin to repeat the sound if it is language. E. Jacobson has shown that action currents are present when we imagine verbally. Construction of the object, with a continuous interchange until a comparative stabilization (gestalt) is reached, seems to be the basic principle for the organization of the senses. It seems that the vestibular apparatus is necessary for the maintenance of this construction. This is understandable, since the vestibular apparatus has such a close relation to the tonic apparatuses.

In smell and taste another motility becomes paramount. In smell, the "object" smell must be drawn in, either through the process of breathing or by sniffing. The turning of the head toward the direction from which the smell comes plays a less important part. It is a "taking in" from the outer world, in order to sample. The tonic principles of the optic and acoustic sphere are replaced by the rhythmic principle of breathing and by the movement of sniffing.

The movements of the mouth which make tasting possible are of a much more complex nature. Sucking occurs when the nipple is put in the mouth of the newborn. However, there are continual movements with the mouth as if the infant were trying to get an object. Later on, the mouth movements combined with movements of the head, follow the object. After nourishment has touched the mouth, the mouth closes tightly and the sucking starts, which accounts for the possibility of taste. In adults, movements of the tongue bring to the receptive surfaces the object of taste, which has to be chewed by the action of the jaws. It is remarkable that even in the imagination of taste, movements of the jaw and tongue occur, and that swallowing is initiated. Secretion of saliva occurs even in the course of imagination, and we have every reason to believe that secretory functions are changed along the whole gastrointestinal tract. In other words, in the whole field of taste, phasic motility is necessary in order for perception to occur, and a reaction occurs in the motility and secretion of the gastrointestinal tract. Secretion and peristalsis are primitive answers to situations. Although they are not voluntary or conscious, they serve the whole attitude of the individual.

It is essential to study basic motor attitudes of the individual in connection with perception. We can turn either to the object or away from it. We have reason to believe that turning toward the object is more primitive than turning away from it. The object appeals to all senses at once. It is primarily perceived as in motion or movable. Only in late development is it perceived at rest. Orientation toward the object and away from the object is represented in voluntary action. Tonic reactions, which are not as fully conscious and voluntary as the majority of phasic actions, are necessarily always present. Every action is based upon a background of posture, in which the individual is oriented to the outside world. As Koffka expresses it, posture is in direct relation to the spatial framework. A posture must necessarily be a reaction to the force of gravitation. Action can only be understood as emerging from the continuous tonic adaptations to one's environment or pulls. When an individual turns towards an object he may either want to touch it or to incorporate it. Incorporation has been considered as the final aim. However, every step in itself is a final end, even if it does not lead to touch or incorporation. We expect the object to offer resistance to the final incorporation. We do not want a world which cannot be completely subdued and incorporated. We need a world we can cling to and lean upon—a world which offers us protection and security. Grasping takes the object partially into the body, a process which is completed when the object is taken into the mouth. But, primarily, grasping does not serve the incorporation of an object into the mouth, but serves as a help in the fight against gravitation.

This whole path—from visual perception or hearing or smelling of the object through tonic and phasic action to final solutions—is from the beginning connected with reactions of secretion, of the smooth muscle of the gastrointestinal tract, and of the whole vasovegetative system.

This entire process gets its color and final shape by the continuous interaction between the tendencies towards and away from the object. The object may be feared as threatening. Data of smell and taste may contribute to flight from it. When the object is introduced into the mouth, vomiting still may occur. Finally, we expel, psychologically at least, a part of the intake by defecation, especially by diarrhea. Furthermore, in organic diseases, particularly in hypochondriasis, the patient frequently feels that something which should come out has remained in the body. It is an arbitrary assumption that the final aim of life is to incorporate objects into one's own body and to devour objects. The construction of the object is essential in itself, and not merely because the object might sooner or later be of immediate use. We need and want an independent world; our own investigations show that even the relation of grasping to the mouth is not a primary one. The individual uses grasp primarily in order to get the support of an independent object.

One should not speak of sensations, feelings, and emotions as units. The primitive unit is a sensory-motor-vegetative unit in a unified attitude, which is either a complete or incomplete action. Objects are necessarily in space. There is a fundamental difference between the space of the body and the space of the outside world. Senses have different modes of action and different spaces. There is an innate tendency to a unification of space by unified motility, which centers around the organs of equilibrium. Action is always a unified action in space. The single decisive action is built upon posture. The importance of tonic changes for the perception of space has been clinically demonstrated by observations involving the vestibular apparatus and the cerebellar and frontal lobe systems. Space is thus very closely related to action. There is a component in space which is tonic and vestibular, and there are space components which are connected with the phasic actions of grasping and groping. W. Mayer-Gross states that in apraxia one deals chiefly with an impairment in the utilization of space in the small realm of hands and fingers and in all performances dependent upon these. It is a disturbance in the sphere of hands and fingers and their space. This is precisely the same conclusion to which I came in *The Image and Appearance of the Human Body,* except that it is expressed in a different way. Space and sensory motor experiences cannot be separated from each other. J. Lange has tried to base the syndrome of finger agnosia on a general difficulty in perceiving directions. But such general disturbances cannot be observed in such cases. The subjects are merely not capable of performing tasks in which they have to use their hands and fingers. They are, furthermore, disoriented concerning right and left, and very often have difficulties in using numbers. These tasks can be made impossible by an impairment either in the sensory or the motor side of experience.

The development of space parallels the development of action. This is a development towards unification of experience, since unified actions in the social world are necessary. Space and the creation of objects, of space, and of one's own body image and the body image of others are all closely related. The space problem is a human problem and the space of physics is a space in which actions take place which have no specific moral significance. The conception that primitive space is two-dimensional is incorrect, as Kurt Koffka has recently pointed out. Space perception is a function dependent on the libidinous structure of the individual. The idea of space develops around the erogenous zones and in close connection with the drives of the individual; it is localized as separate units until these are finally united under the influence of genitality. Space distortions taking place on the genital level signify either the genitals as such or the distance from persons. The final appreciation of space is dependent upon our appreciation of personalities.

Space is decidedly a social phenomenon. In some obsession neuroses there are feelings of distortions in space in relation to erogenous zones. Aggressiveness crosses the borderline of space. Space shrinks between erogenous zones and the objects. The sexually desired part is brought near or to one's own body. The space of the body and the organs of the body may be extended into the outer world, and a dismembered part of one's body may become a part of the outer optic space, where it is subject to the aggression of the outer world. The aggressiveness of the depressive patient often leads to the distortion of space relations similar to that of obsessional neurotic patients. There is a physiological structure, rather impersonal, in the periphery of the personality. Even here, constructive processes go on continually.

The primitive unit of space is a tridimensional unit in connection with sensory motor impressions and in particularly close relation to the drives based upon the libidinous structure. This primitive space is not unified, at least no more than the libidinous urges are. The unification takes place by development of libido to the genital sphere. In the physiological sphere continuous action makes the construction of a unified space possible. Libidinous and so-called physiological processes are in a continuous interplay. The physiological processes are linked with the ego instincts, in the psychoanalytic sense.

Space and time are closely related. There is a perception of time as well as of space. The separation of space and time occurs in the course of a differentiating process which is based upon action and experience. Everywhere we find that development has started from the union of space and time in movement. Only in later development does the object become stabilized, that is, extended in time. Rhythm belongs to primitive experiences. It is a repetition in regular intervals. The world certainly contains comparatively stabilized objects, but it also contains rhythm and repetition. Primitive experience is prone to put greater emphasis upon the perception of rhythm, and may even perceive and act rhythmically where developed perception does not find sufficient basis for perception and assumption of rhythm. The function of the organism is, in many respects, rhythmical and periodical. All senses function in a rhythmical way. Rhythm is also very important for many forms of primitive activity. The vegetative organs function rhythmically; so does the bowel movement. The electric phenomena connected with the activities of the nerves and the central nervous system are rhythmical. This is merely an arbitrary enumeration and far from being complete. Upon closer inspection, one very often sees that neither the rhythm in the outside world nor the rhythm of the body are regular. Continuous adaptations take place between the rhythm outside and the rhythm inside. Rhythm signifies continuous dissatisfaction. Finally, one wishes to reach a stabilized object and some kind of rest. We eventually understand that events in the outside world are not always rhythmical; they are not always repetitions. Irregular changes occur and, furthermore, the factor of duration is also present. Rhythm, change, motion, and duration are practical particularities of the world which have to be perceived by a constructive process. The experience of time emerges from this process of adaptation to rhythm, to change, to perception of the outside world and one's own body.

Time perception has, as has any other perception, an objective and a subjective side. The immediate experience of time compares with sensation in other perceptions. The immediate time experience depends on libidinous factors. It is changed in *déjà vu,* and in depersonalization, obsession, depression, and schizophrenia. Narcissistic, voyeuristic, and sadistic elements in depersonalization remove the immediate experience of the present into the past. Present means that we are able to enjoy ourselves and to progress into the future. To the obsessional neurotic, time is an eternity of tortures. In depressions the passage of time also ceases, since only eternity guarantees the continuation of destructive and self-torturing impulses. Schizophrenic patients lose, with loss of love objects, the immediate living experience of the ego in time. Obsessional neurotic patients may treat time like a valuable object equated with money.

In intoxication with hashish or mescal, time may be extremely slowed and space extremely extended. The change in time experience is closely related to changes in the motion of perceptions and changes in motility and tone. Similar phenomena can be observed in patients with alcoholic hallucinosis with vestibular symptomatology and in patients with vestibular and cerebellar lesions. In diffuse lesions of the brain after infectious disease, time may be experienced as lengthened or shortened.

Exact appreciation of length of time passed in sleep and hypnosis is based upon the utilization of immediate time experiences by a constructive effort.

In Korsakoff patients past experiences cannot be arranged in their correct temporal order. A specific psychic function guarantees the reconstruction of the correct sequence of events in the past, but only when a constructive effort is made. The actual time experience is preserved in Korsakoff patients in whom the secondary elaboration is impaired. This function is partially dependent on lesions in the periventricular gray, but especially on cortical structures.

Psychic life contains an immediate experience of the future. The future is experienced as foreshortened, and words without definite contents become hiding places for unanalyzed symbolic expectations. To understand the symbolic character of the life expectations of patients is a fundamental problem in psychotherapy.

The concept of a continuous flow of time extending from the eternal past into an eternal future is due to a process of complicated elaboration and reveals as little of the psychological facts as does the physicist's approach to time.

The concepts of philosophers concerning time have neglected the immediate psychological experiences and substituted abstract thinking, which is not sufficient.

Space and time are in the closest relation to action and drives in quite the same way as is any other perception of the senses. Since space and time in their final elaboration are correlated to unified action, they have a very close relation to the great unifying force represented in the vestibular apparatus. A theory of human action is therefore a necessary corollary to a theory of perception. Action takes place in a framework which is tonic and also partially phasic and rhythmic. In human action there are also figure and background. The structure of action is closely correlated to the structure of the perceptual world.

Action is not based upon reflexes. The most successful attempt to consider human action as the result of a mosaic of reflexes is Pavlov's experimental work on conditioned reflexes. However, Pavlov's conditioned reflex is not a reflex at all. It is a complicated biological attitude concerning food which expresses itself by salivary secretion. It is a part of an action only in that the experimental conditions are devised in such a way as to make complete action impossible. J. Beritoff has pointed out this fact. It has been shown that Pavlov's idea that irritation spreads over the cortex and that irradiation takes place is not a physiological conception but merely the translation of psychological facts into a pseudophysiological terminology. When the conditioned reflex occurs, first at every sound and later merely at a specific sound, one deals with an increased experience by trial and error and not with a physiological concentration.

The different types of inhibition described by Pavlov, external inhibition and internal inhibition (with the subgroups of extinction, delay, trace inhibition, conditioned inhibition, inhibition by differentiation) are merely the expression of psychological attitudes. They express a gradual adaptation to an actual situation. There is no question that these attitudes are dependent upon the functioning of a specific apparatus in the brain. However, this relation is much more complicated than Pavlov realized. Physiological experimentation must culminate with the same conclusions as psychological experimentation and experience if both are planned and interpreted correctly. If psychology has proved that psychic life is not a mosaic of psychic elements, physiology cannot prove that the functioning of the central nervous system is a mosaic of excitation and inhibition. One of these interpretations must be wrong. There cannot be much doubt that Pavlov's psychology is wrong. On the other hand it cannot be denied that the experimental work of Pavlov and his pupils is of extreme importance and that, correctly interpreted, it opens the way to deeper psychological insight. Pavlov's experiments show very clearly that we are continually guided by our needs and that every situation which seems to grant us these needs is taken as a definite unit, and that it is assumed as a matter of course that the signal which once led to satisfaction or dissatisfaction will in the future do the same. When a sequence has once led to satisfaction, the repetition of the first part of the sequence provokes the expectation of the complete sequence. This expectation is given up only when disappointment has taken place several times. Whereas, in the beginning, the signal is not completely understood in its nature, it is better understood after several repetitions and can then be differentiated from signals which have no effect, especially when the signal without effect has been given between effective signals, and it has been demonstrated that nothing follows. The signal is at first comparable to a general concept, or better, to a concept which is taken as the sign of the object as long as the opposite has not been proved.

Pavlov's experiments help us to a deeper understanding of signal function, and of language in general. A word which becomes the signal for an object is at first vague and general in its signal function. By a process of trial and error a differentiation of the signal function takes place, or a general concept is replaced by a more specific one. Words and sentences have signal functions. They are signals for objects. Objects are not merely given to the individual by passive reception but also by a continuous process of construction and reconstruction. The individual takes parts of the objects, puts them together, rejects other parts, molds and remolds the object. This remolding, reconstructing, and rebuilding is based upon a continuous interplay between sensory and motor function. The meaning of a word and of a sentence is the sum total of the sensory-motor attitudes concerning the expected object. This sum total is unified in the preparedness for action or in an action as such.

Words get their signal function as by-products of the process of getting food and sexual objects. Signal functions have social significance for the whole community. Signal functions are at first inexact indicators of objects with biological importance. The material for a signal function is taken from the vague background of continuous motor activity and unrest of the small child. A constructive process also gives motor perfection to language. The further elaboration of language takes place by trial and error, biological satifaction and disappointment, which lead from the careless use of single experiences as a pattern for action to individualized action fitting specific situations.

Thinking and imagination have a direction toward expression in words, and tend to signalize themselves to the community. The verbalization may be complete or incomplete. The sign function also has an importance for unconscious thinking. In aphasia, the disturbance is chiefly in the signal function of language. The impairment of the thinking proper is less evident. One type of thinking has closer relation to the core of the personality, and the other type of thinking has less relation to the core of the personality. This latter type of thinking has closer relation to speech and to formulation in words.

In schizophrenia the patient uses similarity and partial identity as a sign of the presence of the strongly desired object. Under the influence of strong desire, the schizophrenic is ready to emphasize the partial identity between the sign (symbol) and the object, and to take the sign for the object. The identification of signal and referent gives magic power to the word. Lack of differentiation between referent and words and sentences is a product of an incomplete development of thought and language construction. Not only in schizophrenics but also in neurotics and normals, sign and referent are not always clearly differentiated from each other. The analysis of the relationship between word and referent may become the nucleus of the psychotherapeutic procedure. The relation between signal and referent is comparatively simple in the case of concrete objects; difficulties usually begin only when the signal covers a multiplicity of referents. The preparedness to action provoked by abstract words and connotations (signals) may then lead to actions which do not fit the referent. When we adhere too closely to the concrete object, we also are not prepared to act. (Abstract and concrete are probably words which stress too strongly the idea of polarity and opposites.) The essence of language consists in being prepared for many possibilities, and we are prepared only when we have handled single situations and are ready to handle a multiplicity of other new situations. Only abstract thinking is flexible enough to cover a multiplicity of possible situations. Thinking is only possible on the basis of past experiences. The organism reacts not only on the basis of the present situation but also on the basis of past situations. This is merely a behavioristic formulation. It is not necessary that the previous experience be fully remembered. It seems that whenever actual performance is changed by a previous experience, there exists the possibility of reviving this previous experience as a memory.

The terms memory and learning indicate a diversity of functions and experiences. An experience one has had can be remembered. It may come back to the mind under specific conditions, especially when the present situation demands a revival of the previous situation. Memory is, therefore, always in the service of the present. Almost every experience can be remembered when the present situation has an important biologic similarity or partial identity with the past situation. Remembering is easier when the previous experience has not been too far distant in time, or when the past situation has occurred not once but many times. In other words, when a situation has occurred repeatedly it is comparatively easy to remember it in the service of the present. We may speak of the process of learning, when the process of remembering has been facilitated by the repetition of experiences. Such a repetition may take place without the intention of the individual, or the individual may be active in provoking the repetitions with the intention of better recall later on. In the latter case we may speak of learning, in the narrower sense. A great deal of learning occurs without the active wish of the subject, and the repetition is merely brought about by outward circumstances. This is the psychological situation in experiences with animals in which the conditioned reflexes are provoked.

It is an everyday life experience that the memories of situations which have occurred repeatedly are organized into a definite pattern which reappears as a unit. It is comparatively difficult and sometimes impossible to remember the single experiences which went into this pattern and to differentiate them from each other. Learning is not an isolated function. It always occurs in an individual who tries to develop attitudes which are useful, and he is more inclined to retain the attitudes the more often they have been used. Laboratory experiments often neglect this factor, and are too apt to treat learning as an isolated activity. Learning is always practical and is given up as soon as the individual can no longer convince himself that he will benefit by it. Schematic attitudes are developed. Learning leads to crystallizations which fit regular sequences. One sees this process of crystallization particularly clearly in the experiments of Frank J. Curran and myself. These experiments reveal the constant grasping and groping in the total field of one's experiences until crystallization occurs. Repeated experience is trace forming.

The psychopathology of memory and learning shows the same basic problems. Amnestic gaps occur if one desires to evade a specific situation. The tendency to run away continues in the attitude toward memory material. It is characteristic that the amnesia patient, in order to become the victim of amnesia, has to run away from the place where he actually lives. Forgetting proves to be an attitude with a goal and an aim which, as Milton Abeles and myself have shown, is rather easy to understand. In *The Image and Appearance of the Human Body* I have demonstrated that turning away from experience may occur in very different layers. In the so-called psychogenic amnesia, the motives for the turning away are in a superficial layer. The many small events which we forget in the course of our everyday life are very often of no significance and we turn away from them. This is another superficial turning away. In repression, we forget because the event has an importance in our life which we do not want to acknowledge. Deeper problems of the personality are involved here. Repression can be directed against problems arising in the present or against problems arising in childhood. The repression directed against the latter material is generally more thorough and the forgetting based upon it originates on a deeper level. The types of forgetting so far mentioned are types of forgetting on the so-called psychological level. There is usually an obvious connection between forgetting and the personal problem. As we have seen, the casual forgetting of everyday life experiences often has no deep relation to the problems of personality; but it is nevertheless true that the final form of this type of forgetting is in many cases determined by an underlying necessity for forgetting, due to personality problems.

After head injuries, retroactive amnesia may occur. This means that events prior to the accident may be forgotten in a more or less extensive way. Here also, the individual turns away from a part of his experiences. However, personal problems have very little to do with this attitude. No specific motives are discernible. Heinz Hartmann and I have called this by the Freudian term of organic repression. It is as if the individual wished to forget, but such a wish is not even present in the unconscious. We deal with an organic condition the nature of which is unknown, and at the present time the psychological description of the event is more adequate than physiological theories.

In so far as this forgetting is impersonal, it reminds us of the common type of forgetting described above. In retrograde amnesia there is only one act of turning away. In the forgetting of everyday life and in the Korsakoff psychosis the individual turns away again and again from the experiences he has recently had. It is also called difficulty in retention.

It is difficult to get along in this world unless one uses the material of the past for the construction and reconstruction of the picture of the world. The Korsakoff patient fails in this requirement. Many investigations have made it probable that this memory material is not actually lost. It is there, but it cannot be used. It is less available than so-called unconscious material. We deal here with another type of organic repression. Psychological motives for this forgetting cannot be found, although it is obvious that the character of the material very often determines whether a specific detail is remembered or not. In other words, communications between personal and impersonal "organic" material exist, and may have an influence on the way in which the forgotten material appears. The forgetting of the Korsakoff patient resembles forgetting in everyday life. It is merely more extensive and, whereas the forgetting of everyday life becomes more outspoken for the remote past, the forgetting in the Korsakoff case is less outspoken concerning the remote past. These cases share the impersonal character and the repetition of the act of forgetting.

I have emphasized the fact that acts of psychological and organic repression are unable to destroy traces; they only make them inaccessible. As Freud also has pointed out, these traces are approximately the same as they were at the time when the event took place. The traces reduplicate the world of the past. As the previous discussions show, constructive processes take place when the concept of this world is built up. The final experience is, therefore, merely a stabilized point in the process of construction. It is probable, although not definitely established, that the trace not only retains the events but also the connection between them. At any rate, the constructive process is not finished with the first creation of the trace, but traces remain alive and a wealth of new relations to organizations are created. These processes are intensified when the individual actually tries to remember. Single memories have to be fitted together, relations have to be created or reconstructed, and memories have to be compared and rectified. A general scheme is drawn, in which the outstanding events of life are at first fixed. For instance, moving, beginning of school, marriage, the death of a beloved person, the birth of a sibling, and so forth.

The reconstruction, therefore, begins with a general plan, which is carried out by a process of trial and error. During this process of reconstruction, instead of the average experiences as such, experiences related in space and time or similar to the original experience are brought forward. In other words, symbols occur. Thinking and memory do not, in this respect, differ from each other.

According to general rules of thinking, every experience is taken as typical, as long as the circumstances permit. Or, in other words—although this formulation is not quite correct—in thinking it does not matter at first whether a concept is general or individual. One concept is also easily taken for another one related to it. That is to say, similarity and partial identity are often taken as signs of complete identity, and only by continuous contact with reality does the final elaboration of memory and thought take place. The use of general concepts, "spheres," condensations and symbolizations is common to thinking as well as to memory, and the process of development of thinking and memory are to a great extent identical. This process of development is very closely related to instincts and drives, which are in close relation to the attitudes towards reality. It is connected with what Freud has called reality-testing.

I have spoken about the development of thought in the "sphere." Difficulties in thinking and memory occur when this constructive flow is interrupted, and it should be possible to differentiate disturbances of memory according to the stage in which the constructive process has been interrupted. In Korsakoff psychosis, because of the interruption in the constructive process of memory, condensation and symbolization take place in the material, but it seems that, while the memory material as such may come up continuously, it cannot be used in the constructive processes which we have emphasized. There is a deep inner relation between memory and intelligence, and it is not probable that the intelligence of the Korsakoff patient can be completely preserved. Indeed, the majority of findings indicate an inner connection between memory and intelligence in the disturbance. However, there is no question that the disturbance of intelligence in Korsakoff cases is not proportionate to the severe impairment of retention of memory material. Memory and intelligence are both in the service of the personality. Organic lesions may impair access to structures of the past and of the present in different degrees.

It is certainly interesting that Korsakoff patients show some learning, where remembering seems to be almost completely absent. It is possible that learning and remembering are not identical from the point of view of brain physiology, although they may have many things in common. It is probable that during the process of learning, memory traces are created, although these memory traces may not be available, even to the unconscious. My own investigations clearly show that unconscious traces are present in such a great number of cases in which learning takes place that we are justified in assuming

(1) that they are always present when learning takes place and (2) the dissociation between learning and memory is simply due to a different degree of availability of traces. Only the observations of G. E. Stoerring and E. Gruenthal seem to contradict this point of view, since these authors state that they have observed a case of complete loss of retention, in which the possibility of learning had completely disappeared. This case, however, showed very severe disturbances in attitudes and reasoning. It is artificial to consider these merely as secondary to the memory disturbances.

Memory and thinking are not isolated entities simply related to emotions. There are specific attitudes connected with memory disturbances. From the emotional point of view, the psyche of the Korsakoff patient differs from the psyche of an individual without memory disturbances. We expect that, in every stage of memory or thought development, arrest is connected with a specific emotional attitude. The attitude when we learn is different from the attitude when we remember, and also different from the attitude when we think, but all these attitudes are connected with emotions.

In its final development the process of thinking, as such, comes nearer to action. It is a more direct preparedness which is again directed towards the outside world and during the whole process this world must also sometimes be present in pictures. There may be phases in which these pictures are absent, at least momentarily, or do not play an important part. This may be especially true when the individual is close to a state of complete preparedness, or when the individual is in the first stages of preparedness. At any rate, the question of whether there are independent entities of thinking has lost importance from our point of view. Disturbances in thinking are incomplete phases in the process of construction. As mentioned above, if the arrest occurs by gross anatomical lesion, then a disturbance occurs in the constructive process in connection with experiences that are peripheral to the aims of the personality. In schizophrenia and neurosis, the disturbance in construction lies in the arrest of the thought development concerning central problems of the individual. Finally, in the thought disturbances of manic depressive psychoses, emotional attitudes change the utilization of the results of the developed thought. It is of course arbitrary to consider the "emotions" of the manic, and the "emotions" of the depressive as mere exaggerations of so-called normal "emotions." J. C. Whitehorn has justly pointed to this. The question remains, whether thinking does introduce a new factor which K. Buehler has called the "aha" experience and which the gestalt school calls insight. The constructive process, in whichever sphere it may occur, leads from time to time to solutions which seem to be satisfactory for the moment and which derive their satisfaction from the fact that they comply with the inner coherence in reality. This satisfactory configuration or gestalt is reached by a constructive process that may take a longer or a shorter time. One may call "insight" the experience of the closure of the gestalt and the experience of the solution which is satisfactory because it satisfies biological needs in close relation to reality; but this is merely an expression of the same basic forces which we have previously discussed and which take place not only in the act of thinking but also in the perception and creation of objects as such.

The functions discussed are the basis of what one may call consciousness. Consciousness is readiness in construction of perception in thinking, and this readiness is a preparedness for action. Generally, we speak of consciousness to designate the sum total of preparedness in perception and action. It is closely connected with a general factor of awareness and vigilance indicating the strength of drives. When we are sleepy, consciousness becomes clouded and we maintain less of the construction work. Consciousness is indeed in close relation to the amount of psychic energy available for adaptation to the outside world. How great is the variation in the psychic energies available for adaptation is not precisely known. Psychoanalysis has shown, at any rate, that we have underrated the stability of psychic energies and that in many cases in which the diminution of psychic energy seemed apparent, energy was merely diverted to other channels. It is doubtful whether we are entitled to speak of the constancy of available psychic energy. At present our measurements of psychic energies are incompetent. We doubtless have a specific function of distributing energy to psychic functions—vigilance—which has a relation to the well-known cerebral apparatus of sleep. Its definite localization in the brain is well known (Paul Schilder and Otto Kauders, *Hypnosis*).

Consciousness is not an independent phenomenon but consists of the process of trial and error in perception and thought until the object and the outside world are reached. The individual has to compare again and again, and must not only know that he perceives but must also be aware of his effort in the construction of perception. The conclusion is, therefore, justified that consciousness is in itself self-consciousness. It is the attempt to bring experiences into a context. We may also call this context the ego, from an analytic point of view.

The psychological creation of an object is a social act, since only objects offer resistances which make final construction possible. Consciousness is therefore dependent on the resistances of the world, which to a great extent are social. Consciousness is a social act and in self-consciousness we consider ourselves as social human beings. At this point we go beyond the aims of the present study. I wish merely to indicate that the "self" is also in close relation with the construction of the outer world and the processes involved in it. To "have experiences" means that we separate these in a constructive effort; it makes no fundamental difference whether these experiences are considered from the point of view of the person or from the point of view of the world. It is our contention that every experience not only refers to these fundamental spheres of "self" and "world" but also to the sphere of the body. Human existence consists in living at once in these three spheres, which form an inseparable unit. We may call the fact that experiences are experiences in the outside world, in the body, and in the self, an *a priori* insight. I would prefer the more modest expression that here we deal simply with an experience which so far has been proved to be correct. One has a right to be skeptical about an experience assumed to be of universal application. One may suspect that it does not lead very far toward the understanding of human situations and toward the handling of human problems in physics and morals. Such a general formulation may sometimes help in going back to concrete problems. We cannot handle single situations and single problems unless we make an attempt to see them in context with more general problems.

The attempt to arrive at a general context from specific experiences is in itself a constructive effort, which nevertheless is probably futile in the final philosophical formulation. Philosophy, however, remains an incentive to construction and so has its pragmatic and behavioristic value, if it does not remain in the sphere of words but tries to go back to the individual problems of life.

BIBLIOGRAPHY

Abeles, Milton, and Paul Schilder. "Psychogenic Loss of Personal Identity." *Archives of Neurology and Psychiatry*, XXXIV (Sept., 1935), 587–604.

Ach, N. Ueber die Willenstätikeit und das Denken. Göttingen, 1905.

Adrian, E. D. The Basis of Sensation. London, 1928.

—— The Mechanism of Nervous Action. Philadelphia, Pa., 1932.

—— "Electrical Activities of the Nervous System." *Archives of Neurology and Psychiatry*, XXXII (Dec., 1934), 1125–36.

Ahringsmann, H., and A. Buch. "Ueber die Wahrnehmung von bewegten Reizen auf der Haut." *Zeitschrift für Biologie*, LXXXIV (1926), 541.

Allers, Rudolf. "Zur Pathologie des Tonus Labyrinthes." *Monatschrift für Psychiatrie und Neurologie*, XXVI (1909), 116.

—— and Ferdinand Scheminzky. "Ueber Actionströme der Muskeln bei motorischen Vorstellungen." *Pfluegers Archiv für die gesamte Physiologie*, CCXII (1926), 169–282.

—— and Jacob Teler. "Ueber die Verwertung umbemerkter Eindrücke bei Associationen." *Zeitschrift für die gesamte Neurologie und Psychiatrie*, LXXXIX (1924), 492–513.

Allport, Floyd H. Social Psychology. Boston, 1924.

Alonnes, Revault, d'. "Rôle des sensations internes dans les emotions et dans la perception de la durée." *Revue Philosophique*, LX (1905), 512.

Baade, W. "Aufgabe und Begriff einer darstellenden Psychologie." *Zeitschrift für Psychologie und Physiologie der Sinnesorgane*, LXXI (1915), 356.

Baerwald, R. Zur Psychologie der Vorstellungstypen. Leipzig, 1916.

Baldwin, J. M. Mental Development in the Child and Race. New York, 1906.

Bárány, R. Physiologie und Pathologie des Bogengangsapparates. Leipzig, 1907.

Bauer, Julius. Allgemeine Konstitutions- und Vererbungslehre. Berlin, 1925.

—— "Der Baranysche Zeigeversuch bei traumatischen Neurosen." *Wiener Klinische Wochenschrift*, XXXVI (1916).

—— and Paul Schilder. "Ueber einige psychophysiologische Mechanismen bei functionelle Neurosen." *Deutsche Zeitschrift für Nervenheilkunde*, LXIV (1919), 279.

Bechterew, Vladimir. Allgemeine Grundlagen der Reflexologie des Menschen. Leipzig and Vienna, 1926.

Bender, Lauretta. "Psychiatric, Neurologic and Neuropathologic Studies in Disseminated Alterative Arteriolitis." *Archives of Neurology and Psychiatry*, XXXVI (Oct., 1936), 790–815.

—— Visual Motor Gestalt Test and Its Clinical Use. New York, 1938.

—— "Gestalt Principles in Sidewalk Drawing and Games of Children." *Journal of Genetic Psychology*, XLI (1932), 192–210.

—— "The Psychology of Children Suffering from Organic Disturbances of the Cerebellum." *The American Journal of Orthopsychiatry*, X (April, 1940), 287–92.

—— "Gestalt Function in Mental Defect." *Proceedings of the 57th Annual Session of the American Association for Mental Deficiency*, 1933.

—— Frank Curran, and Paul Schilder. "Organization of Memory Traces in the Korsakoff Syndrome." *Archives of Neurology and Psychiatry*, XXXVIII (1938), 482–87.

—— and Paul Schilder. "Form as a Principle in the Play of Children." *Journal of Genetic Psychology*, XLIX (1936), 254–61.

—— "Encephalopathia Alcoholica." *Archives of Neurology and Psychiatry*, XXIX (1933), 990.

Benussi, Vittorio. "Kinematohaptische Auffassungsformung." *VI Kongress für experimentelle Psychologie* (1914).

—— Psychologie der Zeitauffassung. Heidelberg, 1913.

—— "La Perception de L'Espace." *Journal de Psychologie*, XXII (1925), 625–66.

Bergson, Henri L Essai sur les données immédiates de la conscience. Paris, 1889.

—— L'Évolution créatrice. Paris, 1907.

Beringer, Kurt. Der Meskalinrausch. Berlin, 1927.

—— and Wilhelm Mayer-Gross. "Der Fall Hahnenfuss." *Zeitschrift für die gesamte Neurologie und Psychiatrie*, XCVI (1925), 209–50.

Beritoff, J. "Ueber die individuellerworbene Tätigkeit des Zentralnervensystems." *Journal für Psychologie und Neurologie*, XXVII (1933), 113–335; *Pfluegers Archiv für die Physiologie*, CCXIII (1926), 370–406.

Bernfeld, Siegfried. Psychologie des Säuglings. Vienna, 1925. Translated as The Psychology of the Infant. New York, 1929.

—— and Sergei Feitelberg. "Bericht ueber einige psychophysiologische Arbeiten." *Imago*, XX (1934), 224.

Bernhard-Leroy, L. "Sur l'illusion dite 'Dépersonalisation'." *Revue Philosophique*, XLVI (1898), 157.

Betlheim, Stephan, and Heinz Hartmann. "Ueber Fehlreaktionen des Gedächtnisses bei der Korsakoffschen Psychose." *Archiv für Psychiatrie,* LXXII (1924), 278.

Bibring-Lehner, Grete. "Ueber die Beeinflussung eidetischen Phänomene durch labyrinthäre Reizung." *Zeitschrift für die gesamte Neurologie und Psychiatrie,* CXII (1928), 496–505.

Bieber, Irwin. "Grasping and Sucking." *Journal of Nervous and Mental Disease,* LXXXV (1937), 196–201.

Bielschowsky, A. "Ueber monokuläre Diplopie ohne physikalische Grundlage nebst Bemerkungen ueber das Sehen Schielender Graefes." *Archiv für Ophthalmologie,* XLVI (1898), 143.

Binswanger, Ludwig. Ueber Ideenflucht. Zurich, 1933.

Bleuler, Eugen. "Die Schizophrenie." *Handbuch für Psychiatrie.* Vienna, 1911.

—— Textbook of Psychiatry, trans. by A. A. Brill. New York, 1930.

Blug, A. "Neue Untersuchungen ueber Scheinbewegungen bei tachistoskopischer Beobachtung." *Zeitschrift für Psychologie,* CXXVI (1932), 290–324.

Boernstein, W. "Ueber die funktionellen Beziehungen der Sinnesorgane unter einander und zum Gesamtorganismus." *Nederlandisch Tydschrift vor Geneeskunde* (1933), p. 331.

Bonnier, P. "L'Aschematie." *Revue Neurologique,* XIII (1905), 605.

Boring, Edwin Garrignes. The Physical Dimensions of Consciousness. New York and London, 1933.

Bouman, L., and A. A. Gruenbaum. "Eine Störung der Chronognosie und ihre Bedeutung im betreffenden Symptomenbild." *Monatschrift für Psychiatrie und Neurologie,* LXXIII (1929), 1.

Bourdon, B. La Perception visuelle de l'èspace. Paris, 1902.

Braly, K. W. "The Influence of Past Experience in Visual Perception." *Journal of Experimental Psychology,* XVI (1933), 613–43.

Brentano, Franz. Psychologie vom empirischen Standpunkt. Leipzig, 1874.

—— Untersuchungen zur Sinnespsychologie. Leipzig, 1907.

Breslauer-Schueck, A. "Hirndruck und Schädeltrauma." *Mitteilungen aus dem Grenzgebiet der Medizin und Chirurgie,* XXIX (1917), 117.

—— "Pathologie des Hirndrucks." *Ibid.,* XXX (1918), 283.

Brodmann, M. "Experimentelle und klinische Beiträge zur Psychopathologie der polyneuritische Psychose." *Journal für Neurologie und Psychiatrie,* I–III (1902–4).

Bromberg, Walter. "Marihuana Intoxication." *American Journal of Psychiatry,* XCI (1934), 303.

Bromberg, Walter, and Paul Schilder. "Attitudes of Psychoneurotics towards Death." *Psychoanalytic Review*, XXIII (1936), 1–25.

—— and Paul Schilder. "On Tactile Imagination and Tactile After-effects." *Journal of Nervous and Mental Disease*, LXXVI (1932), 33.

—— and Paul Schilder. "Olfactory Imagination and Olfactory Hallucinations." *Archives of Neurology and Psychiatry*, XXXII (Sept., 1934), 467.

—— and Paul Schilder. "Psychologic Considerations in Alcoholic Hallucinosis—Castration and Dismembering Motive." *International Journal of Psychoanalysis*, XIV (1933), 206–24.

—— and Paul Schilder. "Death and Dying: A Comparative Study of the Attitudes and Mental Reactions toward Death and Dying." *Psychoanalytic Review*, XX (1933), 133–83.

Brown, Thomas Graham. "The Intrinsic Factors in the Act of Progression in the Mammal." *Proceedings of the Royal Society of London*, Series B, LXXXIV (1911).

Brunner, H., and H. Hoff. "Das Nebelsehen bei Labyrinthreizung." *Zeitschrift für die gesamte Neurologie und Psychiatrie*, CXX (1929), 796.

Brunswik, E. Wahrnehmung und Gegenstandswelt, Grundlegung einer Psychologie vom Gegenstand her. Leipzig and Vienna, 1934.

—— and E. C. Tolman. "The Organism and the Causal Texture of the Environment." *Psychological Review*, XLII (1935), 43–77.

Brush, E. N. "Observations on the Temporal Judgment During Sleep." *American Journal of Psychology*, XLII (1930), 408.

Buch, Anne Marie. "Zur Pathologie von Gestaltswahrnehmungen an der Haut." *Verhandlungen der Gesellschaft deutscher Nervenärzte*, Leipzig, 1926.

Buehler, Charlotte. Der menschlische Lebenslauf. Leipzig, 1933.

Buehler, Karl. "Tatsachen und Probleme zu einer Psychologie der Denkvorgänge." *Archiv für die gesamte Psychologie*, XI–XII (1907).

—— Die geistige Entwicklung des Kindes. Jena, 1924.

Buerger, Hans. In *Monatschrift für Psychiatrie und Neurologie*, XL (1928).

Buerger-Prinz, H., and M. Kaila. "Ueber die Struktur des amnestischen Symptomenkomplexes." *Zeitschrift für die gesamte Neurologie und Psychiatrie*, CXXIV (1933), 553.

Bykof, K. M., and A. Speransky. In *Zentralblatt für die gesamte Neurologie und Psychiatrie*, XXXIX (1925).

Carpenter, C. B. "A Field Study of the Behavior and Social Relations of Howling Monkeys." *Comparative Psychology Monograph*, X (1934), 168.

Carr, H. A. "The Autokinetic Sensation." *Psychological Review*, XVII (1910), 42.

Cason, Hulsey. "Pleasure Pain Theory of Learning." *Psychological Review*, XXXIX (1932), 440–66.

Charcot, J. M. "Cas de suppression brusque et isolée de la mémoire des signes." *Progrès médicale*. Paris, 1883.

Claparède, E. "Note sur la localisation du Moi." *Archives du Psychologie*, XIX (1924), 172.

Coghill, George E. "Biologic Basis of Conflict in Behavior." *Psychoanalytic Review*, XX (1933), 4.

—— Anatomy and the Problem of Behavior. Cambridge, Mass., 1929.

Cohen, G. "Zur Bedeutung des Zeitfaktors für die Pathologie des Temperatursinnes." *Deutsche Zeitschrift für Nervenheilkunde*, XCVI (1927), 43–60.

Curran, Frank J., and Paul Schilder. "Experiments in Repetition and Recall." *Journal of Genetic Psychology*, LI (1937), 163–87.

Cyon, Elie von. Das Ohrlabyrinth als Organ der mathematischen Sinne für Raum und Zeit. Berlin, 1908.

Davis, Hallowell. "The Physiological Phenomena of Audition," in Handbook of General Experimental Psychology, ed. by Carl Murchison. Worcester, Mass., 1934.

—— and Paula A. Davis. "Action Potentials of the Brain." *Archives of Neurology and Psychiatry*, XXXIV (1935), 1214–24.

—— and Leon J. Saul. "Action Currents in the Central Nervous System." *Ibid.*, XXIX (1933), 255–59.

Delbrueck, Anton. Grundfragen der Sprachforschung. Strassburg, 1901.

Demetriades, Theodor D. "Die Wechselbeziehungen zwischen Labyrinth und vegetativem Nervensystem." *Wiener Klinische Wochenschrift*, XL (1927), 48–49.

Dimmick, F. L. "An Experimental Study of Visual Movement and the Phi Phenomenon." *American Journal of Psychology*, XXXI (1920), 217–32.

Dittler, R., and H. Koellner. "Ueber Halluzinationen." *Zeitschrift der Neurologie*, LIII (1920), 169.

Ebbinghaus, H. Ueber das Gedächtnis. Leipzig, 1885. Translated by H. A. Rueger as Memory. New York, 1913.

Economo, Constantin von. "Der Schlaf." *Jahreskurse für ärztliche Fortbildung*, V (1929), 65.

—— "Encephalitis Lethargica." *Jahrbücher für Psychiatrie und Neurologie. Verhandlungen der deutschen medizinischen Kongress*, VIII (1923), 191.

Economo, Constantin von. "Ueber den Schlaf." *Handbuch der Physiologie,* XVII (Vienna, 1925).

—— "Schlaftheorie." *Ergebnisse der Physiologie,* XXVIII (1929), 312–39.

—— A. Fuchs, and Otto Poetzl. "Die Nachbehandlung der Kopfverletzungen." *Zeitschrift für die gesamte Neurologie und Psychiatrie,* XLIII (1918), 276–341.

Ehrenwald, Hans. "Versuche zur Zeitauffassung des Unbewussten." *Archiv für die gesamte Psychologie,* XLV (1923), 144–56.

—— "Störung der Zeitauffassung, der raumlichen Orientierung, bei einem Hirnverletzten." *Zeitschrift für die gesamte Neurologie und Psychologie,* CXXXII (1931), 518.

—— "Ueber den Zeitsinn und die gnostische Störung der Zeitauffassung beim Korsakow." *Ibid.,* CXXXIV (1931), 512.

—— "Gibt es einen Zeitsinn? Ein Beitrag zur Psychologie und Hirnpathologie der Zeitauffassung." *Klinische Wochenschrift,* X (1931), 1481.

Eisenson, John. "Confirmation and Information in Reward and Punishment." *Archives of Psychology,* CLXXXI (1935).

Eisinger, K., and Paul Schilder. "Träume bei Labyrinthläsionen." *Monatschrift für Psychiatrie und Neurologie,* LXXIII (1929), 314.

Esper, Erwin A. "Language," in Handbook of Social Psychology, ed. by Carl Murchison. Worcester, Mass., 1935.

Exner, S. "Optische Bewegungsempfindungen." *Biologie Zentralblatt,* VII, 188–89.

—— "Ueber Sensomobilität." *Pfluegers Archiv für die gesamte Physiologie,* XLVIII (1891).

Federn, P. "Reality of the Death Instinct." *Psychoanalytic Review,* XIX (1932), 129–51.

—— "Ueber zwei typische Traumsensationen." *Jahrbuch für psychoanalytische Forschungen,* VI (1914), 89.

—— "Some Variations in Ego-Feeling." *International Journal of Psychoanalysis,* VII (1926), 434.

Ferenczi, Sándor. "Schwindelempfindung nach Schluss der Analysestunde." *Internationale Zeitschrift für ärztliche Psychoanalyse,* II (1914), 272–74.

Ferree, C. E. "The Streaming Phenomenon." *American Journal of Psychology,* XIX (1915), 484–503.

Feuchtwanger, Erich. "Körpertonus und Aussenraum." *Archiv für Psychiatrie,* C (1933), 439–90.

Fischer, Franz. "Zeitstruktur und Schizophrenie." *Zeitschrift für die gesamte Neurologie und Psychiatrie,* CXXI (1929), 544.

—— "Raum-Zeitstruktur und Denkstörung in der Schizophrenie." *Ibid.,* CXXIV (1930), 241–56.

Fischer, Max Heinrich. Die Regulationsfunktion des menschlichen Labyrinthes. München, 1928.

—— "Die Orientierung im Raume bei Wirbeltieren und beim Menschen." *Handbuch der normalen und pathologischen Physiologie,* XV (1931), 909.

—— and E. Wodak. "Beiträge zur Physiologie des menschlichen Vestibularapparates." *Archiv für die gesamte Physiologie,* CCII (1924), 523.

Flach, Auguste. "Ueber symbolische Schemata im produktiven Denkprozess." *Archiv für die gesamte Psychologie,* LII (1925), 369–440.

—— and C. Palisa. "Zur Psychopathologie des Zeiterleben im postencephalitischen Blickkrampf." *Psychiatrisch-neurologische Universitätsklinik in Wien,* CLIV (1935), 599–620.

Forster, E. "Selbstversuch mit Meskalin." *Zeitschrift für die gesamte Neurologie und Psychiatrie,* CXXVII (1930), 1–14.

French, T. M. "Interrelations Between Psychoanalysis and the Experimental Work of Pavlov." *American Journal of Psychiatry,* XII (May, 1933), 1165–205.

—— "Reality Testing in Dreams." *Psychoanalytic Quarterly,* VI (1937), 62–77.

—— "Beziehungen des Unbewussten zur Funktion der Bogengänge. *Internationale Zeitschrift für Psychoanalyse,* XVI (1930), 73–86.

Freud, Sigmund. Collected Papers, trans. by L. M. Baines. 4 vols. London, 1925; Gesammelte Schriften, Vienna, 1924.

—— Hemmung Symptom und Angst. Vienna, 1936.

Frey, M. von. "Die Tangorezeptoren des Menschen." *Handbuch der normalen und pathologischen Physiologie,* II (1926), 94–128. (Bibliography.)

—— and A. Goldman. "Der zeitliche Verlauf der Einstellung bei den Druckempfindungen." *Zeitschrift für Biologie,* LXV (1914), 183.

—— and W. Metzger. "Die Raumschwelle der Haut bei Sukzessivreizung." *Zeitschrift für Psychologie,* XXIX (1902), 161.

Frisch, K. von. "Der Farbensinn und Formensinn der Biene." *Zoologisches Jahrbuch,* XXV (1915), 1–182.

Frobenius, K. "Ueber die zeitliche Orientierung im Schlaf und einige Aufwachphänomene." *Zeitschrift für Psychologie und Physiologie der Sinnesorgane,* CIII (1927), 100.

Froebe, Josef. Lehrbuch der experimentellen Psychologie. Freiburg, 1923.

Fuchs, W. Ueber das Sehen der Hemianoptiker, psychologische Analysen Hirnverletzter, ed. by K. Goldstein and A. Gelb. Leipzig, 1920.

Gamper, Edward. "Bau und Leistungen eines menschlichen Mittel-
hirnwesens." *Zeitschrift für die gesamte Neurologie und Psychiatrie,*
CII (1921), 154.
—— "Der chronische Alkoholiker." *Ibid.,* CIV (1926), 49.
—— "Zur Frage der Polioencephalitis Hemorraghica." *Deutsche Zeit-
schrift für Nervenheilkunde,* CII (1928), 122–29.
Gardner, William A. "Influence of the Thyroid Gland on the Conscious-
ness of Time." *American Journal of Psychology,* XLVII (1935), 698–
701.
Garten, Siegfried. "Ueber die Grundlagen unserer Orientierung im
Raum." *Abhandlungen der mathematisch-physikalischen Klasse der
sächsischen Akademie ueber Wissenschaften,* XXXIII (1920), 433.
Garvey, C. R. "A Study of Conditioned Respiratory Changes." *Journal of
Experimental Psychology,* XVI (1933), 471–503.
Gebsattel, E., Baron von. "Zeitbezogenes Zwangsdenken in der Melan-
cholie." *Nervenarzt,* V (1932), 275–87.
Gelb, Adhénar. "Die psychologische Bedeutung pathologischer Störungen
der Raumwahrnehmung." *IX Kongress für experimentelle Psychologie,*
1925.
—— and Kurt Goldstein. "Zur Psychologie des optischen Wahrneh-
mungs- und Erkennungsvorganges." *Zeitschrift für die gesamte Neurologie und Psychiatrie,* XLI (1918), 1.
—— and Kurt Goldstein. "Ueber den Einfluss des vollständigen Verlustes
des optischen Vorstellungsvermögens auf das taktile Erkennen." *Zeitschrift für Psychologie und Physiologie der Sinnesorgane,* LXXXIII
(1919), 1.
—— and Kurt Goldstein. Psychologische Analysen hirnpathologischer
Fälle. Leipzig, 1920.
Gerard, Ralph. "Factors Influencing Brain Potentials." *Transactions of the
American Neurological Association,* LXII (1936), 55–57.
Gerstmann, Joseph. "Ueber eine eigenartige Orientierungsstörung."
Wiener medizinische Wochenschrift, XXVII (1926), 1–6.
—— and A. Kestenbaum. "Monokuläres Doppelsehen bei cerebralen Er-
krankungen." *Zeitschrift für die gesamte Neurologie und Psychiatrie,*
CXXVIII (1930), 42–56.
Goethe, J. W. von. Zur Morphologie. Tübingen, 1923.
Goldschmidt, B. F. Die quantitative Grundlage von Vererbung und Aus-
lese. Berlin, 1920.
Goldstein, Kurt. "Ueber monokuläre Doppelbilder." *Jahrbücher für Psy-
chiatrie und Neurologie,* LV (1922), 16–38.
—— "Beobachtungen ueber die Veränderungen des Gesamtverhaltens

bei Gehirnschädigung." *Monatschrift für Psychiatrie und Neurologie,* LXVIII (1928), 217–42.

—— "Das Wesen der amnestischen Aphasie." *Schweizer Archiv für Neurologie und Psychiatrie,* XV (1924), 163–74.

—— "Kritisches und tatsächliches zu einigen Grundfragen der Psychopathologie." *Ibid.,* XXXIV (1934), 2–40.

—— Der Aufbau des Organismus. The Hague, 1934. (Bibliography.)

—— "Das Kleinhirn." *Handbuch der normalen und pathologischen Physiologie,* X (Berlin, 1927), 222 ff.

—— and Frieda Reichmann. "Beiträge zur Kasuistik und Symptomatologie der Kleinhirnerkrankungen." *Archiv für Psychiatrie,* LI (1915–16), 466–521.

Goodenough, Florence L. Measurement of Intelligence by Drawing. Yonkers, N.Y., 1926.

Gottschaldt, K. "Ueber den Einfluss der Erfahrung auf die Wahrnehmung von Figuren 'I und II,' " *Psychologische Forschungen,* VIII (1926), 261–317; XII (1929), 1–87.

Gregor, A. "Beiträge zur Psychopathologie des Gedächtnisses." *Monatschrift für Neurologie und Psychologie,* XXV (1909).

Gross, Alfred. "Zeitsinn und Traum." *Internationale Zeitschrift für Psychoanalyse,* XIX (1933), 613.

Gruenbaum, A. A. "Ueber Apraxie." *Zentralblatt für die gesamte Neurologie und Psychiatrie,* LV (1930), 788.

Gruenthal, E., and G. E. Stoerring. "Ueber das Verhalten bei umschriebener völliger Merkunfähigkeit." *Monatschrift für Psychiatrie und Neurologie,* LXXIV (1930), 354–69.

Guenther, H. "Ueber Nachempfindungen besonderer Sensoreniterationen." *Deutsche Zeitschrift für Nervenheilkunde,* LXXVI (1923), 320.

Guettich, O. "Beobachtungen ueber die Dauer der Abweichreaktion bei Reizung des Vestibularis." *Passov-Schaeffers Beiträge,* XII (1919).

Harnik, J. "Die triebhaft-affektiven Momente in Zeitgefühl." *Imago,* XI (1925), 321.

Hartmann, Heinz. "Gedächtnis und Lustprinzip; Untersuchungen an Korsakoffkranken." *Zeitschrift für die gesamte Neurologie und Psychiatrie,* CXXVI (1930), 496–518.

—— "Halluzinierte Flächenflagen und Bewegungen." *Monatschrift für Psychiatrie und Neurologie,* LVI (1924), 1.

—— "Cocainismus und Homosexualität." *Deutsche medizinische Wochenschrift,* 1918.

—— and Paul Schilder. "Körperinneres und Körperschema." *Zeitschrift*

402   BIBLIOGRAPHY

für die gesamte Neurologie und Psychiatrie, CIX (1927), 666–75.
—— and Paul Schilder. "Zur Klinik und Psychologie der Amentia."
    Monatschrift für Psychiatrie und Neurologie, LV (1923), 321–26.
Hartshorne, Charles. The Philosophy and Psychology of Sensation. Chi-
    cago, 1934.
Head, Henry. Aphasia and Kindred Disorders of Speech. 2 vols., Cam-
    bridge, England, 1926.
—— "Certain Mental Changes That Accompany Cerebral Disease." *Brain,*
    XXIV (1901).
Heidegger, M. Sein und Zeit. Halle, 1929.
Helmholz, H. Treatise on Physiological Optics. Ithaca, New York, 1924.
Henning, Hans. "Die neuentdeckte Erlebnisskala der Eidetik, die Urbilder
    und der Konstitutionstypus." *Deutsche Zeitschrift für Nervenheilkunde,*
    LXXXI (1924), 180.
—— "Starre eidetische Klang- und Schmerzbilder." *Zeitschrift für Psy-*
    chologie und Physiologie der Sinnesorgane, XLII (1923), 137.
Hering, E. Grundzüge der Lehre vom Lichtsinn. Leipzig, 1920.
Hermann, Imre. "Studien zur Denkpsychologie." *Acta Psychologica,* V
    (1940), 22–102.
Hess, W. R. "Ueber die Wechselbeziehungen zwischen psychischen und
    vegetativen Funktionen." *Schweizer Archiv für Neurologie und Psy-*
    chiatrie, XVI (1925), 285.
Heveroch, M. Quoted by Rudolf Allers in "Zur Pathologie des Tonuslaby-
    rinthes." *Monatschrift für Psychiatrie und Neurologie,* II (1909),
    116.
Hillebrand, M. I. "Untersuchungen ueber Vergangenheits- und Zukunfts-
    reaktionen." *Archiv für die gesamte Psychologie,* LXXXII (1931), 153.
Hoagland, Hudson. "The Physiological Control of Judgment of Dura-
    tion." *Journal of General Psychology,* IX (1933), 261.
Hoff, Hans. "Die zentrale Abstimmung der Sehsphäre." *Abhandlungen*
    aus der Neurologie und Psychiatrie, LIV (Berlin, 1930).
—— "Beiträge zur Relation der Sehsphäre und des Vestibularapparates."
    Zeitschrift für die gesamte Neurologie und Psychiatrie, CXXI (1929),
    751–62.
—— and O. Poetzl. "Zeitrafferwirkung." *Ibid.,* CLI (1934).
—— and O. Poetzl. "Polyopie als Nischensymptom." *Ibid.,* CLII (1934),
    449.
—— and Paul Schilder. Die Lagereflexe des Menschen. Vienna, 1927.
—— and Paul Schilder. "Zur Kenntnis der Symptomatologie vestibulärer
    Erkrankungen." *Deutsche Zeitschrift für Nervenheilkunde,* CIII
    (1928), 145.

—— and M. Silbermann. "Aenderungen der akustischen Wahrnehmungs-welt bei Temporallappenläsionen." *Zeitschrift für die gesamte Neurologie und Psychiatrie*, CXLIV (1933), 657–64.

Hoffman, F. B. Die Lehre vom Raumsinn des Auges. Berlin, 1925.

—— "Handbuch der gesamte Augenheilkunde." *Physiologische Optik*, III, 1–613. Berlin, 1922.

—— and Fruboese. "Ueber das Erkennen der Hauptrichtungen im Sehraum." *Zeitschrift für Biologie*, LXXX (1927), 91.

Hollos, Istvan. "Des Zeitgefühl." *Internationale Zeitschrift für Psychoanalyse*, VIII (1924), 421.

Hornbostel, Erich M. von. "Die Einheit der Sinne." *Melos Zeitschrift für Musik*, IV, 290–97.

Hudgins, C. V. "Conditioning and the Voluntary Control of the Pupillary Light Reflex." *Journal of General Psychology*, VIII (1933), 3–51.

Hull, Clark L. "Functional Interpretation of Conditioned Reflex." *Psychological Review*, XXXVI (1929), 498–511.

Hunt, W. A. "The Relation of Bright and Dull Pressure to Affectivity." *American Journal of Psychology*, XLIII (1931), 87–92.

—— "The Pressure Correlate of Emotion." *Ibid.*, 600–605.

—— "Localization of Bright and Dull Pressure." *Ibid.*, 308–13.

Hunter, W. S. "The After-effect of Visual Motion." *Psychological Review*, XXI (1914), 245.

—— "Retinal Factors in Visual After-movements." *Ibid.*, XXII (1915), 479–89.

Husserl, Edmund. Logische Untersuchungen. Halle, 1913.

Isakower, O., and Paul Schilder. "Optischräumliche Agnosie und Agraphie." *Zeitschrift für die gesamte Neurologie und Psychiatrie*, CXIII (1928), 102–42.

Ischlondsky, N. E. Neuropsyche und Hirnrinde. Berlin and Vienna, 1930.

Jacobson, Edmund. Progressive Relaxation. Chicago, 1929.

—— You Must Relax. New York, 1934.

—— "Electrophysiology of Mental Activity." *American Journal of Physiology*, CLIV (1932), 677–99.

Jaensch, E. R. Ueber den Aufbau des Bewusstseins. Leipzig, 1930.

—— Die Eidetik und die typologische Forschungsmethode. Leipzig, 1925.

—— and A. Kretz. "Experimentell-strukturpsychologische Untersuchungen ueber die Auffassung der Zeit unter Berücksichtigung der Personaltypen." *Zeitschrift für Psychologie*, CXXVI (1932), 312–75.

—— and others. Grundformen menschlichen Seins. Berlin, 1929.

Jaensch, W. Grundzüge der Physiologie und Klinik der psychophysischen Persönlichkeit. Berlin, 1926.

Janet, Pierre M. In *Journal de Psychologie normale et pathologique*, VI (1908), 488.

Jelliffe, Smith Ely. Psychopathology of Forced Movements and the Oculogyric Crises of Encephalitis Lethargica. New York and Washington, 1932.

Jones, Ernest. Papers on Psychoanalysis. London, 1923.

Jung, Carl Gustav. Ueber die Psychologie der Dementia Praecox. Halle and Zurich, 1907.

—— Psychological Types. London, 1923.

Kanner, Leo, and Paul Schilder. "Ueber Bewegungen an Vorstellungsbildern und ihre Beziehungen zur Pathologie." *Nervenarzt*, III (1930), 406–11.

—— and Paul Schilder. "Movements in Optic Images, and Optic Imagination of Movement." *Journal of Nervous and Mental Disease*, LXXII (1930), 489–517.

Kant, F., and E. Krapf. "Ueber Selbstversuche mit Haschisch." *Archiv für experimentelle Pathologie und Pharmakologie*, CXXIX (1928), 319.

Karsten, Anitra. "Psychische Sättigung." *Psychologische Forschung*, X (1928), 142–254.

Katz, D. Der Aufbau der Tastwelt. Leipzig, 1925.

Kauders, Otto. "Drehbewegungen um die Körperlängsachse." *Zeitschrift für die gesamte Neurologie und Psychiatrie*, XCVIII (1925), 602–14.

Keller, Hans. "Psychologie des Zukunftsbewusstseins." *Zeitschrift für Psychologie*, CXXIV (1932), 211.

Keynes, J. M. "Treatise on Probability," cited by Bertrand Russell, in Philosophy. New York, 1927.

Kleist, Karl. "Hirnpathologie," in *Handbuch der pathologischen Erfahrungen im Weltkrieg*. Berlin, 1933.

Kluever, Heinrich. Behavior Mechanism in Monkeys. Chicago, 1933.

—— Mescal—The "Divine" Plant and Its Psychological Effects. London, 1928.

—— "The Study of Personality and the Method of Equivalent and Nonequivalent Stimuli." *Character and Personality*, II (1936), 92–112.

—— "The Eidetic Type." *Proceedings of the Association for Research in Nervous and Mental Disease*, XIV (1933).

—— "The Eidetic Child," in Handbook of Child Psychology, ed. by Carl Murchison. Worcester, Mass., 1933.

—— "Do Personality Types Exist?" *American Journal of Psychiatry*, X (1931), 781–88.

—— "Visual Disturbances after Cerebral Lesions." *Psychological Bulletin*, XXIV (1927), 316.

Knauer, A., and W. Y. Maloney. "A Preliminary Note on the Psychic Action of Mescalin." *Journal of Nervous and Mental Disease*, LXXII (1930), 397.

Koehler, Wolfgang. Gestalt Psychology. New York, 1929.

—— The Mentality of Apes. New York and London, 1927.

—— "Gestalt Probleme und Anfänge einer Gestalttheorie." *Jahresbücher der gesamten Physik*, V (1924), 12–39.

Koffka, Kurt. Principles of Gestalt Psychology. New York, 1935.

Kornmueller, Alois E. "Biolektrische Untersuchungen ueber den Pathomechanismus des Zentralnervensystem." *Deutsche Zeitschrift für Nervenheilkunde*, CXXXIX (1936), 81–89.

—— Gesellschaft deutscher Neurologen und Psychiater. Dresden and Berlin, 1936.

Korzybski, Alfred. Science and Sanity. Lancaster, Pa., 1933.

Krause, Fedor. "Die Sehbahn in chirurgischer Beziehung und faradische Reizung des Sehzentrums." *Klinische Wochenschrift*, III (1924), 1260–65.

Krauss, Stephan. "Untersuchung ueber Aufbau und Störung der menschlichen Handlung. I: Die Korsakowsche Störung." *Archiv für die gesamte Psychologie*, LXXVII (1930), 649–92.

Kretschmer, Ernst. Physique and Character. New York, 1925.

Kronfeld, Arthur. Das Wesen der psychiatrischen Erkenntnis. Berlin, 1920.

Kubie, Lawrence S. "Die Beziehung des bedingten Reflexes zur psychoanalytischen Technik." *Internationale Zeitschrift für Psychoanalyse*, XIX (1933), 213.

Kuelpe, Otto. "Der gegenwärtige Stand der experimentellen Aesthetik." *III Kongress für experimentelle Psychologie* (1906–7).

Lange, J. Brain Mechanisms and Intelligence. Chicago, 1929.

—— "Fingeragnosie und Agraphie." *Monatschrift für Psychiatrie und Neurologie*, LXXVI (1930), 129.

Lashley, K. S. "Integrative Functions of the Cerebral Cortex." *Physiological Review*, XIII (1933), 1–42.

—— "Nervous Mechanisms in Learning," in Handbook of General Experimental Psychology. Worcester, Mass., 1934.

Latif, Israel. "The Physiological Basis of Linguistic Development and of the Ontogeny of Meaning." *Psychological Review*, XLI (1934), 55–85, 153–76, 246–64.

Leidler, Rudolf. "Versuch einer psychologischen Analyse des Schwindels." *Monatschrift für Ohrenheilkunde*, LV (1921), 144.

Leidler, Rudolf. "Der Schwindel." *Handbuch der Neurologie des Ohres* (Berlin and Vienna, 1922), I, 553–58.

—— and Paul Loewy. "Der Schwindel bei Neurosen." *Monatschrift für Ohrenheilkunde,* LVII (1923), 1–174.

Lemaître, Auguste. La vie mentale de l'adolescent et ses anomalies. Saint-Blaise, 1910.

Lenz, A. Habilitationschrift. Breslau, 1922.

Lewin, Kurt. "Ueber die Umkehrung der Raumlage auf dem Kopf stehender Worte und Figuren in der Wahrnehmung." *Psychologische Forschung,* IV (1923), 210–61.

—— Dynamic Theory of Personality. New York, 1935.

Liepmann, H. "Apraxie." *Ergebnisse der Medizin von Bruges,* I (1920), 516.

Lindemann, L. W. "Experimentelle Untersuchungen ueber das Entstehen und Vergehen von Gestalten." *Psychologische Forschung,* II (1922), 5–60.

Lindworsky, J. Das schlussfolgende Denken. Freiburg, 1916.

—— Der Wille. Leipzig, 1918.

Lockhart, L. W. Word Economy; a Study in Applied Linguistics. London, 1931.

Loewy, Paul. "Psychophysiologische Mechanismen bei funktionellen Neurosen." *Deutsche Zeitschrift für Nervenheilkunde,* LXIV (1919), 279.

—— "Die Beziehung zwischen Psyche und Statik." *Zeitschrift für die gesamte Neurologie und Psychiatrie,* LXV (1921), 321.

Luria, A. R. "Die moderne russische Physiologie und die Psychoanalyse." *Internationale Zeitschrift für Psychoanalyse,* XII (1926), 40.

Mach, E. Beiträge zur Analyse der Empfindungen. Jena, 1918.

Magnus, Rudolf. Körperstellung. Berlin, 1924.

—— and A. de Kleijn. "Die Abhängigkeit des Tonus von der Körperstellung." *Pflueger's Archiv für die gesamte Physiologie,* CXLV (1912), 455.

Marie, Pierre, and R. Béhague. "Syndrome de désorientation dans l'èspace consécutif aux plaies profondes du lobe frontal." *Revue Neurologique,* XXXV (1919), 3.

Matthaei, Rupprecht. Das Gestaltproblem. München, 1929. (Bibliography.)

Mayer-Gross, Wilhelm. "Ueber einige Abänderungen der Sinnestätigkeit im Meskalinrausch." *Zeitschrift für die gesamte Neurologie und Psychiatrie,* CI (1926), 354.

—— "Pathologie der Wahrnehmung." *Bumkes Handbuch der Geisteskrankheiten,* I (1928).

—— and H. Stein. "Veränderte Sinnestätigkeit im Meskalinrausch." *Deutsche Zeitschrift für Nervenheilkunde,* LXXXIX (1926), 112.

Messer, K. "Experimentelle Beiträge ueber das Denken." *Archiv für die gesamte Psychologie,* VIII (1906).

Metzger, W. "Ueber das physiologische Substrat der optisch-motorischen Erlebniseinheit." *Zentralblatt für die gesamte Neurologie und Psychiatrie,* XLVI (1925), 520.

Meyer, Paula. "Ueber die Reproduktion eingeprägter Figuren und ihrer räumlichen Stellungen bei Kindern und Erwachsenen." *Zeitschrift für die Psychologie und Physiologie der Sinnesorgane,* CXIV (1913), 34-91.

Minkowsky, Eugene. "Bleulers Schizoidie und Syntonie und das Zeiterlebnis." *Zeitschrift für die gesamte Neurologie und Psychiatrie,* LXXXII (1923), 212-30.

—— La Schizophrenie. Paris, 1927.

—— Le Temps vècu. Paris, 1933.

—— "Zeit- und Raumproblem in der Psychopathologie." *Wiener Klinische Wochenschrift,* XLIV (1931), 346-80.

Morgan, C. Lloyd. Instinct and Experience. New York, 1913.

Mourgue, Raoul. Neurobiologie de l'hallucination. Bruxelles, 1932.

—— "Une découverte scientifique: la durée bergsonienne." *Revue Philosophique,* XVI (1935), 35-367.

Mueller, G. E. Die Analyse der Gedächtnistätigkeit. Leipzig, 1917.

Mueller, Johannes. Ueber die phantastischen Gesichtserscheinungen. Coblenz, 1826.

Nachmansohn, D. "Ueber experimentellerzeugte Träume nebst kritischen Bemerkungen zur psychoanalytischen Methode." *Zeitschrift für die gesamte Neurologie und Psychiatrie,* CVIII (1926), 556.

—— "Zur Frage des Schlafzentrums." *Ibid.,* CVII (1927), 342-401.

Nafe, John P. "An Experimental Study of the Affective Qualities." *American Journal of Psychology,* XXXV (1924), 507-44.

Oberndorf, Clarence P. "Depersonalization in Relation to Erotization of Thought." *International Journal of Psychoanalysis,* XV (1934), 271.

Ogden, Clarence Kay. Opposition, a Linguistic and Psychological Analysis. London, 1932.

—— and I. A. Richards. The Meaning of Meaning. New York, 1925.

Orton, Samuel T. Reading, Writing and Speech Problems in Children. New York, 1936.

Pálàgy, W. Wahrnehmungslehre. Leipzig, 1925.

Parker, S., and Paul Schilder. "Das Koerperschema im Lift." *Zeitschrift für die gesamte Neurologie und Psychiatrie,* CXXVIII (1930), 777.

408   BIBLIOGRAPHY

Parker, S., and Paul Schilder. "Acoustic Imagination and Acoustic Hallucination." *Archives of Neurology and Psychiatry*, XXXIV (1935),
744–57.

Pavlov, Ivan Petrovich. Conditioned Reflexes. New York, 1927.

—— Lectures on Conditioned Reflexes. New York, 1928.

—— Letter to the Editor, in *Journal of the American Medical Association*,
XCIX (1932), 1012–13.

Pick, Arnold. "Ueber Hyperaesthesie der peripherischen Retinaab-
schnitte." *Monatschrift für Psychiatrie und Neurologie*, XXIV (1908),
382.

—— "Ueber Beeinflussung von Visionen durch cerebellar ausgelöste
vestibuläre und ophthalmostatische Störungen." *Zeitschrift für die gesamte Neurologie und Psychiatrie*, LVI (1920), 213.

Pick, Ernst. "Ueber Schlaf und Schlafmittel." *Mitteilungen des Volksge-
sundheitsamtes*, VI (1927).

Piéron, H. Thought and the Brain. New York, 1927.

Pikler, Julius. Schriften zur Auffassungstheorie des Empfindungsvor-
ganges. Budapest, 1926.

Poetzl, Otto. Biologie und Klinik des Schlafs. Munich, 1929.

—— "Bemerkungen ueber den Augenmassfehler der Hemianopiker."
Wiener klinische Wochenschrift, XLII (1918), 114.

—— "Die Aphasielehre. Optisch-agnostische Störungen." *Aschaffenbergs
Handbuch für Psychiatrie*. Vienna, 1928.

—— "Experimentell erregte Traumbilder." *Zeitschrift für die gesamte
Neurologie und Psychiatrie*, XXXVII (1917), 278.

—— "Tachystoskopisch provozierte optische Halluzinationen bei einem
Fall von Alkoholhalluzinose mit rückgebildeter cerebraler Hemianop-
sie." *Jahrbücher für Neurologie und Psychiatrie*, XXXV (1914–15), 141.

—— "Zur Topographie der Schlafzentren." *Monatschrift für Psychiatrie
und Neurologie*, LXIV (1927), 1–24.

—— and Georg Hermann. "Ueber die Agraphie." *Abhandlungen der Neurologie und Psychiatrie*, XXXV (1926), Berlin.

—— and E. Redlick. "Demonstration eines Falles bilateraler Affektion der
Occipitallappen." *Wiener klinische Wochenschrift*, XXIV (1911), 517.

Poppelreuter, W. "Zur Psychologie und Pathologie der optischen Wahrnehmung." *Zeitschrift für die gesamte Neurologie und Psychiatrie*,
LXXXIII (1923), 26–152.

—— "Ueber den Versuch einer psychophysischen Lehre von der elemen-
taren Assoziation und Reproduktion." *Monatschrift für Psychiatrie und
Neurologie*, XXXIII (1915).

Purdy, D. M. "The Structure of the Visual World. I. Space Perception and the Perception of Wholes." *Psychological Review,* XLII (1935), 399–424.

—— "The Structure of the Visual World. II. The Action of Motor Impulses on Sensory Excitations." *Ibid.,* 528–536.

—— "The Structure of the Visual World. III. The Tendency towards Simplification of the Visual Field." *Ibid.,* XLIII (1936), 59–82.

Quix, F. H. "L'Examen clinique des symptomes otolithiques." *Société Belge d'Oto-Rhinologie et de Laryngologie,* II (1924), 24.

Rabiner, A. M. "Significance of Panic and States of Consciousness in Grasping Movements." *Archives of Neurology and Psychiatry,* XXXIII (1935), 976–85.

Rado, Sándor. "Anxious Mother." *International Journal of Psychoanalysis,* IX (1928), 219–26.

Ranschburg, P. Reflexologie und Psychologie. Poznan, 1932.

Ransom, S. W. "The Hypothalamus: Its Significance for Visceral Innervation and Emotional Expression." *Transactions of the College of Physicians of Philadelphia,* II and III (1934).

Reichardt, M. "Hirnstamm und Psychiatrie." *Monatschrift für Psychiatrie und Neurologie,* LXVIII (1928), 470.

Reik, Theodor. Wie Man Psychologe Wird. Vienna, 1927.

Richter, Curt P. "The Grasping Reflex in the Newborn Monkey." *Archives of Neurology and Psychiatry,* XXVI (1931), 784–90.

—— and L. H. Bartemeier. "Decerebrate Rigidity of the Sloth." *Brain,* XLIX (1926), 207–25.

—— and others. "A Biologic Approach to Manic Depressive Insanity." *Transactions of the Association for Research in the Nervous and Mental Diseases,* LX (1930).

Rieger, J. "Ueber Apparate in dem Hirn." *Arbeit aus der psychiatrischen Klinik aus Wuerzburg,* V (1909).

Romberg, M. F. Lehrbuch der Nervenkrankheiten. Leipzig, 1857.

Rosenfeld, Max. Die Störungen des Bewusstseins. Leipzig (1929).

Ross, Nathaniel. "Hallucinatory Experiences of Changes in Visual Perception." *Journal of Nervous and Mental Disease,* LXXXIII (1936), 671–78.

Rossel, F. Das Hilfsschulkind: Beihefte zur Hilfsschule. Halle, 1925.

Rubinow, O., and L. Frankl. "Die erste Dingauffassung beim Säugling; Reaktionen auf Wahrnehmung der Flasche, mit Einleitung und Schluss von Charlotte Buehler." *Zeitschrift für Psychologie,* CXXXIII (1934), 1–71.

Russell, Bertrand. Philosophy. New York, 1927.

410   BIBLIOGRAPHY

Sander, F. "Structure, Totality of Experience and Gestalt," in Psychologies of 1930, ed. by Carl Murchison. Worcester, Mass., 1930.

Schilder, Paul. Gedanken zur Naturphilosophie. Vienna, 1927.

—— Introduction to a Psychoanalytic Psychiatry. New York and Washington, 1928.

—— Medizinische Psychologie für Aerzte und Psychologen. Berlin, 1924.

—— Seele und Leben. Berlin, 1923.

—— Selbstbewusstsein und Persönlichkeitsbewusstsein. Berlin, 1914.

—— Wahn und Erkenntnis. Berlin, 1918.

—— "Bemerkung ueber Zeitprobleme," *Nervenarzt*, V (1932), 361–65.

—— "Clinical Studies on Particular Types of Depressive Psychoses." *Journal of Nervous and Mental Disease*, LXXX (1934), 501–27, 658–83.

—— "Conditioned Reflexes." *Archives of Neurology and Psychiatry*, XXII (1929), 425–44.

—— "Corticale Encephalitis." *Journal für Neurologie und Psychiatrie*, XXXVII (1928), 293.

—— "Elementäre Halluzinationen des Bewegungsehens." *Zeitschrift für die gesamte Neurologie und Psychiatrie*, LXXX (1922), 424.

—— "Experiments on Imagination, After-Images and Hallucinations." *American Journal of Psychiatry*, XIII (1933), 597.

—— "Psychische Symptome bei Mittel- und Zwischenhirnerkrankung." *Wiener Klinische Wochenschrift*, XL (1927), 1147–48.

—— "Psychoanalyse und Eidetik." *Zeitschrift für Sexualwissenschaft*, XIII (1926), 56.

—— "Psychopathology of Time." *Journal of Nervous and Mental Disease*, LXXXIII (1936), 531–46.

—— "Self-Consciousness and Optic Imagination in a Case of Depression." *Psychoanalytic Review*, XXI (1934), 316–28.

—— "Space, Time, Perception." *Psyche*, XIV (1934), 124–39.

—— "Studien ueber den Gleichgewichtsapparat." *Wiener Klinische Wochenschrift*, XXXI (1918), 1350.

—— "The Vestibular Apparatus in Neurosis and Psychosis." *Journal of Nervous and Mental Disease*, LXXVIII (1933), 110–11.

—— "Ueber autokinetische Empfindungen." *Archiv für die gesamte Psychologie*, XXV (1912); *Zeitschrift für Psychologie*, LXXII (1915), 318.

—— "Ueber Gedankenentwicklung." *Zeitschrift für die gesamte Neurologie und Psychiatrie*, LIX (1920), 250–64.

—— "Ueber Halluzinationen." *Ibid.*, LIII (1930), 169–98.

—— "Ueber Identifizierung auf Grund der Analyse eines Falles von Homosexualität." *Ibid.*, LIX (1920), 217.

—— "Ueber monokuläre Polyopie bei Hysterie." *Deutsche Zeitschrift für Nervenheilkunde*, LXVI (1920), 250.

—— "Unity of the Body, Sadism, and Dizziness." *Psychoanalytic Review*, XVII (1930), 114.

—— "Vestibulooptik und Koerperschema in der Alkoholhalluzinose." *Zeitschrift für die gesamte Neurologie und Psychiatrie*, CXXVIII (1930), 784.

—— "Zur Kenntnis der Psychosen bei chronischer Encephalitis Epidemica." *Ibid.*, CXVIII (1929), 327–45.

—— and Otto Kauders. Hypnosis. New York and Washington, 1927.

—— and David Wechsler. "The Attitude of Children towards Death." *Journal of Genetic Psychology*, XLV (1934), 406–11.

—— and Max Weissmann. "Aetherisierung Geisteskranker." *Zeitschrift für die gesamte Neurologie und Psychiatrie*, CX (1927), 779–92.

—— and Max Weissmann. "Amente Psychose bei Hypophysengangtumor." *Ibid.*, 767–78.

Schumann, F. "Beiträge zur Analyse der Gesichtswahrnehmungen." *Zeitschrift für Psychologie und Physiologie der Sinnesorgane*, XXIII (1900).

—— "Die Lokalisierung bei Blickbewegungen." *Zeitschrift für Psychologie*, CXXVII (1932), 113–28.

—— "Psychologie des Lesens." *II Kongress für experimentelle Psychologie* (1906).

Selz, Otto. Die Gesetze des geordneten Denkverlaufes. Stuttgart, 1913.

—— "Komplextheorie und Constellationstheorie." *Zeitschrift für Psychologie und Physiologie der Sinnesorgane*, LXXXIV (1920).

Senden, M. von. Raum- und Gestaltauffassung bei operierten Blindgebornen. Leipzig, 1932.

Sherrington, Sir Charles Scott. The Integrative Action of the Nervous System. New Haven, 1911.

Shipley, W. C. "An Apparent Transfer of Conditioning." *Journal of General Psychology*, VIII (1933), 282–391.

Shuey, Herbert. "Recent Trends in Science and the Development of Modern Typology." *Psychological Review*, III (1924), 207–36.

Silberer, Herbert. "Bericht ueber eine Methode, gewisse symbolische Halluzinationserscheinungen hervorzurufen." *Jahrbuch für Psychoanalyse*, I (1909), III (1912).

Silbermann, M., and M. Tamari. "Audiometrische Untersuchungen bei Erkrankungen des Temporallappens." *Jahrbücher für Psychiatrie und Neurologie*, L, 89–114.

Skranlik, E. von. "Ueber Tastwahrnehmungen." *Zeitschrift für Sinnesphysiologie*, LVI (1925), 256.

Spiegel, E. A. "Rindenerregung durch Labyrinthreizung," *Zeitschrift für die gesamte Neurologie und Psychiatrie.* CXXXVIII (1932), 178–96.

—— "Electrothalmogram." *Proceedings of the Society for Experimental Biology and Medicine,* XXXIII (1936), 574.

—— "Labyrinth and Cortex." *Archives of Neurology and Psychiatry,* XXXI (1939).

—— Die Zentren des autonomen Nervensystems. Berlin, 1928.

—— and Ch. Inaba. "Zur zentralen Lokalisation von Störungen des Wachzustandes." *Klinische Wochenschrift,* V (1926), 2408.

Spielrein, Sabina. "Die Zeit im unterschwelligen Seelenleben." *Imago,* IX (1923), 300–317.

Spitzer, E. "Anatomie und Physiologie der zentralen Bahnen des Vestibularis." *Arbeit aus dem Neurologischen Institut der Wiener Universität,* XXV (1924).

Staples, Ruth. "The Responses of Infants to Color." *Journal of Experimental Psychology,* XV (1932), 119–41.

Stein, C. Schwindelautokinesis externa und interna. Leipzig, 1924.

Stein, Felix. "Ueber psychische Zwangsvorgänge und Angstzustände bei Blickkrampf." *Archiv für Psychiatrie,* LXXXI (1927).

Stein, J., and V. von Weizsaecker. "Zur Pathologie der Sensibilität." *Ergebnisse der Physiologie,* XXVII (1928), 657.

Stekel, Wilhelm. Peculiarities of Behavior. London and New York, 1924.

Stengel, Erwin. "Ueber taktile Bewegungs- und Scheinbewegungswahrnehmung bei Störung der Oberflächensensibilität." *Deutsche Zeitschrift für Nervenheilkunde,* XCIX (1927), 31.

—— "Zur Klinik und Pathophysiologie des postencephalitischen Blickkrampfes." *Monatschrift für Psychiatrie und Neurologie,* LXX (1928), 305.

Stern, Clara, and William Stern. Die Kindersprache. Leipzig, 1922.

Stern, Robert. "Ueber die Aufhellung der Amnesien bei pathologischen Rauschzuständen." *Zeitschrift für die gesamte Neurologie und Psychiatrie,* CVIII (1927), 601–24.

Stern, William. Psychology of Early Childhood. London and New York, 1924.

Stertzinger, Othmar. "Chemopsychologische Untersuchungen ueber den Zeitsinn." *Zeitschrift für Psychologie,* CXXXIV (1935), 100.

Stoerring, G. E. "Ueber den ersten reinen Fall eines Menschen mit völligem isoliertem Verlust der Merkfähigkeit." *Archiv für Psychiatrie,* LXXXI (1931), 257–385.

Storch, E. Muskelfunktion und Bewusstsein. Wiesbaden, 1901.

Stransky, Erwin. Ueber Sprachverwirrtheit. Halle, 1905.

—— and E. F. ten Cate. "Die correlative Empfindlichkeitsschwankung." *Wiener Klinische Rundschau,* XIV (1900), 290.

Stratton, G. M. "Vision without Inversion of the Retinal Image." *Psychological Review,* IV (1897), 314.

Straus, Erwin. "Die Formen des Räumlichen: ihre Bedeutung für die Motorik und die Wahrnehmung." *Nervenarzt,* III (1930), 633–56.

—— "Das Zeiterlebnis in der endogenen Depression und in der psychopathischen Verstimmung." *Monatschrift für Psychiatrie und Neurologie,* LXVIII (1928), 640.

Struempell, A. "Ueber das Zeitbewusstsein." *Neurologisches Zentralblatt,* XXXVIII (1919), 642.

Stumpf, Carl. "Ueber Gefühlsempfindungen." *Zeitschrift für Psychologie,* XLIV (1906), 1–49.

Szekely, Lejos. "Ueber den Aufbau der Sinnesfunktionen." *Zeitschrift für Psychologie,* CXXVI (1932), 227–65.

Thorndike, Edward. Human Learning. New York and London, 1931.

Titchner, E. B. Elementary Psychology of Feeling and Attention. 1908.

Troemner, Ernst. "Reflexuntersuchungen an einem Anencephalus." *Journal für Neurologie und Psychiatrie,* XXXV (1928), 194.

Trowbridge, M. H., and H. Cason. "An Experimental Study of Thorndike's Theory of Learning." *Journal of General Psychology,* VII (1932), 245–60.

Urbantschitsch, Viktor. "Ueber Störungen des Gleichgewichtes und Scheinbewegungen." *Zeitschrift für Ohrenheilkunde,* XXXI (1897).

—— Ueber subjektive optische Anschauungsbilder. Vienna, 1907.

Vogt, H., and W. Grant. "A Study of the Phenomenon of Apparent Movement." *American Journal of Psychology,* XXXVIII (1927), 72.

Walshe, F. M. R., and E. Graeme Robertson. "Observations upon the Form and Nature of the 'Grasping' Movements and 'Tonic Innervation' Seen in Certain Cases of Lesion of the Frontal Lobe." *Brain,* LVI (1933), 40–70.

Washburn, M. F. The Animal Mind. New York, 1926.

—— Movements and Mental Imagery. New York, 1916.

Watson, John Broadus. Behaviorism. New York, 1933.

Weaver, E. G., and C. Bray. "The Nature of Acoustic Responses; the Relation Between Sound Frequency and Frequency of Impulses in the Auditory Nerve." *Journal of Experimental Psychology,* XIII (1930), 373–87.

Wechsler, Israel. "Partial Cortical Blindness with Preservation of Cortical Vision." *Archives of Ophthalmology,* IX (1933), 957.

Weil, H. "Studien zur Psychologie menschlicher Typen; sinnespsychologische Kriterien menschlicher Typen." *Zeitschrift für Psychologie und Physiologie der Sinnesorgane*, CIX (1929), 241.

Weizsaecker, Viktor, Baron von. "Ueber einige Täuschungen in der Raumwahrnehmung nach Erkrankungen des Vestibularapparates." *Deutsche Zeitschrift für Nervenheilkunde*, LXIV (1919), 1.

―― "Ueber eine systematische Raumsinnstörung." *Ibid.*, LXXXIV (1925), 179.

―― "Kasuistische Beiträge zur Lehre vom Funktionswandel bei stato-opto-sensiblen Syndromen." *Ibid.*, CXVII (1931), 716–36.

―― "Ueber neurotischen Aufbau bei inneren Erkrankungen." *Verhandlungen der Gesellschaft deutscher Nervenärzte* (1925), 169.

Werner, Heinz. "Raum und Zeit in der Urform der Künste." *Bericht ueber den Kongress für Aesthetik und Kunstwissenschaft*, 1930.

―― Einführung in die Entwicklungspsychologie. Leipzig, 1926.

―― Comparative Psychology of Mental Development. New York, 1934.

―― and H. Creuzer. "Ueber einen Fall von 'Schichtspaltung' beim Bewegungssehen." *Zeitschrift für Psychologie*, CII (1927), 335.

Wertheimer, Max. "Untersuchungen zur Lehre von der Gestalt." *Psychologische Forschung*, IV (1923), 332–37.

White, William A. "The Frustration Theory of Consciousness. Mind as Energy." *Psychoanalytic Review*, XVI (1929), 143–62.

Whitehorn, J. C. "Material of Human Nature and Conduct Symposium: Material in the Hands of the Biochemist." *American Journal of Psychiatry*, XCII (1935), 315–23.

Wilder, Joseph. "Ueber Schief- und Verkehrtsehen." *Deutsche Zeitschrift für Nervenheilkunde*, CIV (1923), 222–56.

Woerkom, W. von. "Ueber Störungen im Denken der Aphasie Patienten." *Monatschrift für Psychiatrie*, LIX (1925).

Wolpert, J. "Störungen der Orientierung im Raum." *Neurologisches Zentralblatt*, CV (1930).

Wundt, Wilhelm Max. Grundzüge der physiologischen Psychologie. Leipzig, 1910.

―― Völkerpsychologie. I. Die Sprache. Leipzig.

Zádor, J. "Meskalinwirkung bei Störungen des optischen Systems." *Zeitschrift für die gesamte Neurologie und Psychiatrie*, CXXVII (1933), 30.

―― "Meskalinwirkung auf das Phantomglied." *Monatschrift für Psychiatrie und Neurologie*, LXXVI (1930), 71.

Zietz, K., and H. Werner. "Ueber die dynamische Struktur der Bewegung." *Zeitschrift für Psychologie*, CV (1927), 226–49.

Zingerle, H. "Weitere Untersuchungen ueber Automatose." *Journal für Psychologie und Neurologie*, XXXI (1925), 400–418.

—— "Klinische Studie ueber Haltungs- und Stellreflexe sowie andere automatische Körperbewegungen beim Menschen." *Zeitschrift für die gesamte Neurologie und Psychiatrie*, CV (1927), 548–98.
—— "Ueber Stellreflexe und automatische Lageänderungen beim Menschen." *Klinische Wochenschrift*, III (1924), 1847–49.
Zuckermann, S. The Social Life of Monkeys and Apes. London. 1926.

INDEX

Abeles, Milton, and Schilder, Paul, 384

Abraham, Karl, 334

Acceleration, perception of, 83, 132

Accommodation, changes in, 98

Ach, N., 304, 311

Acoustic imaginations, 76; tonic changes in connection with, 77

Acoustic nuclei, 86

Action, 233-41, 374; reality testing, 150, 211, 371; a dynamic change in body image, 233; continuous, necessary for child, 250; perception, representation, and thoughts lead to, 305; by wish only, 320; pleasure and reality principles in, 324-39; in distance and by mere contiguity, 359; always a unified action in space, 375; relation of space and time to, 379; theory of human, a necessary corollary to a theory of perception, 379; phasic, *see* Grasping; Sucking

Adaptation, tonic, 236

Adler, Alfred, 302, 342

Adrian, E. D., 366, 368, 369

Affect and thinking, 320

Afterimage, of movement, 19; tingling character, tendency to motility, 63

Aggression, 211; of depressive patients, 198; in neurotic cases, 306

Agnosia, optic, 34, 35; movement not perceived, 225

Ahringsmann, H., 72

A la recherche du temps perdu (Proust), 229

Alcoholic encephalopathy, time perception in, 225

Alcoholic hallucinosis, 9, 136; with macroptic and microptic hallucinations, 46; aftereffects in tactual sphere, 72; tendency to rhythm and repetition in, 77; acute, 109

Alcoholic intoxication, frequency of amnesias, 276

Alcoholic psychoses, tactile perception in, 70

Alexia, perception of movement in, 34

Allers, Rudolf, 86, 97, 104, 128, 322

Allonnes, Revault d', 215

Allport, F. H., 250

Amnesia, 384, 385

Amnestic gaps, 275, 384; time perception, 227

Anal eroticism, relations between ideas of time and, 219

Anger, 269

Angle cannot be drawn by young child, 351

Angles, perception of, 350, 351

Animals, salivation of dogs, 154 ff., 252 ff.; behavior, 174; tonic reaction, 234; hibernation, 344; *see also* Monkeys

Antinomies, 360, 361-64

Anxiety neurosis, 112; dizziness in, 127; space perception in, 209

Aphasia, impairment in signal function of language, 262 ff. *passim*, 267

Apraxia, 376

Asphyxiation, results of, 280

Association, 155; no disturbance in, in psychic life, 279; experiments, 309

Atom, 257

Atropine delirium, 46, 98; movement and change in, 143

Attitudes, formation of, 289; continually changing, 305

Auditory field, frequency of impulses in, 367

Autokinetic phenomena, 16

Autoscopy, 318

Autosymbolic phenomena, 313

Babbling, 247, 250

Baldwin, J., 146

Bárány, R., 90

Barbital intoxication, 115, 116